A
GLOSSARY
OF
OCEAN SCIENCE AND UNDERSEA TECHNOLOGY
TERMS

An authoritative compilation of over 3,500 engineering and scientific terms
used in the field of underwater sound, oceanography, marine sciences, underwater physiology and ocean engineering.

EDITED BY

LEE M. HUNT and DONALD G. GROVES

Staff Members
National Academy of Sciences
National Research Council

PREFACE BY

HARRIS B. STEWART, JR.
Deputy Assistant Director
Office of Oceanography
U. S. Coast and Geodetic Survey

COMPASS PUBLICATIONS, INC. • Arlington, Virginia • 1965

Compass Publications, Inc.

617 Lynn Building

1111 N. 19th Street

Arlington, Virginia 22209

Publishers of

Undersea Technology

and

A Guide to Sunken Ships In American Waters

66/ 6303

Oversize
+
DRS
1
H

PREFACE

Oceanography is not a science, but rather it is
the magnificent combination of all other sciences
that are in any way applicable to the watery seven
tenths of our planet. Just as the study of the
oceans unifies all the sciences, so too has the
lexicon of oceanography become a unification of
those of such diverse fields as physiology, acoustics,
invertebrate ecology, geology, hydrodynamics, and
organic chemistry to name only a few. With this uni-
ficiation - this polygamous marriage of the specialized
languages of many sciences - has come the very real
problem of communication among those who deal with
the ocean.

Ten years ago there were so few people concerned
with oceanography that they could talk the same language to each other and no one else was concerned.
Today, however, interest in our global sea has reached
national proportions. With this has come increased
support for an intensified effort to learn about the
sea for a variety of reasons   This in turn has brought
into the field many companies, scientists, engineers,
and technicians to whom at least part of the language
of oceanography is new. This book is for those people.
It is also for those with any interest in the sea and
for those who want to understand them.

The need for such a glossary has long been felt.
Many have urged that it be undertaken, but all were
staggered by the enormity of the task. Lee Hunt and
Don Groves also felt the need. They were also staggered by the task, but they have accomplished it.
They themselves admit that this is just a beginning,
but it is a good one and a highly useful one, and
oceanography will be in their debt until a large team
representing many specialities and working for many
years does a better job. In the meantime this glossary
of the terms of ocean science and technology will be
the standard handbook and will be found on the desk
of every oceanographer, marine engineer, and technician
engaged in any aspect of finding out about or working
with the ocean. It will also be found on the book-
shelves of the many who are merely fascinated by the
ocean and want to read and learn all they can about it.

Harris B. Stewart, Jr.
Deputy Assistant Director
Office of Oceanography
U. S. Coast and Geodetic Survey

v

As Dr. Stewart states in the Preface of this book, many people are only now beginning to "discover" the oceans of the world. These are people of diversified background, academic training, and professional interest - businessmen, engineers, technicians, lawyers, teachers, sportsmen and medical men - to name only a few. However, because of their growing interest in the oceans, each is now a potential contributor to that fund of knowledge which will be required to successfully exploit, for every man's benefit, the resources of the oceans of the world.

It appears that this potential would be enhanced by the existence of an appropriate glossary which would help to establish a common plane of understanding for the many varied terms which are used in connection with oceanography, ocean engineering and the marine sciences.

It was with this basic consideration in mind that this glossary was conceived. However, it must be clearly recognized that an effort such as this represents only the nucleus of more comprehensive efforts which will be required - indeed is required now - in order to satisfy the objective of this publication. While the editors particularly desire that their work be viewed and assessed in this light, they also feel their efforts have produced the first relatively complete and publicly available oceanic glossary.

Department of Defense weapon systems and project names have purposely been omitted in spite of the fact that much work in these endeavors have had and will continue to have a direct effect upon the progress of ocean science and undersea technology.

The mode of operation adopted in compiling the information contained in this glossary has been to describe the most important terms in the following basic areas:

Oceanography, including Physical, Biological, Chemical, Geological, and Meteorological;
Oceanographic Instrumentation;
Underwater Sound;
Ocean Engineering;
Diving Physiology; and
General Terms, including abbreviations and acronyms.

In providing the greatest comprehensive coverage within the limits of time and space available, definitions and terms were researched from the most authoritative sources of information (both published and unpublished) - including texts, technical reports, scientific papers, and other such documents. In the majority of cases definitions have been quoted verbatim from these references. However, in the area of oceanographic instrumentation many of the published descriptions have been edited. Terms in this classification have been predicated upon furnishing the reader with broad, generic descriptions representative of the classes of instruments and devices in use, since many of the specific instruments used in ocean science and engineering are constantly changing, improving and expanding in scope.

The extent of detailed description devoted to every term, and the number of important terms to be covered for each of the areas mentioned, involved judgment equated to a definite predetermined amount of space available for the book. Such judgments can certainly be fallible. Hence, it is recognized that some errors of omission and commission may have been made. These will, hopefully, be rectified by the more comprehensive work in compiling a revised and expanded follow-on glossary which is scheduled for future publication.

The number in parenthesis following a term indicates the source of the definition and is the same as the reference number listed on pages 171 and 172.

ACKNOWLEDGMENTS

The editors wish to express their sincere appreciation to the following organizations, government agencies and publications for their assistance and cooperation in preparing this glossary.

Addison-Wesley Publishing Co., for permission to reproduce materials from "Introduction To Physical Oceanography" by von Arx, copright Addison-Wesley Co., Reading, Mass.

Allen, George & Unwin. Ltd., for permission to reproduce materials from "Oceanography and Marine Biology" by Barnes, copyright 1959, London.

American Geological Institute, for use of materials from "Glossary of Geology and Related Sciences," 1960.

American Institute of Physics, for use of materials from "Glossary of Terms Frequently Used in Acoustics," 1960.

American Meteorological Society, for use of materials from "Glossary of Meteorology," 1959.

American Standards Association, for permission to reproduce materials from "American Standard Acoustical Terminology" copyright 1960 by ASA, copies of which may be purchased from the American Standards Association, 10 East 40th St., New York, N. Y. 10016.

Atomic Energy Commission, for use of materials from "Atomic Terms To Live With."

Beach Erosion Board, for use of materials from "Shore Protection, Planning and Design," 1961.

Dryden Press, The, reproduction of material from "Botany" by Wilson.

Edward Brothers, Inc., Ann Arbor, Michigan, "Dictionary of Geological Terms."

Instrument Society of America, for use of materials from "Marine Sciences Instrumentation," Vol. 1, 1961.

Interagency Committee On Oceanography.

McGraw-Hill Book Co., Inc., for permission to reproduce material from "Invertebrate Fossils" by Moore, Lalicker and Fischer, copyright 1952; for permission to reproduce materials from "General Zoology" by Storer, copyright 1943; also to reproduce material from "McGraw-Hill Yearbook of Science and Technology," copyright 1960.

National Aeronautics And Space Administration, for use of materials from "Short Glossary of Space Terms," 1962.

National Defense Research Committee.

National Science Foundation.

Prentice-Hall, Inc., for permission to reproduce materials from "The Oceans," by Sverdrup, Johnson & Fleming, copyright 1942, by Prentice-Hall, Inc., Englewood Cliffs, N. J.

Reinhold Publishing Co., for reproduction of materials from "Mechanical Properties and Tests," July 1954.

Taggart, Robert Inc., for use of materials from "Handbook of Underwater Engineering, Part I, The Environment," an unpublished manuscript.

Terry, Richard D., for permission to reproduce from an unpublished manuscript, "Oceanography -- Its Tools, Methods, Resources and Applications."

U.S. Air Force Missile Test Center, for use of material from "Missile Glossary."

U.S. Coast & Geodetic Survey.

U.S. Naval Institute, for permission to reproduce materials from "Fundamentals of Sonar," copyright 1959 by U.S. Naval Institute, Annapolis, Md.

U.S. Naval Oceanographic Office, The authors acknowledge in particular the contributions by Joseph M. Bensadon, Sidney H. Upham, and Fred Alt of the Instrumentation Center for descriptions of terms relating to oceanographic instrumentation.

U.S. Navy, Bureau of Naval Personnel.

U.S. Navy, Bureau of Ships.

U.S. Navy Underwater Sound Laboratory.

AAAS. American Association for the Advancement of Science.

AAG. Association of American Geographers.

ABAF. In a direction nearer dead astern than dead ahead. The opposite is forward. (17)

ABAF THE BEAM. Bearing more than 090° relative but less than 270° relative. The opposite is forward of the beam. (17)

ABDUCTOR. A muscle that draws a part away from the axis of the body or a limb, or separates two parts (such as that which opens the valves of clams). (19)

ABEAM. Bearing approximately 090° relative (abeam to starboard) or 270° relative (abeam to port). The term is often used loosely for abroad on the beam, or bearing exactly 090° or 270° relative. Also called on the beam. (17)

ABLATION. 1. The combined processes (such as sublimation, melting, evaporation) which remove snow or ice from the surface of a glacier, snow-field, etc.; in this sense, the opposite of ALIMENTATION. Particularly in glaciology, the term may be applied to reduction of the entire snow-ice mass, and may also include losses by wind action and by CALVING.
   Air temperature is the dominant factor in controlling ablation, precipitation amounts exercise only secondary control. During the ablation season, an ablation rate of about two millimeters per hour is typical of most glaciers.
   2. The amount of snow or ice removed by the above described processes; in this sense, the opposite of ACCUMULATION. (24)

ABROLHOS SQUALLS. Rain or thunder squalls of the frontal type experienced near the Abrolhos Islands (18°S.) off Brazil, mainly from May through August. (24)

ABSOLUTE ISOHYPSE. A line that has the properties of both constant pressure and constant height above mean sea level. Therefore, it can be any contour line on a constant-pressure chart, or any ISOBAR on a constant-height chart. (24)

ABSOLUTE ZERO. The zero point of the Kelvin temperature scale, of fundamental significance in thermodynamics and statistical mechanics. It may be interpreted as the temperature at which the volume of a perfect gas vanishes, or more generally the temperature of the cold source which would render a Carnot cycle 100 per cent efficient. The value of absolute zero on the centigrade scale is now estimated to be -273.16° ±.01. (24)

ABSORPTION. See SOUND ABSORPTION.

ABSORPTION HYGROMETER. A type of HYGROMETER with which the water vapor content of the atmosphere is measured by means of the absorption of vapor by a hygroscopic chemical. The amount of vapor absorbed may be determined in an absolute manner by weighing the hygroscopic material, or in a non-absolute manner by measuring a physical property of the substance that varies with the amount of water vapor absorbed. The lithium chloride humidity strip and

carbon-film hygrometer element are examples of the latter. (24)

ABSORPTION LOSS. Absorption loss is that part of the transmission loss which is due to dissipation or the conversion of sound energy into some other form of energy, usually heat. This conversion may take place within the medium itself or upon a reflection at one of its boundaries. (9)

ABYSS. A very deep, unfathomable place. The term is used to refer to a particularly deep part of the ocean, or to any part below 3000 fathoms. (17)

ABYSSAL-BENTHIC ZONE. See BENTHIC DIVISION.

ACANTHIN. The strontium sulphate material which makes up the skeletons of some plankton organisms (especially the Acantharia). (13)

ACCELEROMETER. A device which measures the forces of acceleration acting upon a body. (35)

ACCPO. Administrative Committee on Coordination Pertaining to Oceanography.

ACCRETION (AGGRADATION). May be either natural or artificial. Natural accretion is the gradual build-up of land over a long period of time solely by the action of the forces of nature, on a BEACH by deposition of water- or air-borne material. Artificial accretion is a similar build-up of land by reason of an act of man, such as the accretion formed by a GROIN, BREAKWATER, or beach fill deposited by mechanical means. (11)

ACCUMULATION. In glaciology, the quantity of snow or other solid form of water added to a glacier or snowfield by ALIMENTATION; the opposite of ABLATION. (24)

ACLINIC LINE (DIP EQUATOR, MAGNETIC EQUATOR). The line through those points on the earth's surface at which the magnetic INCLINATION is zero. The aclinic line is a particular case of an ISOCLINIC LINE.
   In South America the aclinic line lies about 15° South latitude; while from central Africa to about Indochina it coincides approximately with the parallel of 10° North latitude. (24)

ACM. A designation for a U. S. Navy Minelayer, Auxiliary Ship.

ACMRR. Advisory Committee on Marine Resources Research of the Food & Agriculture Organization of the United Nations.

ACOUSTIC, ACOUSTICAL. These two qualifying adjectives can be confused and in fact are often misused. The qualifying adjective acoustic is used when the term which it modifies designates something which has the properties, dimensions, or physical characteristics associated with sound waves. The adjective acoustical, on the other hand, is used when the term being qualified does not innately contain some property, dimension, or physical characteristic which is intimately associated with sound. Thus, we speak of an acoustic impedance, but we speak of the Acoustical Society of America. (9)

ACOUSTIC ATTENUATION CONSTANT. The acoustic attenuation constant is the real part of the acoustic propagation constant. The commonly used unit is the neper per section or per unit distance. (2)

ACOUSTIC AXIS. See Axis of Acoustic Symmetry.

ACOUSTIC DISPERSION. Acoustic dispersion is the change of speed of sound with frequency. (9)

ACOUSTIC ENERGY. That form of energy which is propagated through a medium having distributed mass and elasticity, and which is made manifest, at any point, as modifications in the mechanical strain and stress which would exist at that point in the absence of this energy. (4)

ACOUSTIC IMPEDANCE. The acoustic impedance of a given surface area of an acoustic medium perpendicular, at every point, to the direction of propagation of sinusoidal acoustic waves of given frequency, and having equal acoustic pressures and equal volume velocities per unit area at every point of the surface at any instance, is the quotient obtained by dividing (1) the phasor corresponding to the acoustic pressure by (2) the phasor corresponding to the volume velocity. (4)

ACOUSTIC INTENSITY. The limit approached by the quotient obtained by dividing the power of the acoustic energy being transmitted at a given time through a given area by the magnitude of this area as the magnitude of this area approaches zero. (4)

ACOUSTIC INTENSITY PER UNIT BAND. The limit approached by the quotient obtained by dividing (1) the intensity of the acoustic energy being transmitted through a given area, at a given time and in a given frequency band, by (2) the width of this band as the width of this band approaches zero. (4)

ACOUSTIC INTERFEROMETER. An acoustic interferometer is an instrument for making physical observations upon standing waves. It may be used, for example, to measure velocity, wave length, absorption, or impedance. (9)

ACOUSTIC OCEAN-CURRENT METER. This device is essentially two sing-around velocimeters in which the directions of pulse transmission are opposite in sense. The instrument is oriented so that the direction of acoustic pulse transmission is parallel to that of the flow to be measured, and so that the time of pulse translation is greater in one velocimeter than the other. The difference in sing-around frequencies is then proportional to ocean-current velocity. The current flow measurement is independent of variations in the velocity of sound. The instrument contains the necessary electronic circuitry to extract the signal with frequency proportional to flow velocity. (30)

ACOUSTIC OHMS. Acoustic impedance is measured in acoustic ohms. One acoustic ohm is equal to one gm/cm^4 sec, or to one dyne sec/cm^5. (4)

ACOUSTIC PHASE CONSTANT. The acoustic phase constant is the imaginary part of the acoustic propagation constant. The commonly used unit is the radian per section or per unit distance. (2)

ACOUSTIC PROPAGATION CONSTANT. The acoustic propagation constant of a uniform system or of a section of a system of recurrent structures in the natural logarithm of the complex ratio of the steady-state particle velocity, volume velocities, or pressures at two points separated by unit distance in the uniform system (assumed to be of infinite length), or at two successive corresponding points in the system of recurrent structures (assumed to be of infinite length). The ratio is determined by dividing the value at the point nearer the transmitting end by the corresponding value at the more remote point. (2)

ACOUSTIC RADIATION PRESSURE. The acoustic radiation pressure is a unit directional steady-state pressure exerted upon a surface exposed to an acoustic wave. Such a steady pressure is usually quite small in magnitude and is readily observable only in the presence of very intense sound waves. (9)

ACOUSTIC RADIOMETER. An acoustic radiometer is an instrument for measuring acoustic radiation pressure by determining the unidirectional steady-state force resulting from reflection or absorption of a sound wave at its boundaries. (9)

ACOUSTIC REFRACTION. Acoustic refraction is the process by which the direction of sound propagation is changed due to variations in the speed of sound in the medium from point to point. Refraction then is due to a nonuniformity of the medium itself. (9)

ACOUSTIC SCATTERING. Acoustic scattering is the irregular reflection, refraction, or diffraction of a sound in many directions. (9)

ACOUSTIC SOUNDING. The indirect evaluation of water depth, using the principle of measuring the length of time necessary for a sound wave to travel to the bottom, reflect and travel back to the water surface. (27)

ACOUSTIC SPECTROGRAPH. An instrument used to analyse the acoustic transmittive and reflective powers of marine life and thermal layers in terms of their effects on particular acoustic frequencies.

ACOUSTIC SYSTEM MARK 1, MOD 4. The Acoustic System Mark 1, Mod 4 measures and records very low-frequency sounds from the low audio ranges down to static pressures. The pressure-sensitive element of this system is essentially an inductance which is varied by changes in pressure and is contained in one arm of an a.c. bridge located on shore. The bridge is driven by a 1,000 c.p.s. oscillator that has good amplitude and frequency stability.

An incremental change in pressure applied to the pressure-sensitive element varies the a.c. output of the bridge. This output is combined with an additional output from the balancing network, and after amplification the combined output is demodulated. The output from the demodulator is filtered and appears as a voltage that varies in accordance with the pressure changes on the underwater element. Frequencies below 1.5 c.p.s., after amplification by a d.c. amplifier, are recorded on a milliammeter. This meter also is used to determine the state of balance of the bridge.

The Acoustic System Mark 1, Mod 4 can operate to a depth of 200 feet and uses cable lengths as much as several miles. This system has been used extensively to obtain wave records over long periods of time off several shorebased stations. (35)

ACOUSTIC THEODOLITE. An instrument designed to provide a continuous vertical profile of ocean currents from the bottom to the surface in a specific location.

ACOUSTICS. Acoustics is the science of sound, including its production, transmission, and effects. (1)

ACRE-FOOT. The amount of water required to cover 1 acre to a depth of 1 foot: equal to 43,560 cubic feet.

ACS. American Chemical Society.

ACSM. American Congress on Surveying and Mapping.

ACTINIC. Pertaining to electromagnetic radiation capable of starting photochemical reactions.

ACTINOMETER. The general name for any instrument used to measure the intensity of radiant energy, particularly that of the sun.

Actinometers may be classified, according to the quantities which they measure, in the following manner: (a) PYRHELIOMETER, which measures the intensity of direct solar radiation; (b) PYRANOMETER, which measures global radiation (the combined intensity of direct solar radiation and diffuse sky radiation); and (c) PYRGEOMETER, which measures the effective terrestrial radiation. (24)

ACTIVE RUDDER. The Active Rudder has played an important role in improving general maneuverability, maintaining course when a vessel is stopped (which is helpful in taking oceanographic data) and proceeding at high speed in strong winds and high seas. In the Active Rudder a submersible electric motor is installed in a rudder of normal design and a propeller is fitted to the motor shaft at the after end about even with the trailing edge of the rudder. The water filled and water lubricated squirrel cage induction motor may range from 20 to 1600 SHP and is arranged for reverse rotation. Thus by swinging the rudder, thrust may be applied either forward or reverse in the direction of the rudder, similar to the manner of steering a small boat with an outboard motor. (30)

ACTIVE SONAR. Active sonar is the method or equipment by which information concerning a distant object is obtained by evaluation of sound generated by the equipment. (1)

ACTIVE TRANSDUCER. An active transducer is a transducer whose output waves are dependent upon sources of power, apart from that supplied by any of the actuating waves, which are controlled by one or more of these waves. (1)

AD. U. S. Navy ship designation for Destroyer Tender.

ADB. Atlantic Development Board (Canada).

ADF BEARING INDICATOR. An instrument used with a radio direction finder to indicate automatically the relative, magnetic, or true bearing (or reciprocal) of a transmitter. A manual type of such an instrument is called an MDF bearing indicator. (17)

ADG. U. S. Navy ship designation for a Degaussing Vessel.

ADIABATIC. Without gain or loss of heat. (17)

ADIABATIC PROCESS. A thermodynamic change of state of a system in which there is no transfer of heat or mass across the boundaries of the system. In an adiabatic process, compression always results in warming, expansion in cooling. In meteorology the adiabatic process is often also taken to be a reversible process. (24)

ADIABATIC TEMPERATURE GRADIENT. The adiabatic temperature change on a vertical distance of 1000 meters. (13)

ADVANCE (OF A BEACH). 1. A continuing seaward movement of the shore line.
2. A net seaward movement of the shoreline over a specified time. Also called progression. (11)

ADVECTION FOG. A type of fog caused by the advection of moist air over a cold surface, and the consequent cooling of that air to below its dew point.
A very common advection fog is that caused by moist air in transport over a cold body of water (SEA FOG). (24)

AE. U. S. Navy designation for an Ammunition Ship.

AEC. Atomic Energy Commission.

AEROEMBOLISM. 1. The formation or liberation of gases in the blood vessels of the body, as brought on by a change from a high, or relatively high, atmospheric pressure to a lower one. 2. The disease or condition caused by the formation or liberation of gases in the body. The disease is characterized principally by neuralgic pains, cramps, and swelling, and sometimes results in death. Also called 'decompression sickness'. (31)
Aeroembolism can occur to scuba swimmers and divers on ascent from even shallow depths. However, it can almost always be prevented by maintaining relaxed respiration upon ascent and avoiding breath holding. Because the disorder forces air bubbles into the blood stream it may be serious, resulting in convulsions, pain, paralysis, reflex spasms or even death. Treatment involves immediate recompression in a pressure chamber. (37)

AEROLOGY. 1. As officially used in the U. S. Navy until early 1957, same as METEOROLOGY; however, this usage tended to be more administrative than scientific. 2. As a subdivision of meteorology, the study of the free atmosphere throughout its vertical extent, as distinguished from studies confined to the layer of the atmosphere adjacent to the earth's surface. (24)

AES. Atlantic Estuarine Society.

AESTIVAL. Of or pertaining to summer. The corresponding term relating to winter is hibernal. (17)

AF. U. S. Navy designation for a Store Ship.

AFAC. American Fisheries Advisory Committee.

"A" FRAME. Gallows used for leading wires over the side of a ship. (38)

AFS. U. S. Navy designation for a Combat Store ship.

AFS. American Fisheries Society.

AG. U. S. Navy ship designation for Miscellaneous Auxiliary.

AGAR. A dried and bleached gelatenous extract obtained from several kinds of red algae. It is used extensively in medicine, chiefly as a laxative, since it is not digested and increases greatly in bulk with the absorption of water. Also used as an essential ingredient in the preparation of a medium for the growth of bacteria and fungi. (18)

AGB. U. S. Navy ship designation for an Icebreaker.

AGC. U. S. Navy designation for an Amphibious Force Flagship. Also AGC is used to mean Automatic Gain Control.

AGDE. U. S. Navy designation for an Escort Research Ship.

AGE, WAVE. The ratio of wave velocity to wind velocity (in wave forecasting theory). (10)

AGEH. U. S. Navy designation for a Hydrofoil Research Ship.

AGGER. See DOUBLE TIDE.

AGGRADATION. The geologic process by means of which various parts of the surface of the earth are raised in elevation or built up by the deposition of material eroded from other sections and transported thereto by water or wind. See ACCRETION. (27)

AGGREGATE. A mixture of substances, separable by mechanical means.

AGI. American Geological Institute.

AGM. U. S. Navy designation for Missile Range Instrumentation ships.

AGMR. U. S. Navy designation for a Major Communications Relay Ship.

AGONIC LINE. See ISOGONIC LINE.

AGOR. U. S. Navy designation for an Auxiliary General Oceanographic Research Ship. This class of ship is 209 feet long with a 39 foot beam.

AGR. U. S. Navy designation for a Radar Picket Ship.

AGS. U. S. Navy designation for an Auxiliary General Survey Ship. These ships are about twice the size of the AGOR ships.

AGSC. U. S. Navy designation for an Auxiliary General Survey Coastal Ship.

AGSL. U. S. Navy designation for a Satellite Launching Ship.

AG(SS). U. S. Navy designation for an Auxiliary Submarine.

AGU. American Geophysical Union.

AH. U. S. Navy designation for a Hospital Ship.

AGULHAS CURRENT. A generally southwestward-flowing ocean current of the Indian Ocean; one of the swiftest of ocean currents.
Throughout the year, part of the SOUTH EQUATORIAL CURRENT turns south along the east coast of Africa and feeds the strong Agulhas current. To the south of latitude 30°S. the Agulhas current is a well-defined and narrow current that extends less than 100 km from the coast. To the south of South Africa the greatest volume of its waters bends sharply to the south and then toward the east, thus returning to the Indian Ocean by joining the flow from South Africa toward Australia across the southern part of that ocean. However, a small portion of the Agulhas current water appears to round the Cape of Good Hope from the Indian Ocean and continues into the Atlantic Ocean. (24)

AIBS. American Institute of Biological Sciences.

AID. Agency for International Development. (Formerly ICA).

AINA. Arctic Institute of North America.

AIR. The mixture of gases comprising the earth's ATMOSPHERE. Since the composition of the atmosphere is slightly variable with respect to certain components, the term "pure air" has no precise meaning, but it is commonly used to imply freedom from nongaseous suspensoids (dust, hydrometeors) and also freedom from such gaseous contaminants as industrial effluents.
By far the most important gas found in air, from the meteorological viewpoint, is water vapor. The term dry air denotes air from which all water vapor has been removed. Pure dry air has a density of 1.2923 gm/cm^3 at a pressure of 1013.25 mb and a temperature of 0°C, a specific heat at constant volume of 0.1707 $cal/gm/^{o}C$; a specific heat at constant pressure of 0.2396 $cal/gm/^{o}C$; and its gas constant (per gram) is 2.8704 x 10^6 $erg/gm/^{o}C$.
The per cent by volume of those gases found in relatively constant amount in dry air is very nearly as follows:

Gases	Per cent
nitrogen (N_2)	78.084
oxygen (O_2)	20.946
argon (A)	0.934
carbon dioxide (CO_2)	0.033
neon (Ne)	0.0018
helium (He)	0.000524
methane (CH_4)	0.0002
krypton (Kr)	0.000114
hydrogen (H_2)	0.00005
nitrous oxide (N_2O)	0.00005
xenon (Xe)	0.0000087

In addition to the above constituents there are many variable constituents. Chief of these is water vapor, which may vary from zero to volume percentages close to four per cent. Ozone, sulfur dioxide, ammonia, carbon monoxide, and other trace gases occur in small and varying amounts.
The sea-level composition of air is now known to prevail up to twenty or twenty-five kilometers without change, and only very slight diffusive separation occurs even at heights as great as fifty kilometers. (24)

AIRBORNE RADIATION THERMOMETER (ART). An instrument carried aboard aircraft to measure ocean surface temperatures. Actually, the radiation thermometer compares the difference in temperature between a self-contained standard temperature reference and the ocean surface.

AIRPLANE STRAND. See WIRE ROPE.

AK. U. S. Navy designation for a Cargo Ship.

AKA. U. S. Navy designation for an Attack Cargo Ship.

AKD. U. S. Navy designation for a Cargo Ship, Dock.

AKL. U. S. Navy designation for a Light Cargo Ship.

AKN. U. S. Navy designation for a Net Cargo Ship.

AKS. U. S. Navy designation for a General Stores Issue Ship.

AK(SS). U. S. Navy designation for a Cargo Submarine.

AKV. U. S. Navy designation for a Cargo Ship and Aircraft Ferry.

ALASKA CURRENT. An ocean current, the northward flowing division of the ALEUTIAN CURRENT, it circulates cyclonically around the Gulf of Alaska. Part of the water passes between the Aleutian Islands into the Bering Sea from which it emerges as the OYASHIO, and part rejoins the Aleutian current.
It enters the Gulf of Alaska along the American west coast and, since it comes from the south, it has the character of a warm current in spite of the fact that it carries subarctic water. It therefore exercises an influence on climatic conditions similar, on a small scale, to that which the NORTH ATLANTIC CURRENT and NORWEGIAN CURRENT exercise on the climates of northwestern Europe. (24)

ALBALINITY. The quantity, when expressed as the number of milli equivalents of hydrogen ions (mg-atoms of H^+), necessary to set free the ions of weak acid in a volume of water which at 20° has a volume of 1 L.

ALBEDO. The ratio of the amount of electromagnetic radiation reflected by a body to the amount incident upon it, commonly expressed as a percentage. The albedo is to be distinguished from the reflectivity, which refers to one specific wavelength (monochromatic radiation). (24)

ALBEDOMETER. An instrument used for the measurement of the reflecting power (the ALBEDO) of a surface. A PYRANOMETER (see ACTINOMETER) adapted for the measurement of radiation reflected from the earth's surface is sometimes employed as an albedometer. (24)

ALEUTIAN CURRENT. An eastward flowing ocean current which lies north of the NORTH PACIFIC CURRENT; it is the northern branch of the KUROSHIO extension which moves northeast then east between 40°N and 50°N. As it approaches the coast of North America it divides to form the northward-flowing ALASKA CURRENT, and the southward-flowing CALIFORNIA CURRENT. (24)

ALGAE. Marine, brackish, and fresh-water plants (including marine seaweeds), ranging in size from microscopic unicellular plants to the giant kelps. Marine algae often have leaflike and stemlike parts similar to those of terrestrial plants but differ from them in cellular structure. (15)

ALIMENTATION. Generally, the process of providing nourishment or sustenance; thus in glaciology, the combined processes which serve to increase the mass of a glacier or snowfield; the opposite of ABLATION. The deposition of snow is the major form of glacial alimentation, but other forms of precipitation along with sublimation, refreezing of melt water, etc. also contribute.
   The additional mass produced by alimentation is termed ACCUMULATION. (24)

ALKALINITY. In sea water, the excess of hydroxyl ions over hydrogen ions, generally expressed as milliequivalents per liter. (24)

ALPHA PARTICLE. Same as the helium atom nucleus, containing two protons and two neutrons and produced or ejected by certain nuclear reactions or rearrangements such as the decomposition of radium and uranium. Each alpha particle has a double positive charge and is spoken of collectively as alpha radiation. (39)

ALS. American Littoral Society.

ALTERNATION OF GENERATIONS. Alternation of generations is the occurrence of two phases, or generations, in the life cycle of an organism which reproduces sexually. One of these generations produces the spores and is called the SPOROPHYTE generation. The other, which produces the GAMETES, is known as the GAMETOPHYTE generation. The word generation refers here to the time interval between the birth of the parents and that of the progeny. (18)

ALTOCUMULUS. A cloud layer (or patches) within the middle level (mean height 6,500-20,000 feet) composed of rather flattened globular masses, the smallest elements of the regularly arranged layers being fairly thin, with or without shading. These elements are arranged in groups, in lines, or waves, following one or two directions, and are sometimes so close together that their edges join. (17)

ALTOSTRATUS. A sheet of gray or bluish cloud within the middle level (mean height 6,500-20,000 feet). Sometimes the sheet is composed of a compact mass of dark, thick, gray clouds of fibrous structure; at other times the sheet is thin and through it the sun or moon can be seen dimly as though gleaming through ground glass. (17)

ALUMINAUT. An aluminum hulled submarine presently under construction by the Electric Boat Division of General Dynamics Corp. It is designed for oceanographic research, will be 50 feet in length, and have a maximum cruising depth of 15,000 feet.

ALUVIUM. Soil (sand, mud, or similar detrital material) deposited by flowing water, or the deposits formed thereby. (10)

ALVEOLAR EXCHANGE. The transposition of oxygen to the blood and the removal of carbon dioxide in the alveolae of the lungs. (37)

ALVEOLI. The lungs can be thought of as two elastic bags containing millions of little distensible air sacs. These air sacs or alveoli are all connected to the air passages, which branch and rebranch like the twigs of a tree. (37)

ALVIN. A manned submersible vehicle (USA). See Appendix Chart.

AM. U. S. Navy designation for a Minesweeper.

AMBIENT NOISE. The composite noise from all sources in a given environment excluding the desired signal and noise inherent in the measuring equipment and platform.

AMCU. U. S. Navy designation for Underwater Locator.

AMERICAN SUBMARINE MODEL 600. A manned submersible vehicle (US).

AMMETER. An instrument for measuring the electron flow in amperes. (36)

AMOS. Acoustic Meteorological Oceanographic Survey.

AMPERE. The basic unit of current flow; a current of one ampere will flow through a conductor having a resistance of one ohm when a potential of one volt is applied. (36)

AMPHIDROMIC POINT. A point on a chart of COTIDAL LINES from which the cotidal lines radiate. (24)

AMPHIDROMIC REGION. An oceanic region whose COTIDAL LINES radiate from one AMPHIDROMIC POINT. (24)

AMPHITRITE. The name of a 65 foot long, 6 ton inflatable ship used as a tender in sea diving operations.

AMPLIDYNE. A type of dc generator used as a power amplifier, (output voltage responds to changes in field excitation).

AMPLITUDE. 1. The semirange of a CONSTITUENT tide. By analogy, it may be applied also to the maximum velocity of a constituent current. (14)
   2. In hydrodynamics, one-half the wave height.
   3. In engineering usage, loosely, the wave height from crest to trough. (10)

AMS. American Meteorological Society.

AMS. U. S. Navy designation for a Minesweeper, Coastal.

AMSFC. Atlantic States Marine Fisheries Commission.

AN. U. S. Navy designation for a Net Laying Ship.

ANCHORAGE BUOY. One of a series of buoys marking the limits of an anchorage. A buoy marking the location of a quarantine anchorage is called a quarantine buoy. (17)

ANCHOR BUOY. A buoy marking the position of an anchor. (17)

ANEMOMETER. The general name for instruments

designed to measure the speed (or force) of the wind. These instruments may be classified according to the means of transduction employed: those used in meteorology include the rotation anemometer, pressure plate anemometer, pressure-tube anemometer, bridled-cup anemometer, contact anemometer, cooling-power anemometer, and sonic anemometer. (24)

ANEROID BAROGRAPH. An ANEROID BAROMETER arranged so that the deflection of the aneroid capsule actuates a pen which graphs a record on a rotating drum. The magnification of the deflection of the capsule may be adjusted so that records of small fluctuations in pressure may be obtained. The aneroid barograph is subject to the uncertainties of the aneroid barometer, and therefore must be calibrated periodically. (24)

ANEROID BAROMETER. An instrument for measuring atmospheric pressure. It is constructed on the following principles: an aneroid capsule (a thin corrugated hollow disk) is partially evacuated of gas, and is restrained from collapsing by an external or internal spring. The deflection of the spring will be nearly proportional to the difference between the internal and external pressures. Magnification of the spring deflection is obtained both by connecting capsules in series and by mechanical linkages.

The aneroid barometer is temperature compensated at a given pressure level by adjustment of the residual gas in the aneroid or by a bimetallic link arrangement. The instrument is subject to uncertainties due to variations in the elastic properties of the spring and capsules, and due to wear in the mechanical linkages. (24)

ANGEL. A radar echo caused by a physical phenomenon not discernible to the eye. Angels are usually coherent echoes and sometimes of great signal strength (up to 40 db above the noise level). They have been ascribed to insects flying through the radar beam, but have also been observed under atmospheric conditions which indicate there must be other causes. Studies indicate that a fair portion of them are caused by strong temperature and/or moisture gradients such as might be found near the boundaries of bubbles of especially warm or moist air. They frequently occur in shallow layers at or near temperature inversions within the lowest few thousand feet of the atmosphere. (24)

ANGLE OF REPOSE. The greatest angle to the horizontal assumed by any unsupported granular, semisolid, or semifluid material. Also called natural slope. (27)

ANGLE OF ROLL. The angle between the lateral axis of a craft and the horizontal. It is considered positive of the port side is higher than the starboard side, but may be designated starboard or port depending upon which side is lower. Also called angle of bank, roll angle. (17)

ANGLE OF YAW. 1. The horizontal angular displacement of the longitudinal axis of a vessel from its neutral position, during a yaw. It is designated right or left according to the direction of displacement of the bow.
2. The angle between a line in the direction of the relative wind and a plane through the longitudinal and vertical axes of an aircraft. It is considered positive if the nose is displaced to the right.
Also called yaw angle. (17)

ANGULAR SPREADING. The lateral extension of ocean waves as they move out of the generating area as swell. (24)

ANGULAR-SPREADING FACTOR. In ocean wave forecasting, the ratio of the actual wave energy present at a point to that which would have been present in the absence of ANGULAR SPREADING. (24)

ANIP. Army-Navy Instrumentation Program.

ANODE. The less noble electrode of an electrolytic cell at which corrosion occurs. The corrosion process involves the change of metal atoms into ions with a liberation of electrons that migrate through the metal to the cathode of the cell. (35)

ANOMALOUS DISPERSIVE. Waves having crests which are short compared to the wavelength.

ANOMALOUS PROPAGATION. In sonar, pronounced and rapid variations in echo strength caused by large and rapid local fluctuations in propagation conditions. (8)

ANOXIA. (Also called HYPOXIA). Oxygen deficiency in the blood cells or tissues of the body in such degree as to cause psychological and physiological disturbances. Anoxia may result from a scarcity of oxygen in the air being breathed or from an inability of the body tissues to absorb oxygen under conditions of low ambient pressure.

Anoxia can occur if large amounts of nitrogen are present in the rebreathing bags of closed or semi-closed circuit rebreathing apparatus and the oxygen supply fails or becomes exhausted. The onset of anoxia is frequently accompanied by a feeling of elation and well being which is so deceiving as to be difficult to recognize even by experienced swimmers. The man usually loses consciousness without warning. In pure oxygen rebreathing units, this can only occur through an error in the diver's technique (poor nitrogen elimination) and should be completely preventable by training. Where nitrogen is intentionally used in the breathing mixture, anoxia can result from mechanical failure of the apparatus or exhaustion of the gas supply. (37)

ANTARCTIC CIRCLE. The line of latitude $66^{\circ}32'S$ (often taken as $66 1/2^{\circ}S$). Along this line the sun does not set on the day of the summer solstice, about December 22nd, and does not rise on the day of the winter solstice, about June 21st. (24)

ANTARCTIC CIRCUMPOLAR CURRENT. The ocean current with the largest volume transport (approximately 110×10^6 m^3/sec), and the swiftest current; it flows from west to east through all the oceans around the Antarctic Continent. It is locally deflected from its course, partly by the distribution of land and sea and partly by the submarine topography. Beside the bends that are associated with the bottom topography, the effects of the distribution of land and sea and of the currents in the adjacent oceans are also evident. On its northern edge it is continuous with the SOUTH ATLANTIC CURRENT, the SOUTH PACIFIC CURRENT and the eastward-flowing extension of the AGULHAS CURRENT in the Indian Ocean.

A flow to the west near the Antarctic Continent is evident only in the Weddell Sea area, where an extensive cyclonic motion occurs to the south of the circumpolar current. (24)

ANTARCTIC FRONT. The semi-permanent, semi-continuous front between the antarctic air of the Antarctic Continent and the Polar air of the southern oceans; generally comparable to the arctic front of the Northern Hemisphere. (24)

ANTARCTIC WHITEOUT. See ARCTIC WHITEOUT

ANTILLES CURRENT. An ocean current, the northern branch of the NORTH EQUATORIAL CURRENT flowing along the northern side of the Great Antilles carrying water that is identical with that of the Sargasso Sea. The Antilles current eventually joins the FLORIDA CURRENT (after the latter emerges from the Straits of Florida) to form the GULF STREAM. (24)

6

ANTERIOR. The forward-moving or head end of an animal, or toward that end. Opposite of posterior. (19)

ANTINODE. See LOOP.

ANTINODE (LOOP). An antinode is a point, line or surface in a standing wave where some characteristic of the wave has a maximum value. (9)

ANTIRESONANCE. For a system in forced oscillation, antiresonance exists at a point when any change, however small, in the frequency of excitation causes an increase in the response at this point. (1)

ANTITRADES. A deep layer of westerly winds in the troposphere above the surface TRADE-WINDS of the tropics. They comprise the equatorward side of the mid-latitude WESTERLIES, but are found at upper levels rather than at the surface.

The antitrades are best developed in the winter hemisphere, and also above the eastern extremities of the subtropical highs. Further west their base is higher and their appearance less regular.

The antitrades were formerly regarded as return currents carrying away, to higher latitudes, the air which rises in the INTERTROPICAL CONVERGENCE ZONES, the westerly component being due to the conservation of angular momentum as the air moves into higher latitudes. Bjerknes, J. ("La Circulation Atmospherique dans les Latitudes Sous-Tropicales," Scientia, 57:1935, pp. 114-123) showed that this explanation is incomplete: the antitrades are dynamical in origin and constitute an essential part of the atmosphere's primary circulation. (24)

ANTLANTNIRO. Atlantic Scientific Research Institute of Fishing Economy and Oceanography (USSR).

ANZAAS. Australian and New Zealand Association for the Advancement of Science.

AO. U. S. Navy ship designation for an Oiler.

AOE. U. S. Navy designation for a Fast Combat Support Ship.

AOG. U. S. Navy ship designation for a Gasoline Tanker.

AOG. Atlantic Oceanographic Group.

AOR. U. S. Navy designation for a Replenishment Fleet Tanker.

AO(SS). U. S. Navy designation for Submarine Oiler.

AP. U. S. Navy designation for a Transport.

APA. U. S. Navy designation for an Attack Transport Ship.

APB. U. S. Navy designation for a Self-Propelled Barracks Ship.

APC. U. S. Navy designation for a Small Coastal Transport.

APD. U. S. Navy designation for a High Speed Transport Ship.

APHOTIC ZONE. See EUPHOTIC ZONE.

APO. Association of Physical Oceanographers.

APOGEAN TIDAL CURRENTS. Tidal currents of decreased speed occurring at the time of apogean tides. (17)

APOGEAN TIDES. Tides of decreased range occurring when the moon is near apogee. The range at this time is called apogean range and usually does not occur until 1 to 3 days after the moon reaches apogee. This lag is called age of parallax inequality, or parallax age. (17)

The apogean range (An) of tide is the average semidiurnal range occurring at the time of apogean tides and is most conveniently computed from the harmonic constants. It is smaller than the mean range where the type of tide is either semidiurnal or mixed, and is of no practical significance where the type of tide is diurnal. (14)

APPARENT COHESION. In soil mechanics, the resistance of particles to being pulled apart due to the surface tension of the moisture film surrounding each particle. Also called MOISTURE FILM COHESION. (27)

APPARENT SOURCE. See EFFECTIVE CENTER.

APPARENT TIME. Time based upon the true position of the sun as distinguished from mean time, which is measured by a fictitious sun moving at a uniform rate. Apparent time is that shown by the sundial, and its noon is the time when the sun crosses the meridian. The difference between apparent time and mean time is known as the equation of time. Although quite common many years ago, apparent time is now seldom used. (14)

AP(SS). U. S. Navy designation for a Transport Submarine.

AR. U. S. Navy designation for a Repair Ship.

ARB. U. S. Navy designation for a Battle Damage Repair Ship.

ARC. U. S. Navy designation for a Cable Repairing or Laying Ship.

ARCHED ICEBERG. An ICEBERG eroded in such a manner that a large opening at the water line extends horizontally through the iceberg forming an arch. (25)

ARCHED SQUALL. See SQUALL.

ARCHIBENTHIC ZONE. See BENTHIC DIVISION.

ARCHIMEDES. A manned submersible vehicle (French).

ARCHIMEDES PRINCIPLE. States that any object wholly or partially immersed in a liquid is buoyed by a force equal to the weight of the liquid it displaces. (37)

ARCHIPELAGIC APRON. A fan-shaped slope around an oceanic island differing from deep-sea fans in having little, if any, sediment cover. (27)

ARCHIPELAGO. A group of islands; a sea studded with many islands. (27)

ARCS. Ridges which are curved, and particularly if parts of them rise above sea level. (oceans) (see ridge)

ARCTIC CIRCLE. The line of latitude 66°32'N (often taken as 66 1/2°N). Along this line the sun does not set on the day of the summer solstice, about June 21, and does not rise on the day of the winter solstice, about December 22. From this line the number of twenty-four hour periods of continuous day or of continuous night increases northwards to about six months each at the North Pole. (24)

ARCTIC CURRENT. See LABORADOR CURRENT.

ARCTIC WHITEOUT. A peculiar condition affecting visibility caused by a snow cover obliterating all landmarks and accompanied by an overcast sky or cirrostratus and/or altostratus clouds. No shadows are cast and the picture is one of an unrelieved expanse of white. Earth and sky blend so that the horizon is not distinguishable. This condition is extremely dangerous to low-flying aircraft, particularly those attempting to land. Pilots have well described the condition as "like flying in a bowl of milk." An analogous condition in the antarctic regions is called an Antarctic whiteout. (25)

ARD. U. S. Navy designation for a Floating Dry-dock.

ARG. U. S. Navy designation for an Internal Combustion Engine Repair Ship.

ARGILLACEOUS. Containing clay particles or of the nature of clay. (27)

ARGUS ISLAND. An oceanographic observation tower located in 194 feet of water on Plantagenet Bank some 25 miles southwest of Bermuda.

ARL. U. S. Navy designation for a Landing Craft Repair Ship.

ARM. An inlet. The term is usually used in connection with the larger body of water of which it is a part, as an arm of the sea. (17)

ARPA. Advanced Research Projects Agency.

ARS. U. S. Navy designation for a Salvage Ship.

ARSD. U. S. Navy designation for a Salvage Lifting Vessel.

ARST. U. S. Navy designation for a Salvage Craft Tender.

ARTHUR REMOTE-INDICATING THERMOMETER. This device consists essentially of a plexiglass indicator case containing the bridge circuit and a sensing unit. The two are connected by a two-conductor light-weight plastic cable. It is used in a manner similar to the casting thermometer except that it is not fitted with a float to hold the sensing unit at the water surface. The cable is marked in meters and fractions, permitting the investigator to examine vertical distribution of temperature. (30)

ARTIFICIAL NOURISHMENT. The process of replenishing a BEACH by artificial means, e.g. by the deposition of dredged material. (11)

ARV. U. S. Navy designation for an Aircraft Repair Ship.

ARVA. U. S. Navy designation for an Aircraft Repair Ship (Aircraft).

ARVE. U. S. Navy designation for an Aircraft Repair Ship (Engine).

AS. U. S. Navy designation for a Submarine Tender.

ASA. American Shellfisheries Association.

ASCENDENT. See GRADIENT.

ASCIDIAN. See TUNICATES.

A-SCOPE. A Cathode Ray Oscilloscope indicator depicting echo intensities by vertical deflections, and ranges by the position of these deflections on the horizontal trace. (7)

ASDEFORLANT. Antisubmarine Defense Force, Atlantic

Fleet. U. S. Naval Base, Norfolk, Virginia.

ASDEFORPAC. See COMASWFORPAC.

ASDIC. British echo-ranging equipment. Letters derived from Anti-Submarine Development Investigation Committee.

ASEXUAL. Any reproductive process which does not involve the union of GAMETES. (18)

ASHERA. A manned submersible vehicle (U.S.).

ASIRC. Aquatic Sciences Information Retrieval Center.

ASLO. American Society of Limnology and Oceanography.

ASNE. American Society of Naval Engineers.

ASP. American Society on Photogrammetry.

ASPECT. The angle made by a target with the line joining it to the observation point is known as the aspect of the target. (4)

ASR. U. S. Navy designation for a Submarine Rescue Vessel. Also ASR means Air-Sea-Rescue Operations.

ASROC. (Contraction of antisubmarine rocket). A 1,000 lb rocket homing torpedo as well as an integrated system composed of acoustical underwater detection gear, fire control computer, and a launcher holding eight missiles which are combinations of missiles, torpedoes, depth charges and sonars.

ASSA. U. S. Navy designation for a Cargo Submarine.

ASSP. U. S. Navy designation for a Transport Submarine.

ASTIA. Armed Services Technical Information Administration. Now called Defense Documentation Center (DDC).

ASTM. American Society for Testing Materials.

ASTOR. A nuclear torpedo.

ASTRONOMICAL TIME. Time formerly used in astronomical calculations in which the day began at noon rather than midnight. The astronomical day commenced at noon of the CIVIL DAY of the same date. The hours of the day were numbered consecutively from 0 (noon) to 23 (11 a. m. of the following morning). Up to the close of the year 1924 astronomical time was in general use in nautical almanacs. Beginning with the year 1925 the American Ephemeris and Nautical Almanac and similar publications of other countries abandoned the old astronomical time and adopted GREENWICH CIVIL TIME for the data given in their tables. (14)

ASW. Anti-Submarine Warfare.

ASWEPS. Anti-Submarine Warfare Environmental Prediction System.

ASWTNS. ASW Tactical Navigation System.

ATA. U. S. Navy designation for an Auxiliary Ocean Tug.

ATF. U. S. Navy designation for a Fleet Ocean Tug.

ATMOSPHERE. The envelope of AIR surrounding the earth and bound to it more or less permanently by virtue of the earth's gravitational attraction; the system whose chemical properties, dynamic motions, and physical processes constitute the subject matter of meteorology.

The earth's atmosphere extends from the solid or liquid surface of the earth to an indefinite height, its density asymptotically approaching that of interplanetary space. At heights of the order of 80 km (50 mi) the atmosphere is barely dense enough to scatter sunlight to a visible degree. At heights of the order of 600 km (370 mi) the atmosphere's density becomes so low that the properties typical of a gas cease to exist and the free molecular paths are long enough that one must consider them as portions of elliptical orbits in the earth's gravitational field. At 1000 km (600 mi) the density of the atmosphere is still sufficient to yield readily observable auroral effects. At about 30,000 km (18,600 mi) above the earth's surface, a molecule moving as if in rigid rotation with the earth could not be held to such an orbit by the earth's gravitational attraction, so this height might be taken as an extreme upper limit of the possible atmosphere.

The atmosphere may be subdivided vertically into a number of ATMOSPHERIC SHELLS, but the most common basic subdivision is that which recognizes a troposphere from the surface to about ten kilometers, a stratosphere from about ten kilometers to about eighty kilometers, and an ionosphere above eighty kilometers; and each of these is often further subdivided.

Because the troposphere contains the bulk (about three-fourths) of the atmospheric mass and because it contains virtually all of the atmospheric water vapor, ordinary weather events are most intimately concerned with the tropospheric phenomena. (24)

ATMOSPHERIC PRESSURE. The pressure exerted by the atmosphere as a consequence of gravitational attraction exerted upon the "column" of air lying directly above the point in question. As with any gas, the pressure exerted by the atmosphere is ultimately explainable in terms of bombardment by gas molecules; it is independent of the orientation of the surface on which it acts.

Atmospheric pressure is one of the basic meteorological elements. It is measured by many varieties of barometer, and is expressed in several unit systems. The most common unit used is the millibar (1 millibar equals 1000 dynes per cm^2). Unique to the science of meteorology is the use of inches (or millimeters) of mercury; that is, the height of a column of mercury that exactly balances the weight of the column of atmosphere whose base coincides with that of the mercury column. Also employed are units of weight per area and units of force per area. A standard atmosphere has been defined in terms of equivalence to each of the above unit systems, and it is used as a unit itself. (24)

ATMOSPHERIC SHELL. Any one of a number of strata or "layers" of the earth's atmosphere.

Temperature distribution is the most common criterion used for denoting the various shells. The TROPOSPHERE (the "region of change") is the lowest 10 or 20 km of the atmosphere, characterized by decreasing temperature with height. The term STRATOSPHERE is used to denote both (a) the relatively isothermal region immediately above the tropopause, and (b) the shell extending upwards from the tropopause to the minimum temperature level at 70 to 80 km; the MESOSPHERE is the shell between about 20 and 70 or 80 km which has a broad maximum temperature at about 40 or 50 km; and the THERMOSPHERE is the shell above the mesosphere with a more or less steadily increasing temperature with height.

The distribution of various physico-chemical processes is another criterion. The OZONOSPHERE, lying roughly between 10 and 50 km is the general region of the upper atmosphere in which there is an appreciable ozone concentration and in which ozone plays an important part in the radiative balance of the atmosphere; the IONOSPHERE, starting at about 70 or 80 km, is the region in which ionization of one or more of the atmospheric constituents is significant; the NEUTROSPHERE is the shell below this which is, by contrast, relatively un-ionized; and the CHEMOSPHERE, with no very definite height limits, is the region in which photochemical reactions take place.

Dynamic and kinetic processes are a third criterion. The EXOSPHERE is the region at the "top" of the atmosphere, above the critical level of escape, in which atmospheric particles can move in free orbits, subject only to the earth's gravitation.

Composition is a fourth criterion. The HOMOSPHERE is the shell in which there is so little photo-dissociation or gravitational separation that the mean molecular weight of the atmosphere is sensibly constant; the HETEROSPHERE is the region above this, where the atmospheric composition and mean molecular weight is not constant. The boundary between the two is probably at the level at which molecular oxygen begins to be dissociated, and this occurs in the vicinity of 80 or 90 km.

The term mesosphere has been given another definition which does not fit into any logical set of criteria, i.e., the shell between the exosphere and the ionosphere. This use of the word mesosphere has not been widely accepted. (24)

ATOLL. A ring-like "coral" island or islands encircling or nearly encircling a lagoon. It should be noted that the term "coral" island for most of these tropical islands is incorrect, as calcareous algae often forms much more than 50% of them. (27)

ATOLL REEF. A ring-shaped, coral reef, often carrying low sand islands, enclosing a body of water. (10)

ATOM. The smallest particle of an elementary substance. It consists of one or more positive protons and neutral neutrons surrounded by such a number of electrons as will balance the positive charge. (36)

ATOMIC NUMBER. The number of positive charges or protons inside the nucleus of an atom; it is also the number of electrons possessed by an uncharged atom. The atomic number distinguishes each one of the chemical elements and starts with hydrogen with the atomic number of 1 and goes through uranium with 92, the last of the natural occurring elements. (39)

ATOMIC WEIGHT. The determination of the weight of an atom as measured arbitrarily with oxygen having the weight of 16.0000. It is found that the weight of atoms can be expressed very nearly as whole numbers. These whole numbers represent the rough atomic weight which also express the sum of the particles in the nucleus of an atom. Most uranium has 92 protons and 136 neutrons. The sum of these, or 238, is the rough atomic weight of the most abundant kind of uranium. (39)

ATS. Air Transportable Sonar.

ATTENUATION ANOMALY. That part of the propagation anomaly which may be identified with that portion of the total loss which appears as a constant fractional change per unit length of path. (4)

AUDIO FREQUENCY. An audio frequency is any frequency corresponding to a normally audible sound wave. (Ranges roughly from 15,000 to 20,000 cycles per second.) (1)

AUGUSTE PICCARD. A manned submersible vehicle (Swiss).

AUSTRALIA CURRENT. Branch of the SOUTH EQUATORIAL CURRENT of the Pacific Ocean, which leaves the latter in the neighborhood of the Fiji Islands and flows southwesterly until it reaches the east coast of Australia where it takes a southerly direction along this coast. (14)

AUTEC. Atlantic Underwater Test and Evaluation Center, a Navy test center located in the Tongue of the Ocean section of the Bahamas.

AUTOTROPHIC. Organisms able to manufacture their own food, such as green plants. (18)

AUXOSPORE. A reproductive cell in diatoms usually resulting from the union of two smaller cells or their contents and associated with rejuvenescence in cells that have become progressively smaller because of repeated divisions. (20)

AV. U. S. Navy designation for a Seaplane Tender.

AVAILABLE POWER. The rate at which a given source would deliver energy to a load having an impedance which is the conjugate of the source impedance is designated as the available power of that source. (4)

AVAILABLE POWER LOSS. The available power loss of a transducer connecting an energy source and an energy load is the transmission loss measured by the ratio of the source power to the output power of the transducer. (4)

AVB. U. S. Navy designation for an Advanced Aviation Base Ship.

AVERAGE AREA OF THE HUMAN BODY. The average area of the human body is about 2500 square inches. (37)

AVERAGE LIMIT OF ICE. Average seaward extent of ice during a normal winter.

AVM. U. S. Navy designation for a Guided Missile Ship.

AVP. U. S. Navy designation for a Small Seaplane Tender.

AVS. U. S. Navy designation for an Aviation Supply Ship.

AVT. U. S. Navy designation for an Auxiliary Aircraft Transport.

AW. U. S. Navy designation for a Distilling Ship.

AXIS OF ACOUSTIC SYMMETRY. For many transducers the three-dimensional directivity is such that it may be represented by the surface generated by rotating a two-dimensional directivity pattern about the axis corresponding to the reference bearing of the transducer. This axis may then be described as an axis of acoustic symmetry, or, more briefly, as the acoustic axis. (4)

AZCHERNIRO. Azov and Black Sea Research Institute of Marine Fisheries and Oceanography (USSR).

AZIMUTH. Azimuth of a body is the arc of the horizon intercepted between the north or south point and the foot of the vertical circle passing through the body. It is reckoned in degrees from either the north or south point clockwise entirely around the horizon. Azimuth of a current is the direction toward which it is flowing, and is usually reckoned from the north point. (14)

AZORES HIGH. See BERMUDA HIGH.

B

BACK. 1. Of the wind, to change direction in a counterclockwise direction in the northern hemisphere, and a clockwise direction in the southern hemisphere. Change in the opposite direction is called veer.
    2. To go stern first, or to operate the engines in reverse. (17)

BACKBEACH. See BACKSHORE.

BACKGROUND NOISE. Background noise is made up of sound from a variety of sources, other than the desired signal, as indicated by the block diagram below:

BACKRUSH. The seaward return of the water following the uprush of the waves. For any given tide stage the point of farthest return seaward of the backrush is known as the limit of backrush or limit of backwash. (10)

BACKSCATTERING. See REVERBERATION.

BACKSCATTERING CROSS SECTION. The acoustic backscattering cross section of an object is an area equal to 4π times the product of the square of a unit distance and the square of the sound pressure scattered by the object, back in the direction from which the sound has come as observed at unit distance from the acoustic center of the object, divided by the square of the sound pressure of the plane wave incident on the object. The unit of the cross section is the square of the unit distance. (2)

BACKSHORE (BACKBEACH). That zone of the shore or beach lying between the foreshore and the coast line and acted upon by waves only during severe storms, especially when combined with exceptionally high water. (10)

BACKWASH. Water or waves thrown back by an obstruction such as a ship, breakwater, cliff, etc. See also BACKRUSH. (10)

BAGUIO. See TYPHON.

BAGUIO. A tropical cyclone. The term is customarily used only in the Philippine Islands. (17)

BALI WIND. A strong east wind at the eastern end of Java. (17)

BALL BREAKER. Coring and sampling activities in deep-sea areas present the problem of determining the moment of contact of the instrument with the bottom in order that the winch may be stopped immediately. When sampling in deep water the weight of the coring device is often a small part of the total weight of the wire out and of the variable loads caused by the ship's rolling. Thus, no apparent drop in tension may be observed on the dynamometer when the bottom is reached. One device used to indicate contact between corer and bottom is the ball breaker. A hollow glass ball, 3 to 5 inches in diameter, is lightly held in a frame attached to the trigger line above the triggering weight of the corer. Above the ball is a weight with a sharp protrusion pointing downward. When the corer strikes the bottom the line becomes slack releasing the weight which strikes the ball. The resulting implosion may be heard on some types of echo sounders or received on a Brush recorder wired to the echo sounder. (35)

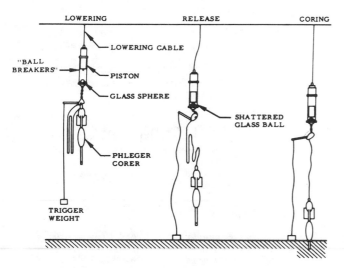

BALL ICE. Numerous floating spheres of SEA ICE having diameters of one to two inches. The balls are very soft and spongy; no internal structure can be distinguished clearly. The balls are generally in belts similar to SLUSH which forms at the same time. Ball Ice has very rarely been reported. (25)

BALNIRO. The Baltic Research Institute of Marine Fisheries and Oceanography (USSR).

BAND ELIMINATION FILTER. A band elimination filter is a wave filter that has a large insertion loss for one frequency band, with the cutoff frequencies for this band neither zero nor infinite. (8)

BAND LEVEL. A given spectrum level is usually associated with a specific frequency. To identify a transmission level measuring the power in a specified frequency band, or the acoustic intensity in a specified frequency band, it may be designated as a band level. (4)

BAND-PASS FILTER. A band-pass filter is a wave filter that has a single transmission band extending from a lower cutoff frequency greater than zero to a finite upper cutoff frequency. (9)

BAND PRESSURE, LEVEL. The band pressure level of a sound for a specified frequency band is the sound pressure level for the sound contained within the restricted band. The reference pressure must be specified. (2)

BAND RATIO. In many problems the ratio, f_b/f_a, between the limiting frequencies of a given band is of more significance than their difference. This ratio, which may be spoken of as the band ratio, is represented graphically by an interval on a logarithmic scale of frequency. (4)

BAND WIDTH. When frequency is plotted against a linear scale any interval along that scale measures the difference, $f_b - f_a$, between the frequency of the upper boundary of the band represented and the frequency of the lower boundary. This difference is known as the band width of the frequency band. Bands having equal widths are represented on a linear frequency scale by intervals of equal length. (4)

BANK. (1) The rising ground bordering a lake, river, or sea. On a river designated as right or left as it would appear facing downstream. (2) An elevation of the sea floor of large area, surrounded by deeper water, but safe for surface navigation; a submerged plateau or shelf, a shoal, or shallow. (10)

BANNER CLOUD. A bannerlike cloud streaming off from a mountain peak in a strong wind. (17)

BAR. 1. An offshore ridge or mound of sand, gravel, or other unconsolidated material submerged at least at high tide, especially at the mouth of a river or estuary, or lying a short distance from and usually parallel to, the beach. (11)
2. A unit of pressure equal to 1,000,000 dynes per square centimeter, 1,000 millibars, 29.53 inches of mercury. (24)

BARALYME. A compressed pill consisting of a blended mixture of barium octohydrate and calcium hydroxide. It is used as a carbon dioxide absorbent in rebreathing (diving) systems.

BARAT. A heavy northwest squall in Menado Bay on the north coast of the island of Celebes, prevalent from December to February. (17)

BAR, BAYMOUTH. A bar extending partially or entirely across the mouth of a bay. (11)

BARBER. 1. A severe storm at sea during which spray and precipitation freeze onto the decks and rigging of boats.
2. (Also spelled berber.) In the Gulf of St. Lawrence, a local form of blizzard in which the wind-borne ice particles almost cut the skin from the face. (24)

BAR BUOY. A buoy marking the location of a bar. (17)

BAR, CUSPATE. A crescent shaped bar united with the shore at each end. It may be formed by a single spit growing from shore turning back to again meet the shore, or by two spits growing from shore united to form a bar of sharply cuspate form. (10)

BARNACLES. Marine crustaceans, most of which attach and grow on hard objects at or below the surface and have a calcareous shell. Some are called Sea Acorns. (15)

BAROCLINITY. The state of stratification in a fluid in which surfaces of constant pressure (isobaric) intersect surfaces of constant density (isosteric). The number, per unit area, of isobaric-isosteric SOLENOIDS intersecting a given surface is a measure of the baroclinity. If the surface is horizontal, this number N is given by

$$N = \frac{\partial \alpha}{\partial x}\frac{\partial \rho}{\partial y} - \frac{\partial p}{\partial x}\frac{\partial \alpha}{\partial y}$$

where α is the specific volume and ρ the pressure. (24)

BAROMIL. The unit length used in graduating a mercury barometer in the centimeter-gram-second system.

(continued on next page)

If the barometer is located at 45° latitude at sea level and its temperature is 0°C, a length increment of one baromil will correspond to a pressure increment of one millibar. Corrections must be applied at other locations. (24)

BAROTRAUMA. A generic term for injury caused by pressure. Although "SQUEEZE" is a colloquialism, it is an excellent descriptive term for all of the phenomena which occur when a rigid closed space within the body or on its surface fails to equalize with external pressure during descent, or is for some reason vented to lower pressure than that acting at the depth. (37)

BAROTROPY. The state of a fluid in which surfaces of constant density (or temperature) are coincident with surfaces of constant pressure; it is the state of zero BAROCLINITY. Mathematically, the equation of barotropy states that the gradients of the density and pressure fields are proportional:

$$\nabla \rho = \beta \nabla p$$

where ρ is the density, P the pressure, and β a function of thermodynamic variables, called the coefficient of barotropy. With the equation of state, this relation determines the spatial distribution of all state parameters once these are specified on any surface. For a homogeneous atmosphere, $\beta = 0$; for an adiabatic atmosphere, $\beta = C_v/C_p\, RT$ where C_v and C_p are the specific heats at constant volume and pressure, respectively, R the gas constant, and T the Kelvin temperature; for an isothermal atmosphere, $\beta = 1/RT$.

It is not necessary that a fluid which is barotropic at the moment will remain so; but the implication that it does often accompanies the assumption of barotropy. In this sense the assumption, or a modification thereof, is widely applied in dynamic meteorology. The important consequences are that absolute vorticity is conserved (to the extent that the motion is two dimensional), and that the geostrophic wind has no shear with height. (24)

BARRANCA. A large rift in piedmont ice or shelf ice. A smaller rift with steep sides is called a donga. (17)

BARRIER BEACH (OFFSHORE BARRIER). A bar essentially parallel to the shore, the crest of which is above high water. (10)

BARRIER ICEBERG. See TABULAR ICEBERG.

BARRIER ISLAND. A wave-built deposit of sand mainly, raised above sea-level by constructive wave action and separated from the shore by a lagoon. Its height may be increased by dune formation. (27)

BARRIER LAYER CELL. For ambient light measurements in the upper 50-100 meters a barrier-layer-type cell generally is used. For example, the Weston photronic cell, responds to light wave lengths between 3,000 and 7,500 Å with a maximum response around 5,500 Å. With the proper detection device this cell has sufficient sensitivity to measure radiation of as little as 10^{-4} gm cal/cm^2/min. (35)

BARRIER REEF. A reef which roughly parallels land but is some distance offshore, with deeper water adjacent to the land, as contrasted with a FRINGING REEF closely attached to the shore. (17)

BARYE. The term "barye" is used in some European countries to mean one dyne per square centimeter, or one microbar as defined in American Standard Acoustical Terminology, S1. 1-1960. See MICROBAR. (1)

BASIC FREQUENCY. Any given oscillation can always be considered to be made up of a number of sinusoidal components each having a different frequency. In any given instance, that frequency which is considered to be the most important is called the basic frequency of the oscillation. (9)

BASIN. 1. A depression of the sea floor more or less equidimensional in form. When the length is much greater than the width, the feature is a TROUGH. (26)
2. An area in a tidal region in which water can be kept at a desired level by means of a gate. Also called tidal basin.
3. A relatively small cavity in the bottom or shore, usually created or enlarged by excavation, large enough to receive one or more vessels for a specific purpose. (27)

BATHOLITH. A large igneous intrusive mass, having an exposed area greater than 40 square miles and no visible or clearly inferable floor. (27)

"BATH SPONGE". See SPONGIN.

BATHYCONDUCTOGRAPH (BC). 1. A device used to measure the electrical conductivity of sea water at various depths.
2. The letters, "BC", are also used as an abbreviation in oceanographic work for Bottom Contour. (35)

BATHYMETER. The Naval Ordnance Test Station developed a device which they call the "bathymeter." This instrument measures temperature, pressure, and sound velocity to depths up to 7 miles. The device is completely transistorized and uses frequency modulation for telemetering. (35)

BATHYMETRIC. Pertaining to depth measurement.

BATHYMETRIC CHART. A topographic chart of the bed of a body of water, or a part of it. Generally, bathymetric charts show depths by contour lines and gradient tints. (17)

BATHYMETRY. The art or science of determining depths of water. (17)

BATHYSCAPH. Literally means "deep-boat". Refers usually to those small submersibles which are designed much more for going to a great depth than for horizontal mobility.

BATHYSYSTEM. A coined word for a permanent sea floor installation.

BATHYTHERMOGRAM. The record obtained by a single immersion of a BATHYTHERMOGRAPH. (4)

BATHYTHERMOGRAPH (BT). The Bathythermograph is an instrument that determines water temperature as a function of depth. When the BT is lowered into the sea a plot of temperature vs. depth is automatically recorded either on smoked glass by a stylus, or with pen and ink on paper. Mechanical as well as electronic Bathythermographs are available. In the mechanical BT the temperature sensing device is a Bourdon tube and the depth finder is a bellows system. In the electronic BT the temperature sensing unit is a thermistor while the depth finder is a Bourdon tube activated potentiometer. (30)

BAY. (1) A recess in the shore or an inlet of a sea or lake between two CAPES or HEADLANDS, not as large as a GULF, but larger than a COVE. (1)
(2) A portion of the sea which penetrates into the interior of the land. It is usually wider in the middle than at the entrance. It may be similar to a gulf, but smaller.
(3) A portion of the sea partly surrounded by ice. See BIGHT. (17)

BAY ICE. Young, flat ice of sufficient thickness to impede navigation. In the antarctic this term also has been used at times for heavy LAND FLOES. (25)

BAYOU. A minor, sluggish waterway or estuarial creek, generally tidal or with a slow or imperceptible current, and with its course generally through lowlands or swamps, tributary to or connecting with other bodies of water. Various specific meanings have been implied in different parts of the southern United States. Sometimes called slough. (17)

BB. U. S. Navy designation for a Battleship.

BCF. Bureau of Commercial Fisheries.

BDHI. Bearing Distance Heading Indicator.

BDI. Bearing Deviation Indicator (on ASW gear).

BEACH. (1) The zone of unconsolidated material that extends landward from the low water line to the place where there is marked change in material or physiographic form... or to the line of permanent vegetation (usually the effective limit of storm waves). The seaward limit of the beach - unless otherwise specified - is the mean low water line. A beach includes FORESHORE and BACKSHORE. (2) Sometimes, the material which is more or less in active transport, alongshore or on-and-off shore, rather than the zone. (11)

BEACH BERM. A nearly horizontal portion of the beach or backshore formed by the deposit of material by wave action. Some beaches have no berms, others have one or several. (10)

BEACHCOMBER. A long, curling wave. Also called comber. (17)

BEACH CUSP. See CUSP.

BEACH EROSION BOARD STEP-RESISTANCE GAUGE. This is a fixed wave gauge which utilizes a 25-foot length of sealed pipe housing a series of electrical contact points spaced at intervals of 0.2 foot. The contact points (made from spark plugs) are connected to a resistance circuit within the pipe. The gauge is mounted vertically on a supporting structure, such as a pier, and the bottom of gauge is set below the lowest expected wave trough. (The top of the gauge must be above the highest expected wave crest.) The exposed tips of the plugs are covered with lead to reduce corrosion effects. In order to overcome the short-circuiting effects of the sea water film which adheres after a wave passes, the gauge pipe and the bases of the spark plugs are covered with neoprene. (35)

BEACH FACE. The section of the beach normally exposed to the action of the wave uprush. The FORESHORE zone of a BEACH. (10)

BEACH, FEEDER. An artificially widened beach serving to nourish downdrift beaches by natural littoral currents or forces. (11)

BEACH PROFILE. The intersection of the ground surface with a vertical plane; may extend from the top of the dune line to the seaward limit of sand movement. (11)

BEACH RIDGE. An essentially continuous mound of beach material behind the beach that has been heaped up by wave or other action. Ridges may occur singly or as a series of approximately parallel deposits. In England they are called fulls. (11)

BEACH SCARP. An almost vertical slope along the beach caused by erosion by wave action. It may vary in height from a few inches to several feet, depending on wave action and the nature and composition of the beach. (11)

BEACH WIDTH. The horizontal dimension of the beach as measured normal to the shore line. (11)

BEAM PATTERN. See DIRECTIONAL RESPONSE PATTERN.

BEAM SEA. Waves moving in a direction approximately 90° from the heading. Those moving in a direction approximately opposite to the heading are called HEAD SEA, those moving in the general direction of the heading are called FOLLOWING SEA, and those moving in a direction approximately 45° from the heading (striking the quarter) are called QUARTERING SEA. See CROSS SEA. (17)

BEAM TIDE. A tidal current setting in a direction approximately 90° from the heading of a vessel. One setting in a direction approximately 90° from the course is called a cross tide. In common usage these two expressions are usually used synonymously. One setting in a direction approximately opposite to the heading is called a head tide. One setting in such a direction as to increase the speed of a vessel is called a fair tide. (17)

BEAM WIDTH. The beam width of a directional transducer at a given frequency in a given plane including the beam axis, is the angle included between the two directions, one to the left and the other to the right of the axis, at which the angular deviation loss has a specified value. Typical values that are used in the specification are losses of 3, 6, or 10 decibels. (9)

BEARING RATE. Rate of change of bearing. (7)

BEATS. Beats are periodic variations that result from the superposition of two simple harmonic quantities of different frequencies. They involve a periodic increase and decrease of amplitude at the beat frequency which is equal to the difference in the frequencies of the two parent signals. Thus, if two pure tones having frequencies of 300 and 400 cycles per second are heard by a listener, then he will also sense a frequency equal to the difference, namely 100 cycles per second. This is a beat frequency. (9)

BEAUFORT WIND SCALE. A system of estimating and reporting wind speeds, invented in the early nineteenth century by Admiral Beaufort of the British Navy. It was originally based on the effects of various wind speeds on the amount of canvas that a full-rigged frigate of the period could carry, but has since been modified and modernized. In its present form for international meteorological use it equates (a) Beaufort force (or Beaufort number), (b) wind speed, (c) descriptive term, and (d) visible effects upon land object or sea surface. (24)

"BEAVER". A manned submersible vehicle (US).

BED. The ground upon which a body of water rests. The term is usually used with a modifier to indicate the type of water body, as river bed. (17)

BEL. The bel is a unit of level when the base of the logarithm is 10. Use of the bel is restricted to level of quantities proportional to power. (1)

BELAT. A strong land wind from the north or northwest which sometimes blows across the southeastern coast of Arabia, and is accompanied by a hazy atmosphere due to sand blown from the interior desert. (17)

BELL BUOY. A buoy equipped with a bell. In United

States waters, a bell buoy is a flat-topped float with a skeleton superstructure supporting the bell. (17)

BENCH. 1. A level or gently sloping erosion plane inclined seaward.

2. A nearly horizontal area at about the level of maximum high water or the sea side of a DIKE. (11)

BENCH MARKS (B.M.). A fixed point used as a reference for elevation. (11)

BENDING. The first stage in the formation of PRESSURE ICE caused by the action of current, wind, tide, or air temperature changes. Bending is more characteristic of thin, plastic ice than heavier forms. (25)

BENDS. See DECOMPRESSION SICKNESS.

BENGUELA CURRENT. The northward flowing current along the west coast of Africa; it is one of the swiftest of ocean currents, the strongest current in the South Atlantic. It is a continuation of the SOUTH ATLANTIC CURRENT. Proceeding toward the equator, the Benguela current gradually leaves the coast and continues as the northern portion of the SOUTH EQUATORIAL CURRENT. (24)

BENTHIC DIVISION. A primary division of the sea which includes all of the ocean floor. The Benthic Division is subdivided into the LITTORAL SYSTEM (the ocean floor lying in water depths ranging from the high water mark to 200 meters or the edge of the continental shelf), and the DEEP-SEA SYSTEM (ocean floor lying in water deeper than 200 meters). The systems are further subdivided into the EULITTORAL ZONE (0-50 meters), SUBLITTORAL ZONE (50-200 meters), ARCHIBENTHIC ZONE (200-1000 meters), and the ABYSSAL-BENTHIC ZONE (1000 meters and greater). (13)

BENTHITHERMOPROBE. This instrument was constructed when it was discovered that the bottom of some shallow bodies of water is significantly warmer than the water immediately above the bottom. The probe is a positive means of placing the sensing element directly on the bottom and positioning it accurately. In a soft bottom it can be forced down in the sediment a short distance to examine temperature gradients in the upper half meter or so. A brass friction fitting at the sensing element end of the probe, resembling the web-ring at the lower end of a ski pole, is moved upward along the probe by the surface of the sediment as the probe is forced into the mud. The maximum extent of penetration into the sediment can thus be determined. The instrument consists of a pair of matched thermistors potted in the end of a slender aluminum tube. It is connected to an indicator case containing the bridge circuit by a two conductor cable. (30)

BENTHOS. The category of marine organisms that live on, in, or close to the bottom of the oceans. (27)

BENTHOS V. A manned submersible vehicle (US).

BERGY BIT. Name applied to a small iceberg about the size of a house. (12)

BERM CREST (BERM EDGE). The seaward limit of a BERM. (11)

BERM EDGE. See BERM CREST.

BERMUDA HIGH. The semi-permanent SUBTROPICAL HIGH of the North Atlantic Ocean, so named especially when it is located in the western part of the ocean. This same high, when displaced toward the eastern part of the Atlantic, is known as the Azores high. On mean charts of sea-level pressure, this high is a principal center of action.

Warm and humid conditions prevail over the eastern United States, particularly in summer, when the Bermuda high is well-developed and extends westward. (24)

BERTH. A place for securing a vessel. (17)

BESET. Surrounded so closely by sea ice that steering control is lost. The term does not imply pressure. If the vessel is incapable of proceeding, it is icebound. If pressure is involved, the vessel is said to be nipped. (17)

BIDIRECTIONAL HYDROPHONE. A bidirectional hydrophone is a HYDROPHONE whose response is a maximum for sound incident at two directions 180° apart. (1)

BIDIRECTIONAL TRANSDUCER. A transducer having maximum response in both directions along a reference axis passing through its center is said to be bidirectional. (4)

BIFILAR CURRENT INDICATOR. An apparatus formerly used for obtaining the direction of the current at different depths. It consisted of several sets of vanes and indicators mounted on a shaft to obtain simultaneously the direction of the current at different depths. Each vane was attached by two wires to an indicator which moved over a PELORUS. (14)

BIFURCATION BUOY. A buoy marking the point at which a channel divides into two branches when proceeding from seaward. The opposite is JUNCTION BUOY. See MIDDLE GROUND BUOY. (17)

BIGHT. A slight indentation in the shore line of an open coast or of a bay, usually crescent shaped. (10)

BILATERAL SYMMETRY. Symmetry such that a body or part can be divided by one median plane into equivalent right and left halves, each a mirror image of the other. (19)

BILATERAL TRANSDUCER. A bilateral transducer is a transducer capable of transmission in either direction between its terminations. (1)

BINARY FISSION. A reproductive process in which an individual organism divides into two halves, often equal, after which each grows to the original form. (19)

BINARY NOTATION. A system of positional notation in which the digits are coefficients of powers of the base 2 in the same way as the digits in the conventional decimal system are coefficients of powers of the base 10. (31)

Binary notation employs only two digits, 1 and 0, therefore is used extensively in computers where the 'on' and 'off' positions of a switch or storage device can represent the two digits.

In decimal notation $111 = (1 \times 10^2) + (1 \times 10^1) + (1 \times 10^0) = 100 + 10 + 1 =$ one hundred and eleven.

In binary notation $111 = (1 \times 2^2) + (1 \times 2^1) + (1 \times 2^0) = 4 + 2 + 1 =$ seven.

BINNACLE. The stand in which a compass is mounted. For a magnetic compass it is usually provided with means of mounting various correctors for adjustment and compensation of the compass. (17)

BIOCHORE. See BIOTOPE.

BIOCOENOSIS. See BIOTOPE.

BIOGENOUS DEPOSITS. Deposits having more than 30 per cent material derived from organisms. (27)

BIOLOGY (MARINE). The study of the life history

and ecology of marine and brackish water plants and animals. (15)

BIOLUMINESCENCE. The emission of light by living organisms. (15)

BIONEPHELOMETER. This is an instrument for recording the intensity of scatter at 90° from a Tyndall beam in a light-tight chamber through which seawater is pumped from an overside collector. It appears that intensity of scatter may be related to settling volume of the water being examined by the instrument. Settling volumes are used by marine biologists as an indication of standing crop of the water. The instrument itself consists of a Tyndall chamber into which seawater is conducted from a plastic hose through an 8° diffuser. Water is conducted from the chamber through an extraction cone to the outlet hose. Extraction ratio in the diffuser is approximately 6:1. A light source and a barrier-layer photocell are situated in the chamber wall at 90° to the flow axis, disposed at 90 to each other. Opposite each is a conical light trap. A plastic window separates the light source and photocell from the seawater. A condensing lens is situated in front of the light source assuring that a parallel beam of light shines through the plastic window into the chamber. Output of the photocell is fed to an amplifier and recorder. (30)

BIONICS. The study of systems which function after the manner of, or in a manner characteristic of, or resembling, living systems. (31)

BIOSPHERE. That transition zone between earth and atmosphere within which most forms of terrestrial life are commonly found; the outer portion of the GEOSPHERE and inner or lower portion of the ATMOSPHERE. (12)

BIOTA. The animal and plant life of a region; flora and fauna collectively. (38)

BIOTOPE. A biotope, or niche, is an area of which the principal habitat conditions and the living forms which are adapted to them are uniform. Smaller habitat anomalies found within the biotope are called facies. The community of forms in a biotope is called a biocoenosis. Biotopes having certain characteristics in common are united into larger divisions known as biochores. (13)

BIPOLAR DISTRIBUTION. See BIPOLARITY.

BIPOLARITY (BIPOLAR DISTRIBUTION). A break in the continuity of distribution of a species or higher division is called discontinuous distribution, and when this occurs in a meridional direction so that the animals involved are absent from the tropical belt, the phenomena is known as bipolarity or bipolar distribution. According to older usage, the term referred only to animals living in arctic and antarctic waters, but now it is used also to indicate those living in the temperate zones. The term bipolarity of relationship is used to indicate a bipolar distribution in which animals of higher latitudes are more closely related taxonomically to each other than to those of lower latitudes. There is also bipolarity of phenomena such as are associated with mass vernal production of diatoms, for example, or with production of great numbers of individuals but of relatively few species. Northern littoral or surface pelagic stenohaline animals that are sufficiently euryhaline and eurybathic, may form a continuous distribution from high northern to high southern latitudes by living in deep water in that part of their meridional range crossing the equitorial region. This is referred to as tropical submergence. The term bipolar-epiplanktonic is used to describe the distribution of related high northern and high southern planktonic animals connected through tropical submergence. (13)

BIPOLARITY OF PHENOMENA. See BIPOLARITY.

BIPOLARITY OF RELATIONSHIP. See BIPOLARITY.

BIRAMOUS. Consisting of or possessing two branches, as a crustacean appendage. (19)

BITTERN. The liquid remaining after sea water has been concentrated by evaporation until salt has crystallized. (24)

BLACK AND WHITE ICEBERG. An ICEBERG having a dark, opaque portion containing sand and stones, and separated from the white portion by a definite line of demarcation. (25)

BLACK ICE. Ice crust which is transparent enough to reveal the color of the sea water beneath. (17)

BLACK STREAM. See KUROSHIO CURRENT.

BLIND ROLLERS. Long, high swells which have increased in height, almost to the breaking point, as they pass over shoals or run in shoaling water. (11)

BLINK. A glare on the underside of extensive cloud areas created by light reflected from snow or ice covered surfaces; also observable in a clear sky. Blink caused by ice surfaces is usually yellowish-white in contrast to the whitish, brighter glare caused by snow surfaces. This distinction is sometimes difficult to perceive. In contrast to SNOW-BLINK and ICEBLINK, the sky is dark above bare land or open water surfaces. (25)

BLOCK. A fragment of SEA ICE ranging in size from 6 to 30 feet across. (25)

BLOCKED ADMITTANCE. The blocked admittance of a transducer is the input admittance when the output terminals are short-circuited. (4)

BLOCKED IMPEDANCE. The blocked impedance of a transducer is its input impedance when its load terminals are open-circuited. (4)

BLOCKY ICEBERG. An ICEBERG with steep, precipitous sides, and with either a horizontal or nearly horizontal upper surface. (25)

BLUE-GREEN ALGAE (MYXOPHYCEAE). A class of algae which contains only small, poorly organized plants, some consisting of only a single cell, while others are multicellular. The blue color is due to a water-soluble accessory pigment, phycocyanin. However, some forms, such as Trichodesmium erythraeum, exhibit a red pigment and is responsible for the red color sometimes observed in surface waters. The Red Sea, for instance, owes its name to this form. Some brackish-water forms are responsible for the sliming occasionally observed in the calm waters of fjords and in the Gulf of Bothnia. Although widespread in both fresh and brackish-water, Myxophyceae is of less general importance in the oceans than GREEN, BROWN, RED and YELLOW-GREEN ALGEA. (13)

BLUE ICE. The oldest and hardest form of GLACIER ICE. It is distinguished by a slightly bluish or greenish color.

BLUE MUD. A common variety of deep-sea mud, having a bluish-gray color due to the presence of organic matter and finely divided iron sulfides; calcium carbonate present in variable amounts to 35 per cent. (27)

BLUFF. A cliff with a broad face, or a relatively long strip of land rising abruptly above surrounding land or a body of water. (17)

BOA-MILS. Broad Ocean Area-Missile Impact Locating System.

BOD. Biological Oxygen Demand.

BOLD COAST. A prominent land mass that rises steeply from the sea. (11)

BOOMERANG SEDIMENT CORER. This (FREE INSTRUMENT type) device can be dropped over the side of a moving ship where it will sink rapidly to the ocean floor, take a core of sediment, release ballast and automatically return to the surface for retrieval. It is designed for nighttime recovery. (35)

BORA. A cold, northerly wind blowing from the Hungarian basin into the Adriatic Sea. (17)

BORASCO. A thunderstorm or violent squall, especially in the Mediterranean. (17)

BORE. A very rapid rise of the tide in which the advancing water presents an abrupt front of considerable height. In shallow estuaries where the range of tide is large, the high water is propagated inward faster than the low water because of the greater depth at high water. If the high water overtakes the low water, an abrupt front is presented with the high-water crest finally falling forward as the tide continues to advance. Also called eager, mascaret, and pororoca. (14)

BORING. Forcing a vessel under power through ice, by breaking a lead. (17)

BOTTOM. The ground under a body of water. The terms bed, floor, and bottom have nearly the same meaning, but bed refers more specifically to the whole hollowed area supporting a body of water, floor refers to the essentially horizontal surface constituting the principal level of the ground under a body of water, and bottom refers to any ground covered with water. (17)

BOTTOM ICE. Ice formed on the bed of a river, lake, or very shallow sea irrespective of its nature of formation. (25)

BOTTOM ICE (ANCHOR ICE). In shoal water and streams particularly where motion is sufficient to cause thorough mixing, freezing temperatures may extend from the surface to the bottom. When this occurs, ice crystals may form at any depth. Because of their decreased density, they tend to rise to the surface, unless they form at the bottom and attach themselves there. This is called bottom ice or anchor ice and continues to grow as additional ice freezes to that already formed. (12)

BOTTOM REVERBERATION. See REVERATION

BOTTOM WATER. The water mass at the deepest part of the water column. It is the densest water that is permitted to occupy that position by the regional topography. In the case of a BASIN, bottom water may be formed locally, or it may represent the densest water that has existed at SILL DEPTH in the recent past. (24)

BOUGUER ANOMALY. A method of stating the isostatic anomaly, derived from gravity observations. It allows for height above sea-level and the visible excess or deficit of mass. It is called after Bouguer, who first noticed that the Andes did not disturb gravity as much as their mass would suggest. (27)

BOUNDARY WAVES. See INTERNAL WAVES.

BOURDON TUBE. A closed curved tube of elliptical cross-section used in some thermometers and barometers. The Bourdon-tube thermometer consists of a Bourdon tube which is completely filled with liquid. The expansion of the liquid due to a temperature change causes an increase in the radius of curvature of the tube. The curvature may then be measured by the travel of the tip of the tube. The Bourdon-tube barometer consists of an evacuated Bourdon tube and operates in a similar manner. In both cases the curvature is a measure of the difference between the pressure inside the tube and that outside. (24)

BOW AND BEAM BEARINGS. Successive relative bearings (right or left) of 45° and 90° taken on a fixed object to obtain a running fix. The length of the run between such bearings is equal to the distance of the craft from the object at the time the object is broad on the beam, neglecting current. The 45° bearing is also called a fourpoint bearing. (17)

BOWEN RATIO. At a water surface, the ratio of the energy flux upward as sensible heat to the energy flux used in evaporation. The Bowen ratio is highly variable and is sometimes negative. It has been estimated that an average value for the ocean surface is about +0.1. (24)

BOX GAGE. A tide gage that is operated by a float in a long vertical box to which the tide is admitted through an opening in the bottom. In the original type of box gage the float supported a graduated rod which rose and fell with the tide, the height of the tide being read on the rod at a point corresponding to a fixed reading mark. When the rod was graduated with numbers increasing toward the float the gage readings increased with the rising tide, but when the rod was graduated from zero upward the gage readings increased with the falling tide. (14)

BOXING THE COMPASS. Naming the points and quarter points of the compass in order clockwise around the circle, beginning with north. (24)

BOYLE'S LAW. States that at a constant temperature the volume of a gas varies inversely as the absolute pressure while the density varies directly as the pressure. (That is, if the pressure on a gas is doubled the density is also doubled, but the volume is decreased to 1/2 of the original volume.) (37)

BRACKISH WATER. Water in which salinity values range from approximately 0.50 to 17.00 parts per thousand. (15)

BRADYCARDIA. A slowing of the heart rate that takes place in all diving mammals including man.

BRANCHIAL. Referring to gills. (19)

BRASH. See BRASH ICE.

BRASH ICE. Small fragments of sea or river ice less than 6 feet in diameter. (15)

BRAVE WEST WINDS. A nautical term for the strong and rather persistent westerly winds over the oceans in temperate latitudes.
    They occur between latitudes 40° and 65° in the northern hemisphere and 35° to 65° in the southern hemisphere, where they are more regular and are strongest between 40° and 50°S (roaring forties). They are associated with the strong pressure gradient on the equatorial side of the frequent depressions passing eastward in sub-polar temperate latitudes; hence they fluctuate mainly between southwest and northwest. (24)

BRAZIL CURRENT. A South Atlantic Ocean current flowing southward and southwestward along the south-

BREAK-DOWN VOLTAGE. The voltage at which an insulator or dielectric ruptures; or the voltage at which ionization and conduction begin in a gas or vapor. (36)

east coast of Brazil, from a point west of Ascension Island nearly to the Rio de la Plata, widening and curving southeastward, and continuing as part of the SOUTH ATLANTIC CURRENT. The Brazil current is the southern branch of the SOUTH EQUATORIAL CURRENT, which divides between Ascension Island and Brazil, and it forms the western part of the general counterclockwise oceanic circulation of the South Atlantic Ocean. (17)

BREAKER. A sea-surface wave which has become too steep to be stable. Waves in shoaling water become higher and shorter (hence steeper) as the water becomes shallower. When the steepness (ratio of wave height to wave length) exceeds 1/7, the laws which govern surface-wave motion can no longer be satisfied and the crest of the wave outraces the body of the wave to form a foaming white turbulent mass of water called a breaker.
　　Roughly, three kinds of breakers can be distinguished, depending primarily on the gradient of the bottom: (a) Spilling breakers (over nearly flat bottom) which form a foamy patch at the crest and break gradually over a considerable distance; (b) Plunging breakers (over fairly steep bottom gradient) which peak up, curl over with a tremendous overhanging mass, and then break with a crash; (c) Surging breakers (over very steep bottom gradients) which do not spill or plunge but surge up the beach face.
　　Waves also break in deep water if they build too high while being generated by the wind, but these are usually short-crested and are termed Whitecaps. (24)

BREAKER DEPTH (BREAKING DEPTH). The still water depth at the point where the wave breaks. (10)

BREAKING DEPTH. See BREAKER DEPTH.

BREAKUP, EARLIEST. Earliest reported date that landfast and pack ice begin to disintegrate prior to final clearance.

BREAKUP, LATEST. Latest reported date that landfast and pack ice begin to disintegrate prior to final clearance.

BREAKWATER. A structure protecting a shore area, harbor, anchorage or BASIN from waves. (11)

BREATHHOLDING. Diving without breathing apparatus requires breath holding during submergence, and methods of prolonging the length of time the breath can be held are always of interest to skindivers and the like. The discomfort which forces a man to resume breathing arises largely from the two main mechanisms concerned with the control of breathing. Rising carbon dioxide tension stimulates the respiratory center directly while falling oxygen tension stimulates it via the chemo-receptors. As the degree of stimulation increases, it becomes more and more difficult to restrain the urge to breathe; and at some point, the individual will "break" and resume breathing. (37)

BRINE. Sea water containing a higher concentration of dissolved salt than that of the ordinary ocean.
　　Brine is produced by the evaporation or freezing of sea water, for, in the latter case, the SEA ICE formed is much less saline than the initial liquid, leaving the adjacent unfrozen water with increased SALINITY. The liquid remaining after sea water has been concentrated by evaporation until salt has crystallized is called BITTERN. (24)

BRITTLE MATERIAL. A nonductile material which fails catastrophically under dynamic loading conditions. CERAMICS are an example of a class of brittle materials.

BROAD ON THE BOW. Bearing 045° relative (broad on the starboard bow) or 315° relative (broad on the

port bow). If the bearings are approximate, the expression on the bow should be used. (17)

BROAD ON THE QUARTER. Bearing 135° relative (broad on the starboard quarter) or 225° relative (broad on the port quarter). If the bearings are approximate, the expression on the quarter should be used. (17)

BROKEN BELT. The transition zone between open water and consolidated ice. (17)

BROKEN ICE. Ice that covers from five-tenths to eight-tenths of the sea surface. Also called loose ice, loose pack ice, open ice, open pack ice, slack ice. (17)

BROKEN WATER. Water having a surface covered with ripples or eddies, and usually surrounded by calm water. (17)

BROWN CLAY. See RED CLAY.

BRUMA. A haze that appears in the afternoons on the coast of Chile when sea air is transported inland. (17)

BRYOZOANS. Minute animals, usually forming plant-like colonies, which attach from the tidal zone to great depths. (15)

B-SCOPE. A Cathode Ray Oscilloscope (CRO) indicator having a rectangular plot of range vs bearing. Spot brightness indicates echo intensity. (5)

BSF&W. Bureau of Sport Fisheries and Wildlife:
　　The BSF&W (U.S. Department of Interior) research program consists of the following two objectives: 1. Life history studies of fish species, to fill gaps in knowledge about distribution in space and time, age, rates of growth, identity, sizes of populations, migratory habits, food habits, reproductive seasons, enemies, parasites, and diseases; and 2. Analysis of environments, to identify and measure factors affecting distribution, movements, abundance, and well-being of game-fish species.
　　Laboratory and field research are at the Bureau's Atlantic Laboratory on Sandy Hook, New Jersey, and its Pacific Laboratory at Tiburon, California.

BT. Bathythermograph.

BUCKET TEMPERATURE. The surface temperature of the sea as measured by a BUCKET THERMOMETER or by immersing a SURFACE THERMOMETER in a freshly-drawn bucket of water. (24)

BUCKET THERMOMETER. A water-temperature thermometer provided with an insulated container around the bulb. It is lowered into the sea on a line until it has had time to reach the temperature of the surface water, then withdrawn and read. The insulated water surrounding the bulb preserves the temperature reading and is available as a SALINITY sample. (24)

BUDDY BREATHING. In SCUBA, the sharing by two or more divers of the same breathing tank. See BUDDY SYSTEM.

BUDDY SYSTEM. In SCUBA diving, divers with few exceptions should work in pairs. This is probably the greatest single aid toward SCUBA safety, especially under unfavorable conditions. The divers should remain in sight of each other. In poor visibility, they should use a "buddy line" 6 - 10 feet long. (37)

BUDOCKS. Bureau of Yards and Docks (USN).

BULKHEAD. 1. A structure separating land and water areas, primarily designed to resist earth pressure. See also SEAWALL.

    2. Walls or partitions within a ship.

BULK MODULUS OF ELASTICITY. The ratio of stress to volume changes in materials subjected to axial loading. It is calculated: $K = \dfrac{E}{3(1 - 2r)}$

where K = Bulk Modulus of Elasticity, psi
        E = Modulus of Elasticity, psi
        r = Poissons Ratio.

BULLPUP. A Navy air-to-surface missile.

BULL'S EYE. 1. The eye or calm central portion of a revolving storm.

    2. A small dark cloud with a reddish center, sometimes seen at sea, often preceding a storm.

    3. A kind of squall on the coast of South Africa. It descends out of a clear sky with great suddenness. Usually called BULL'S EYE SQUALL. (17)

BULL'S EYE SQUALL. A squall forming in fair weather, characteristic of the ocean off the coast of South Africa. It is named for the peculiar appearance of the small isolated cloud marking the top of the invisible vortex of the storm. (17)

BUMED. Bureau of Medicine and Surgery.

BUND. An embankment or embanked thoroughfare along a body of water. The term is used particularly for such structures in the far east. (17)

BUOY. A floating object, other than a lightship, moored or anchored to the bottom as an aid to navigation. Buoys may be classified according to shape, as Spar, Cylindrical or Can, Conical Nun, Spherical, Cask, Keg, Dan, or Pillar Buoy. They may also be classified according to the color scheme, as a Red, Black, or Checkered Buoy. A buoy fitted with a characteristic shape at the top to aid in its identification is called a Topmark Buoy. A Sound Buoy is one equipped with a characteristic sound signal, and may be further classified according to the manner in which the sound is produced, as a Bell, Gong, Horn, Trumpet, or Whistle Buoy. A Lighted Buoy is one with a light having definite characteristics for detection and identification during darkness. If the light is produced by gas, it may be called a Gas Buoy. A buoy equipped with a marker radiobeacon is called a Radiobeacon Buoy. A buoy with equipment for automatically transmitting a radio signal when triggered by an underwater sound signal is called a Sonobuoy. A Combination Buoy has more than one means of conveying intelligence; it may be called a Lighted Sound Buoy if it is a lighted buoy provided with a sound signal. Buoys may be classified according to location, as Channel, Mid-Channel, Middle Ground, Turning, Fairway, BIFURCATION, JUNCTION, SEA or FAREWELL BUOY. A DANGER Buoy is one marking an isolated danger to navigation. A Bar Buoy marks the location of a bar. A buoy marking a hazard to navigation may be classified according to the nature of the hazard, as Obstruction, Wreck, Telegraph, Cable, Fish Net, Dredging, or Spoil-Ground Buoy. Buoys used for particular purposes may be classified according to their use, as Anchor, Anchorage, Quarantine, Mooring, Warping, Swinging, Marker, Station, Watch, or Position Buoy. A lightweight buoy especially designed to withstand strong currents is called a River Buoy. An Ice Buoy is a sturdy one used to replace a more easily damaged buoy during a period when heavy ice is anticipated. (17)

BUOY ANCHORS. The most common buoy anchor is constructed of concrete, cast iron or scrap material (e.g. railroad wheels). Some buoys have employed either explosive or specially designed anchors. Explosive anchors are useful in hard bottoms but are complex and expensive for general use. Specially designed anchors dig into the bottom and provide high drag for their weight. (28)

BUOY FLOATS. Floats have wide ranges of size, weight, and shape. This is probably a result of the large number of factors that must be considered in float design, including buoyancy, stability, strength, drag, and weight. The relative importance of these factors in any particular experiment determines shape of the buoy float to be used. Subsurface floats are probably easier to design since only positive buoyancy and strength need to be considered. Surface floats are more complicated than subsurface floats, and surface floats with telemetering capabilities are probably the most complicated. Telemetry demands that antennae be stable and free from immersion.

    The most commonly used float shapes are cylindrical and toroidal. Cylindrical floats used by the Canadian Air Force, the Navy Electronics Laboratory, and the Office of Naval Research range in size from a 45-gallon drum to a 0.5- by 30-foot hydrophone buoy. The toroidal buoy devised by WHOI is constructed mainly of styrofoam wrapped in fiberglass and provides 6,000 pounds of positive buoyancy with a total weight of only 700 pounds. (28)

BUOY MOORING LINES. The most popular mooring line material is polypropylene. This material is strong (1.5 tons' breaking strength for 1/2 inch diameter), light in weight, buoyant and flexible. It stretches and tends to eliminate kinks under tension.

    Nylon and dacron are also used. Nylon is about one and 1/2 times as strong as polypropylene but it permanently elongates under heavy loading.

    All plastic line, unless braided, tends to unwrap when twisted against the lay. The use of plastic line is also limited to independent transducer moors since it cannot carry electrical signal.

    Wire rope is also used as a mooring material for buoys. This material tends to kink.

    For telemetering oceanographic variables at depths, the mooring line must contain electrical conductors. Armored electrical cable has the same disadvantage as wire rope -- it kinks. Watertight electrical swivels can be used to reduce kinking of these cables, but swivels are troublesome and short-lived. Rigid rod sections, which screw together to form a solid rod, have been tested by the Navy Sofar Station. However, a rigid moor is more susceptible to fatigue and mechanical shock.

    Most moors are composed of chain near the anchor. Chain is strong, difficult to tangle, and unaffected by chafing. Chain buffers vary in length from 50 to several hundred feet and are generally selected with breaking strengths commensurate with the rest of the moor. In many cases, the chain is connected to a weak link which is usually a short piece of small-diameter plastic line. The weak link permits only the anchor to be lost when the moor is broken by exceptionally high strain.

    The ratio of moor length to water depth for a particular buoy depends somewhat on the variable to be measured. Naturally, currents are difficult to measure from a very slack moor. On the other hand, the more taut the system, the more difficult it is to anchor. The largest moor length to water depth ratio (1.4/1) of present buoys occurs on the NOMAD. (28)

BUOY POWER SUPPLIES. Buoy power is almost exclusively furnished by wet cells, dry cells, and nickel-cadmium batteries. Batteries are reliable and inexpensive. Their major disadvantages are limited life and excessive weight. Many exotic power supplies, such as fuel cells, solar cells, and wave generators, are being tested. Use of 5-

watt wind generators for charging batteries appears to be the only successful modification in power supplies. These generators have been successfully tested on the NOMAD buoy in the Gulf of Mexico.

Until the reliability of electronics and mooring systems is greatly increased, there will be little requirement for long-lived power supplies. Atomic batteries, butane engine-generators, and similar sources of power will undoubtedly be popular as buoys become larger and long-lived. (28)

BUOY SENSORS. Many organizations have employed hydrophones as sensors in their buoy projects. Among these are the Naval Electronics Laboratory; Maritime Air Command, Halifax; and the Office of Naval Research. Both slack and taut moors are used, but the mooring line must contain electrical conductors to carry the output signals. Many hydrophone arrays are designed to telemeter. These systems, whether drifting or anchored, offer excellent platforms for continuous, multilevel monitoring of acoustic data.

Savonius rotor current meters have been widely adapted for use in buoys. WHOI; the Army Corps of Engineers; the Navy Sofar Station; Marine Advisors, Incorporated; the Department of Health, Education, and Welfare; and the U. S. Coast Guard are using these meters on buoys.

Temperature is also often recorded from buoys. WHOI, Scripps Institute of Oceanography, the Navy Electronics Laboratory, and the Office of Naval Research have done research in buoy temperature sensors.

Other less commonly used transducers adapted for buoy use measure radioactivity, moor strain, and moor tilt. (28)

BUOYAGE. A system of buoys. One in which the buoys are assigned shape, color, and number distinction in accordance with location relative to the nearest obstruction is called a cardinal system. One in which buoys are assigned shape, color, and number distinction as a means of indicating navigable waters is called a lateral system. (17)

BUOYANCY. By definition, buoyancy is the upward force exerted on a floating, or immersed, body and is independent of the weight of the body. The state of buoyancy refers to the ratio between the weight of the body and the weight of the displaced fluid. In the case of submarines, the buoyancy are considered: (1) positive buoyancy. (2) neutral buoyancy, and (3) negative buoyancy.

1. POSITIVE BUOYANCY exists when the weight of the body is less than the weight of an equal volume of the displaced fluid.

2. NEUTRAL BUOYANCY exists when the weight of the body is equal to the weight of an equal volume of the displaced fluid. A body in this state remains suspended, neither rising nor sinking, unless acted upon by an outside force.

3. NEGATIVE BUOYANCY exists when the weight of the body is greater than the weight of an equal volume of the displaced fluid and the body sinks.

Theoretically, a submarine is designed with its main ballast tanks of such volume that when they are flooded, the ship is in the state of neutral buoyancy. Negative buoyancy is gained by flooding the negative tank. (33)

BUOYANT ASCENT. See FREE ASCENT.

BUREAU OF YARDS AND DOCKS. This engineering bureau is charged with the design, construction, and maintenance of the Navy Shore Establishment. It tests and evaluates techniques, equipment, and materials used in the construction of shore installations and bases. (40)

BUSH. The mass of spray or dense water vapor thrown outward from around the base of a waterspout. Also called bonfire, cascade. (17)

BUPERS. The U. S. Navy Bureau of Naval Personnel.

BUSANDA. U. S. Navy Bureau of Supply and Accounts.

BUSHIPS. The U. S. Navy Bureau of Ships.

BUSTDS. The National Bureau of Standards.

BUWEPS. The U. S. Navy Bureau of Naval Weapons.

BUYS BALLOT'S LAW. (Also called baric wind law.) A law describing the relationship of the horizontal wind direction in the atmosphere to the pressure distribution: if one stands with his back to the wind, the pressure to the left is lower than to the right in the Northern Hemisphere. In the Southern Hemisphere, the relation is reversed.

This law was formulated in 1857 by the Dutch meteorologist Buys Ballot and is a qualitative statement of the GEOSTROPHIC WIND equation. (24)

C

CA. U. S. Navy designation for a Heavy Cruiser.

CABLE. A nautical unit of horizontal distance, equal to 600 feet (100 fathoms) and approximately one-tenth of a nautical mile. See also WIRE ROPE. (24)

CABLE BUOY. 1. A buoy used to mark one end of a cable being worked on.
2. A floating support of a submarine cable. (17)

CABLE LAID ROPE. See WIRE ROPE.

CAG. U. S. Navy ship designation for a Guided Missile Heavy Cruiser.

CAKE ICE. See ICE CAKE.

CALCAREOUS ALGAE. Marine plants which form a hard external covering of calcium compounds. Calcareous algae are found in all oceans and frequently form reefs. (15)

CALCOFI. California Cooperative Oceanic Fishery Investigation.

CALDRON. A small basin or deep of a generally circular or oval shape, constituting an irregularity in the bottom of the ocean. (17)

CALIFORNIA CURRENT. The ocean current flowing southward along the west coast of the United States from approximately Washington to northern Baja California. It is the major branch of the ALEUTIAN CURRENT. As a whole, the current represents a wide body of water that moves sluggishly toward the southeast. Off Central America, the California current turns toward the west and becomes the NORTH EQUATORIAL CURRENT. (24)

CALIFORNIA FOG. Fog peculiar to the coast of California and its coastal valleys. Off the coast, winds displace warm surface water, causing colder water to rise from beneath, resulting in the formation of fog. In the coastal valleys, fog is formed when moist air blown inland during the afternoon is cooled by radiation during the night. (17)

CALLIPPIC CYCLE. A period of four METONIC CYCLES equal to 76 Julian years, or 27759 days. Devised by Callippus, a Greek astronomer, about 350 B.C. as a suggested improvement on the Metonic cycle for a period in which new and full moon would recur on the same day of the year. Taking the length of the synodical month as 29.530588 days, there are 940 lunations in the Callippic cycle, with about 0.25 day remaining. (14)

CALM. 1. The absence of apparent motion of the air. In the BEAUFORT WIND SCALE, this condition is reported when smoke is observed to rise vertically, or the surface of the sea is smooth and mirror-like. In the United States weather observing practice, the wind is reported as calm if it is determined to have a speed of less than one mile per hour (or one knot). (24)

CALM BELT. A belt of latitude in which the winds are generally light and variable. The principal calm belts are the HORSE LATITUDES (the CALMS OF CANCER and of CAPRICORN) and the DOLDRUMS. (24)

CALMS OF CANCER. Along with the "calms of Capricorn", the light variable winds and calms which occur in the centers of the SUBTROPICAL HIGH-PRESSURE BELTS over the oceans.

They are named after the Tropics of Cancer and Capricorn, although their usual position is at about latitudes 30°N and S, the HORSE LATITUDES. (24)

CALMS OF CAPRICORN. See CALMS OF CANCER.

CALVED ICE. A fragment of floating GLACIER ICE ranging in size from an ICEBERG to a GROWLER. (25)

CALVING. The breaking away of a mass of ice from its parent ICEBERG, GLACIER, or SHELF ICE formation.

Calving may take place above, at, or below the water line, relieving stresses set up by temperature changes and responding to vibrations from sound or wave action. ICEBERGS at any time may calve off large sections of ice which, after falling into the water, may bob up to the surface with great force, often at a considerable distance away. In the calving of the largest valley glaciers of Greenland, masses of ice of the order of 1/40 to 1/20 cubic mile are spalled off--one of the most gigantic natural spectacles on earth. The waves which are produced in the fjords rise several tens of yards along the banks and therefore compare favorably with the largest waves of the sea.

Icebergs are often so balanced that this calving, or merely melting of the under surface, will cause a shift in the center of gravity with consequent capsizing and readjustment of mass to a new state of equilibrium. (25)

CANAL. An artificial watercourse cut through a land area for use in navigation, irrigation, etc. (11)

CANARY CURRENT. A North Atlantic Ocean current flowing southwestward along the northwest coast of Africa, from the Canary Islands to the vicinity of the Cape Verde Islands, where it divides into two branches, the western branch augmenting the NORTH EQUATORIAL CURRENT and the eastern branch curving southeast and continuing as the GUINEA CURRENT. The Canary current forms the southeastern part of the general clockwise oceanic circulation of the North Atlantic Ocean. (17)

CAN BUOY. A buoy the above-water part of which is in the shape of a cylinder. Sometimes called cylindrical buoy. (17)

CANDLE ICE. Ice fingers normal to the original free surface in rotten or disintegrating SEA ICE. The fingers may be equal in length to the thickness of the ICE CAKE prior to disintegration. CANDLE ICE is also a feature of disintegrating lake and river ice. (25)

CANISTERS. The absorption canister is a component of CLOSED-CIRCUIT SCUBA. It is a container for the chemical absorbent that removes carbon dioxide from exhalation. It may take a variety of shapes. Most often it is cylindrical. The design must provide for adequate filling so that the absorbent does not settle in use leaving a bypass channel along the canister wall.

Most canisters are made of nonferrous metal with a protective coating for corrosion resistance. Canisters are rugged enough to withstand normal handling. They usually have watertight filling caps for easy filling or changing of the absorbent. They may have baffles to insure against channeling and to increase the path of gases through the absorbent without increasing breathing resistance excessively. (37)

CANYON (SUBMARINE CANYON). A relatively narrow, deep depression with steep slopes, the bottom of which grades continuously downward. (26)

CAPACITANCE. The ability to store electrical energy, measured in farads, microfarads, or micro-microfarads. (36)

CAPACITOR. Two electrodes, or sets of electrodes, in the form of plates, separated from each other by an insulating material called the dielectric. (36)

CAPACITOR HYDROPHONE. See ELECTROSTATIC TRANSDUCER.

CAPE. An area of land projecting into a body of water, either as a peninsula or as an angle of the coast line. A cape is similar to but generally more prominent than a point. (17)

CAPE DOCTOR. The strong southeast wind which blows on the South African coast. (17)

CAPE HORN CURRENT. That part of the west wind drift current flowing eastward in the immediate vicinity of Cape Horn, and then curving northeastward to continue as the FALKLAND CURRENT. (17)

CAPILLARY WAVE. (Also called RIPPLE, CAPILLARY RIPPLE.) A wave, on a fluid interface, of sufficiently short WAVE LENGTH that the restoring force is surface tension.

The PHASE SPEED C of these waves on a free surface decreases with increasing wave length:

$$C = \sqrt{2\pi\, T/\rho\, L}$$

where T is the surface tension of the fluid, ρ the density, and L the wave length. For a water-air surface, the wave length of a wave moving 1m/sec is about 0.04 cm. (24)

CAPTURE AREA. The effective, or apparent, area of the receiving surface of a hydrophone may be computed as the quotient of the available power of the acoustic energy divided by its equivalent plane wave intensity. The value of the area determined in this manner, for a given hydrophone, is known as its capture area. (4)

CARBON DIOXIDE. A heavy, colorless gas of chemical formula CO_2. It is the fourth most abundant constituent of dry air, now present to the extent of 0.033 per cent by volume.

Over 99 per cent of the terrestrial CO_2 is found in the oceans, but its solubility is strongly temperature-dependent, so changes in sea surface temperatures can lead to marked local changes in CO_2 content. (14)

CARBON DIOXIDE EXCESS. In diving CO_2 excess is a possibility wherever carbon dioxide absorbing canisters are used or where, because apparatus design does not reduce apparatus deadspace, some carbon dioxide is re-inhaled. The chief symptoms, which furnish ample warning to trained men, are increased effort of breathing, a sense of breathlessness and headache. Unheeded warning may result in exhaustion and unconsciousness. The incidence is low. Assuming that the design of the apparatus is adequate for the purpose for which it is used, prevention is accomplished by using fresh soda lime with each dive, correct canister loading, and care in keeping the soda lime dry. (37)

CARBON MONOXIDE POISONING. In diving this type of accident usually occurs as a result of contamination of the diver's air supply by exhaust gases from an internal combustion engine. (37)

CARIBBEAN CURRENT. An ocean current flowing westward through the Caribbean Sea. It is formed by the comingling of part of the waters of the NORTH EQUATORIAL CURRENT with those of the GUIANA CURRENT. It flows through the Caribbean Sea as a strong current and continues with increased speed through the Yucatan Channel; there it bends sharply to the right and flows eastward with great speed out through the Straits of Florida to form the FLORIDA CURRENT. (24)

CAROTENOIDS. The yellow or orange pigments of the plant cell, found in the plastids. (18)

CARPOGONIUM. The flask-shaped egg-bearing portion of the female reproductive branch in some thallophytes (as the red algae) in which fertilization occurs and which usually terminates in an elongate receptive trichogyne. (20)

CARPOSPORE. A diploid spore of a red alga that is produced terminally by a GONIMOBLAST that germinates to produce the diploid TETRASPORIC plant. (20)

CASK BUOY. A buoy in the shape of a cask. (17)

CATAMARAN. A twin-hulled ship.

CATHODE. 1. The more noble electrode of a corrosion cell where the action of the corrosion current reduces or eliminates corrosion. (35)
2. The electrode in a vacuum tube which provides electron emission. (36)

CATHODIC PROTECTION. A means of reducing or eliminating the corrosion of a metal by means of making current flow to it from a solution such as, by connecting the metal to the negative pole of some source of current. The source of this current may be another metal, such as zinc, magnesium, or aluminum and the current may be derived from a rectifier, generator or battery applied through an appropriate anode which may be consumed by the applied current, as in the case of steel, or remain substantially unaffected by the current, as in the case of graphite or platinum. (35)

CAT'S PAW. A light breeze affecting a small area, such as would cause a patch of ripples on the surface of a still water surface. (24)

CAUSTIC. In refraction of waves, the name given to the curve to which adjacent orthogonals of waves, refracted by a bottom whose contour lines are curved, are tangents. The occurrence of a caustic always marks a region of crossed orthogonals and high wave convergence. (11)

CAUSWAY. A raised road, across wet or marshy ground or across water. (11)

CAVITATION. Sonically induced cavitation in a liquid is the formation, growth, and collapse of gaseous and vapor bubbles due to the action of intense sound waves. (1)

CAVITATION NOISE. Cavitation noise is the noise produced in a liquid by the collapse of bubbles that have been created by CAVITATION. (19)

CAY. See KEY.

CB. U. S. Navy ship designation for a Large Cruiser.

CBASF. Current Bibliography for Aquatic Sciences and Fisheries (UNESCO).

CBI. Chesapeake Bay Institute.

CBO. Conference of Baltic Oceanographers.

CC. U. S. Navy designation for a Command Ship.

CC. Caribbean Commission.

CCO. Coordinating Committee on Oceanography.

CCOFI. California Cooperative Oceanographic Fisheries Investigation.

CCTA. Commission for Technical Cooperation in Africa.

CCTA/CSA. Commission de Cooperation Technique en Afrique au Sud du Sahara; conseil Scientifique pour L'afrique au Sud du Sahara.

CELESTIAL LONGITUDE. See LONGITUDE.

CELESTIAL MECHANICS. The study of the theory of the motions of celestial bodies under the influence of gravitational fields. (31)

CELLULOSE. The carbohydrate forming the wall of plant cells; also in the mantle of tunicates. (19)

CENTER, ACOUSTIC. See EFFECTIVE ACOUSTIC CENTER.

CENTER OF BUOYANCY. The center of buoyancy is the center of gravity of the displaced water or the location of the upward or buoyant force. It is the geometric center of volume of the displaced water. The center of buoyancy should not be confused with the center of gravity of the immersed or floating body. The center of gravity is the effective center of all the weights in a ship. The total weight acts downward on the ship as if it were concentrated at the center of gravity. (33)

CERC. Coastal Engineering Research Center (formerly Beach Erosion Board).

CERMET (CERAMAL). A material or body consisting of ceramic particles bonded with a metal. According to the American Society Testing Materials the ceramic phase must be present in 15% or more of the body. A ceramic foam or porous ceramic is not a cermet because the bonding of the ceramic structure is not dependent on or due to the metal.

CEROF. Committee on Effects of Atomic Radiation on Oceanography and Fisheries.

CG. U. S. Navy ship designation for a Guided Missile Cruiser.

CGC. U. S. Coast Guard designation for a Coast Guard Cutter.

CGOU. U. S. Coast Guard designation for a Coast Guard Oceanographic Unit.

CGS. Coast and Geodetic Survey.

CGRS. Central Gyro Reference System.

CHALK. Soft earthy sandstone of marine origin, composed chiefly of minute shells. It is white, gray, or buff in color. Part of the ocean bed and some shores are composed of chalk, notably the "white cliffs of Dover", England. (17)

CHANNEL. 1. That part of a body of water deep enough for navigation through an area otherwise not suitable. It is usually marked by a single or double line of buoys and sometimes by ranges.
    2. The deepest part of a stream, bay, or strait, through which the main current flows.
    3. A large strait, as the English Channel.
    4. A hollow bed through which water does or may run.
    5. That part of a water aerodrome designated for the take-off and landing of aircraft in a given direction.
    6. A band of radio frequencies within which a radio station must maintain its modulated carrier frequency to prevent interference with stations on adjacent channels. Also called frequency channel.
    7. Any circuit over which telephone, telegraph, or other signals may be sent by an electric current.
    8. A lead (ice). (17)

CHANNEL BUOY. A buoy marking a channel. (17)

CHARACTERISTIC WAVE HEIGHT. See SIGNIFICANT WAVE HEIGHT.

CHARLES' LAW. States that at a constant pressure the volume of a gas varies directly as the absolute temperature. (37)

CHARTED DEPTH. The vertical distance from the tidal datum to the bottom. (17)

"CHARYBDIS". See GALOFARO.

CHECKERED BUOY. A buoy painted with quadrilaterals of alternate colors. (17)

CHELICERA. One of the most anterior pair of appendages on arachnids such as spiders, scorpions, and the king crab. (19)

CHELIPED. The first thoracic appendage (pincer) of a crayfish and related crustaceans. (19)

CHEZY'S FORMULA. An empirical formula for the velocity of a uniform flow of water through a section of a stream. The formula is usually written as follows: $v = C\sqrt{RS}$; in which v denotes the velocity of flow; R, the hydraulic radius of the section, which is obtained by dividing the area of the section by its wetted perimeter; S, the slope of the water surface; and C, a coefficient depending upon the roughness of the wetted perimeter and also upon the values of R and S. Chezy's formula derived its name from Antoine de Chezy, a celebrated French engineer of the eighteenth century. (14)

CHILEAN CURRENT. See PERU CURRENT.

CHINFO. Chief of Information - U. S. Navy.

CHIP LOG. A line marked at intervals (commonly 50 ft), and paid out over the stern of a moving ship. By timing the intervals at which the markers appear as the line is pulled out by a drag (the "chip"), the ship's speed can be determined. The wave length of ocean waves can be estimated by noting the position of wave crests relative to the markers. (24)

CHITIN. The nonprotein secreted in the exoskeleton on arthopods and some other animals. Some plants, such as blue-green algae, build their cell walls of chitin instead of cellulose. (19,13)

CHLORINITY. The number giving the chlorinity in grams per kilogram of a sea-water sample is identical with the number giving the mass in grams of "atomic weight silver" just necessary to precipitate the halogens in 0.3285233 kilograms of sea-water sample.

CHLOROPHYLL. The green pigment, located in the CHLOROPLASTS, which is necessary to the process of photosynthesis. (18)

CHLOROPLAST. A specialized body in the cytoplasm which contains chlorophyll. (18)

CHLOROSITY. Chlorosity is the property corresponding to the chlorinity expressed as grams per 20°-liter. Chlorosity is obtained by multiplying the chlorinity of a water sample by its density at 20°. (13)

CHOP (WIND CHOP). The short-crested waves that may spring up quickly in a fairly moderate breeze, and break easily at the crest. (10)

CHOPPY SEA. Popularly, descriptive of short, rough irregular wave motion on a sea surface. (24)

CHORDATA. The phylum of animals with a notochord, persistent or transient; includes the vertebrates, amphioxus, tunicates, and tongue worm; the chordates. (19)

CHROMOTOGRAPHY. A chemical process of separating closely related compounds by permitting a solution of them to filter through an absorbent so that the different compounds become absorbed in separate colored layers comprising a chromatogram.

CHROMATOPHORE. A pigment cell containing granules or coloring material and responsible for color markings on many animals (and plants). (19)

CHROMOSOME. One of the small bodies ordinarily definite in number of cells of a given species into which the chromatin of a cell nucleus resolves itself previous to the mitotic division of the cell. (Webster Dictionary definition).

CHUBASCO. A very violent wind and rain squall, attended by thunder and vivid lightning, often encountered during the rainy season along the west coast of Central America. (17)

CIAT. Commission Inter-American del Atun Tropical.

CIC. Combat Information Center.

CIERZO. See MISTRAL.

CIESMM. Commission Internationale pour L'Exploration de la Mediterranee.

CIG. International Committee on Geophysics of ICSU.

CILIA. Microscopic hairlike processes attached to a free cell surface; usually numerous, often arranged in rows, and capable of vibration. (19)

CIM. Committee on International Geophysics (or Geodesy).

CINCLANT. Commander-in Chief, Atlantic (USN/Allies).

CINCLANTFLT. Commander in Chief, Atlantic Fleet (USN).

CINCNELM. Commander in Chief, Naval Forces, Eastern Atlantic and Mediterranean.

CINCPAC. Commander in Chief, Pacific (USN/USA/USAF).

CINCPACFLT. Commander in Chief, Pacific Fleet (USN).

CIPP. Counseil Indo-Pacifique des Peches.

CIRA. Commission for the International Reference of the Atmosphere.

CIRCULARLY POLARIZED SOUND WAVE. A circularly polarized sound wave is a special case of an elliptical sound wave, in which case the two major axes of the ellipse are identical.(9)

CIRROCUMULUS. High clouds (mean lower level above 20,000 feet) composed of small white flakes or of very small globular masses, usually without shadows, which are arranged in groups or lines, or more often in ripples resembling those of sand on the seashore. Cirrocumulus is composed of ice crystals. (17)

CIRROSTRATUS. Thin, whitish, high clouds (mean lower level above 20,000 feet) sometimes covering the sky completely and giving it a milky appearance and at other times presenting, more or less distinctly, a formation like a tangled web. These clouds often produce halos around the sun and moon but do not blur their outlines. Cirrostratus is composed of ice crystals. (17)

CIRRUS. Detached high clouds (mean lower level above 20,000 feet) of delicate and fibrous appearance, without shading, generally white in color, and often of a silky appearance. Cirrus appears in the most varied forms, such as isolated tufts, lines drawn across a blue sky, branching feather-like plumes, curved lines ending in tufts, etc. It is often arranged in parallel bands which cross the sky in great circles and appear to converge toward a point on the horizon, Cirrus is always composed of ice crystals. Cirrus proceeding from cumulonimbus, and composed of the debris of the upper frozen parts of the cloud, is called false cirrus. If in the form of a cap or hood it may be called a cap cloud. A scarf cloud is a thin cirrus-like cloud sometimes observed above a developing cumulus. (17)

CIRRUS. A small, slender, and usually flexible structure or appendage (such as that found in many marine worms). (19)

CIVIL DAY. A mean solar day commencing at midnight. (14)

CIVIL TIME. Time in which the day begins at midnight as distinguished from the former ASTRONOMICAL TIME in which the day began at noon. (14)

CL. U. S. Navy ship designation for a Light Cruiser.

CLAA. U. S. Navy ship designation for a Anti-Aircraft Light Cruiser.

CLAMSHELL SNAPPER. There are several sizes of clamshell snappers for taking small disturbed sediment samples. The largest of those presently in use aboard Navy survey ships is about 30 in. long and weighs about 60 lbs. It is ruggedly constructed of stainless steel. The cast stainless steel snapper jaws are closed by a heavy arm actuated by a strong spring and lead weight. In the open position a foot device extends below the jaws so that it strikes the bottom first. The impact moves the arms up releasing the jaws which snap shut trapping about a pint of bottom material. The snapper is equipped with a tailfin and may be lowered from the oceanographic winch. (35)

CLAPOTIS. 1. The French equivalent for a type of STANDING WAVE.
          2. In American usage it is usually associated with the standing wave phenomenon caused by the reflection of a wave train from a breakwater, bulkhead, or steep beach. (11)

CLARKE BATHYPHOTOMETER. The submerged unit of the Clarke bathyphotometer consists of a photomultiplier tube and a depth-sensing element. The deck unit contains a high-voltage power supply, depth indicator, and a vacuum tube microammeter. Other necessary equipment includes an oscillograph amplifier, a recorder on which flashes from bioluminescent organisms (down to 3750 meters) can be recorded, and a calibration unit. This unit has been used to depths as great as 800 meters. The spectral sensitivity is 3200 - 6500 Å, with a maximum at 4800 Å. It is capable of receiving illumination as low as 10^{-11} gm cal/cm^2/min (Clarke and Wertheim, 1956), or recording radiation from full sunlight down to a value of about $10^{-7}\mu$ w/cm^2. (35)

CLARKE-BUMPUS PLANKTON SAMPLER. Principle features are: a brass tube five inches in diameter and six inches long; a straining sleeve of silk bolting cloth attached to the tube by means of a ring with a bayonet-type lock, and a collecting bucket at the cod end; a propeller mounted in the tube, geared to a counter which registers the number of revolutions, and with calibration, the volume of water sampled; and two vanes, one on each side of the tube, which assist in holding the tube in a horizontal position. This apparatus may be opened or closed at desired depths by means of a messenger-actuated trigger.
     The sampler is equipped with a flow meter so that quantitative plankton investigations can be made. An impeller is geared to the meter so that the number of revolutions made by the impeller is recorded by the counter. From the reading, the volume of water which has passed through the sampler can be determined. This quantity of water filtered by the sampler per revolution of the impeller is determined by calibrating the meter, either in a laboratory equipped with flume tanks or in the field. As a result of many calibrations, an approximate rating of 4 liters per revolution has been found to be satisfactory for all instruments whose impellers spin freely when blown on by the operator.
     The sampler is equipped with a shutter; this is opened or closed by means of a specially shaped messenger which travels along the wire to which the sampler is attached. When the shutter is in the open position, water passes through the flow meter causing the impeller to spin and on through the net thus filtering out zooplankton and phytoplankton. The impeller stops spinning when the shutter is closed by a second messenger. Thus, a sample can be taken at a desired depth by means of this sampler without contamination from plankton in the overlying water strata.
     The Clarke-Bumpus sampler is therefore unique in that an uncontaminated sample can be taken from any desired depth, and an estimate of the filtered volume of sea water can be determined.
     This sampler designed to be towed horizontally from a wire kept as nearly vertical as possible (by means of a weight attached to the lower end), is limited to the collection of net plankton; macroplankton are able to avoid capture because of the small opening in the tube. It will not sample efficiently at high speeds (10 to 15 knots) or over long distances; nor will it withstand the added stresses of such speeds. (35)

CLAY. Fine grained sediments with particle size smaller than approximately 0.00008 inch (0.004 millimeter). When not separately designated on a bottom sediment chart, clay is classed as mud. (16)

CLC. U. S. Navy designation for a Tactical Command Ship.

CLG. U. S. Navy ship designation for a Guided Missile Light Cruiser.

CLINOMETER. A device for measuring the amount of roll aboard ship.

CLK. U. S. Navy designation for a Hunter Killer Ship.

CLOSED CIRCUIT SCUBA. In the simplest type of closed circuit equipment, oxygen is stored in cylinders under high pressure, and is admitted to a breathing bag either (1) through a manually operated valve, (2) by a slow steady flow through a pressure reducing valve, or (3) through a demand valve system similar in construction to that described for the OPEN CIRCUIT equipment. When methods (2) or (3) (automatic oxygen supply)are used, a manually operated emergency valve is also fitted. Oxygen admitted into the breathing bag mixes with the reservoir of purified exhaled gas. The swimmer inhales from the breathing bag through a check valve. The slight pressure of exhalation closes the inhaling valve and opens an exhaling valve causing the exhaled gas to re-enter the breathing bag through a canister which contains carbon dioxide absorbent, normally soda-lime or BARALYME. The rate of oxygen utilization from the cylinders is determined by the diver's metabolic consumption of oxygen rather than by the larger volume of gas required for ventilation as in the open circuit type. Because of the danger of oxygen poisoning, present operating doctrine limits use of closed circuit oxygen apparatus to a depth of 30 feet for a period of 45 minutes. (37)

CLOSED SEA. 1. That part of the ocean enclosed by headlands, within narrow straits, etc.
2. That part of the ocean within the territorial jurisdiction of a country. The opposite is open sea. (17)

CLOUD. 1. A visible assemblage of numerous tiny droplets of water, or ice crystals formed by condensation of water vapor in the air, with the base above the surface of the earth. Clouds may be classified according to some common characteristic, as high clouds, middle clouds, low clouds, or clouds with vertical development. High clouds may be further classified as cirrus, cirrocumulus, or cirrostratus. False cirrus is the debris of the upper frozen parts of cumulonimbus. If in the form of a cap or hood it may be called a cap cloud. Middle clouds may be further classified as altocumulus or altostratus. Low clouds may be further classified as stratocumulus, stratus, or nimbostratus. A characteristic raincloud is sometimes called nimbus. Clouds with vertical development are classified as cumulus or cumulonimbus. Such a cloud having an anvil-like upper part may be called an anvil cloud. A thundercloud is a cumulonimbus or well-developed cumulus. Large, rounded cumulus with light edges, often appearing before a thunderstorm, may be called thunderhead. Prefixes such as alto-, or cirro-, are combining terms, used to indicate cloud height, while cirriform, cumuliform, and stratiform are terms describing clouds pertaining to or resembling the general form of their respective prefixes. Basic cloud names may also be modified by suitable adjectives, to better describe their appearance, as lenticular, having the shape of a lens; mammatus, having the form of pouches or breasts; radiatus, having parallel bands apparently radiating from a point on the horizon; and undulatus, having elongated and parallel elements, as ocean waves. Fracto- is a prefix indicating a torn, ragged, scattered appearance. Clouds may be classified according to their position, as a stationary cloud or standing cloud appearing over a mountain peak or ridge. Such a cloud resting over a mountain peak is called a cap cloud or banner cloud. One over a mountain ridge is called a crest cloud. A crest cloud may be called sansan in the Canadian Rockies, or tablecloth if appearing over Table Mountain in South Africa. A scarf cloud is a thin cirrus-like cloud sometimes observed above a developing cumulus. Squall clouds are small eddy clouds formed below the leading edge of a thunderstorm cloud. Clouds may be classified as to their shape. A funnel cloud is the characteristic tornado cloud; a pocky cloud is one having the under surface in the form of pouches or breasts; mares' tails originate as long slender streaks of cirrus. Scud consists of shreds or small detached masses of rapidly-moving clouds. A veil is nearly invisible, it may be called fumulus. Wisps or falling trails of precipitation are called virga. An iridescent cloud is one having brilliant spots or a border of colors. Such a cloud seen in the stratosphere during twilight is called a nacreous cloud or mother of pearl cloud. A similar assemblage in contact with the surface of the earth is called fog.
2. A visible assemblage of tiny particles of any substance, as a dust cloud.
3. Star cloud. (17)

CLOUD CLASSIFICATION. A system of grouping cloud types according to some common characteristic. The groups commonly used are: a. high clouds (mean lower level above 20,000 feet), consisting of cirrus, cirrocumulus, cirrostratus; b. middle clouds (mean level 6,500 to 20,000 feet), consisting of altocumulus, altostratus; c. low clouds (mean upper level under 6,500 feet), consisting of stratocumulus, stratus, nimbostratus; d. clouds with vertical development, consisting of cumulus and cumulonimbus. (17)

CMC. Commandant, Marine Corps.

CMM. Commission of Maritime Meteorology.

CMR. Common Mode Rejection.

CNO. Chief of Naval Operations.

CNRS. Centre National de al Recherche Scientifique.

COAST. A strip of land of indefinite width (may be several miles) that extends from the seashore inland to the first major change in terrain features. (11)

COASTAL AREA. The land and sea area bordering the shore line. (11)

COASTAL ICE. See FAST ICE.

COASTING LEAD. A light deep sea lead (30 to 50 pounds), used for sounding in water 20 to 60 fathoms. (17)

COAST LINE. (1) Technically, the line that forms the boundary between the COAST and the SHORE.
(2) Commonly, the line that forms the boundary between the land and the water. (11)

COAXIAL CABLE. A transmission line consisting of one conductor, usually a small copper tube or wire, within and insulated from another conductor of larger diameter, usually copper tubing braid. The outer conductor may or may not be grounded. Radiation from this type of line is practically zero. Coaxial cable is sometimes called concentric line. (36)

COCKEYED BOB. A thunder squall occurring during the southern hemisphere summer, on the northwest coast of Australia. (17)

CO-CUMULATIVE SPECTRUM. (Abbreviated C.C.S.) In ocean-wave studies, the integral of an energy spectrum. The area under a particular energy spectrum from a given frequency value to infinity is given by the value of the C.C.S. curve at that frequency. (24)

COCKTAIL PARTY EFFECT. Anyone who has ever attended a cocktail party is aware of the fact that as people gather and time progresses, the noise level in the room where the party is being given gets louder and louder until finally the room is quite noisy indeed. By our usual notions of masking, it should be almost impossible to understand any of the conversation, yet we all know that people will gather together in groups of two or more and carry on quite satisfactory conversations. This means that a human being is able in some way to focus his attention upon a desired source of sound, and to some extent ignore other masking sounds that may be present in the environment. This particular effect has been called the "cocktail party effect." It may be added that the phenomenon can show up in any number of situations, not just at a cocktail party. (9)

CODC. Canadian Oceanographic Data Center.

COEC. Comité Central d´Océanographie et d´Étude des Côtes.

COEFFICIENT OF THERMAL EXPANSION. The relative increase of the volume of a system (or substance) with increasing temperature in an isobaric process. In symbols this coefficient is

$$\frac{1}{V}\left(\frac{\partial V}{\partial T}\right)_p,$$

where V is the volume, T the temperature, and p the pressure. (24)

COELENTERATES. A group of marine animals which includes jellyfishes, corals and hydroids. (15)

COLD-FRONT-LIKE SEA BREEZE (SEA BREEZE OF THE SECOND KIND). A SEA BREEZE which forms out over the water, moves slowly toward the coast and then moves inland quite suddenly. Often associated with the passage of this type of sea breeze are showers, a sharp wind shift from seaward to landward, and a sudden drop in temperature. The leading edge of such a sea breeze is sometimes called the sea-breeze front. (Defant, F., in Compendium of Meteorology, 1951, p. 659). (24)

COLD WALL. A term used to indicate the line or surface along which two water masses of significantly different temperature are in contact. The amount of mixing along a cold wall may be very small. The encounter between the warm waters of the Gulf Stream and the cold waters of the Labrador Current is an example. (12)

COM. Commander. Prefix applied to abbreviations of Naval commands only (e.g. DESLANT becomes COMDESLANT).

COMASWFORPAC (ASDEFORPAC). Commander Antisubmarine Warfare Force, Pacific Fleet. Ford Island, Pearl Harbor, Honolulu, Hawaii.

COMASFORPAC/COMASWFORLANT. Commander Antisubmarine Warfare Force, Pacific Fleet, Ford Island, Pearl Harbor, Honolulu, Hawaii. Atlantic Force, U. S. Naval Base, Norfolk, Virginia.

COMBER. (1) A deep water wave whose crest is pushed forward by a strong wind, much larger than a whitecap; (2) A long-period spilling breaker. (11)

COMBINATION BUOY. A buoy having more than one means of conveying intelligence, as a lighted sound buoy. (17)

COMB JELLIES. Common names for members of the phylum Ctenophora; small jellyfish-like animals which live in the surface layers of the ocean, usually spheroidal and with comb plates. They are common marine animals, often occurring in enormous concentration; many species are strongly bioluminescent. (15)

COMEX. Comité d´Exploitation des Oceans.

COMMENSALISM. The association of two or more individuals of different species in which one kind or more is benefited and the others are not harmed. (19)

COMOPTEVFOR. Commander Operational Test and Evaluation Force. U. S. Naval Base, Norfolk, Virginia.

COMPASS. An instrument used in determining the azimuth or direction of a body relative to the meridian of a place. There are two kinds of compasses in use -- namely, the magnetic compass which is actuated by the earth's magnetism and the gyrocompass which is actuated by a rapidly spinning rotor which tends to place its axis of rotation parallel to the earth's axis of rotation. The first is subject to certain errors known as the variation and deviation of the compass and may also be affected by other local attractions. The gyrocompass is free from these disturbances and indicates direction relative to the true meridian of the earth. (14)

COMPASS DIRECTION. Direction as indicated by a compass without any allowances for compass error. The direction indicated by a magnetic compass may differ by a considerable amount from the true direction referred to a meridian of the earth. (14)

COMPASS ERROR. The amount by which a compass direction differs from the true direction. The error is usually expressed in degrees and is marked plus (+) or minus (-) according to whether the compass direction as read in degrees of azimuth is less or greater than the true azimuth. The error is to be applied according to sign to the compass reading to obtain the true direction. The compass error combines the effects of the deviation and variation of the compass. (14)

COMPASS POINTS. The four principal points of the compass -- north, east, south, and west, are called the cardinal points. Midway between the cardinal points are the intercardinal points: northeast, southeast, southwest, and northwest. Midway between each cardinal and intercardinal point is a point with a name formed by combining that of the cardinal and intercardinal point, the former being placed first, as north-northeast, east-northeast, and so forth. Midway between the points already indicated are points bearing the name of the nearest cardinal or intercardinal point followed by the word by and the name of the cardinal point in the direction in which it lies, as north by east, northeast by north, and so forth. In all, there are 32 points separated by intervals of 11 1/4°. Each of these intervals is subdivided into quarter points. (14)

COMPENSATION DEPTH. The depth at which the light intensity is just sufficient to bring about a balance between the oxygen produced by algae through photosynthesis and that consumed by them through respiration. (13)

CONDUCTION. The transmission of heat directly from MOLECULE to molecule through a substance or through materials which are in contact with each other. An unprotected diver loses heat to the water around him mainly by direct conduction through his skin. (37)

COMPLETE FREEZING, EARLIEST. The earliest reported date when ten-tenths ice coverage was observed at a specific location.

COMPLETE FREEZING, LATEST. The latest reported date when ten-tenths ice coverage was observed at a specific location.

COMPONENT. (1) Same as CONSTITUENT.
(2) That part of a tidal force or current velocity which by resolution is found to act in a specified direction. (14)

COMPOSITE MATERIALS. Structural materials of metal alloys or plastics with built-in strengthening agents which may be in the form of filaments, foils, or flakes of a strong material. (31)

COMPOUND PANCAKE ICE. See PANCAKE ICE.

COMPOUND TIDE. A tidal CONSTITUENT with a speed equal to the sum or difference of the speeds of two or more elementary constituents. Compound tides are usually the result of shallow-water conditions. (14)

COMPRESSED AIR INTOXICATION. See NITROGEN NARCOSIS.

COMPRESSIONAL WAVE. A compressional wave is a wave in an elastic medium which causes an element of the medium to change its volume without undergoing rotation. (1)

CONAD. Continental Air Defense Command (USN/USA/USAF).

CONCENTRATION CELL. An electrolytic cell consisting of an electrolyte and two electrodes of the same metal or alloy that develop a difference in potential as a result of a difference in concentration of ions or oxygen at different points in a solution. (35)

CONCENTRATION, ICE. The percentage of ice cover in a given area of water, usually expressed in tenths.

CONCENTRATION POLARIZATION. Occurs in corrosion because of concentration changes which take place at the electrode/solution interface when the electrode reaction proceeds. Since the electrode reactions are dependent upon the rate at which the participating ions are brought up to the interface, it is evident that migration, diffusion, and convection are the controlling factors. Thus temperature, agitation, current density, ion concentration, and time may all be influential. (35)

CONCURRENT LINE. A line on a map or chart passing through places having the same current hour. (14)

CONDUCTANCE. The ability of a material to conduct or carry an electric current. It is the reciprocal (opposite) of the resistance of the material, and is expressed in mhos. (36)

CONDUCTIVITY-TEMPERATURE INDICATOR (CTI). This instrument was designed primarily for estuarine studies. Thus, it has a conductivity range for salinities from 0% to 35% and a temperature range of -2° to 32°C; it contains no depth measuring element. The underwater element consists of a two-electrode, H-type conductivity cell and a nickel resistance thermometer. Temperature in degrees centigrade and conductivity in millimhos are indicated on a pair of four-digit counters mounted on the housing for the amplifier and servomechanism. (35)

CONFUSED SEA. A highly disturbed water surface without a single, well-defined direction of wave travel. A series of waves or swell crossing another wave system at an angle is called CROSS SEA. (17)

CONICAL BUOY. A buoy the above water part of which is in the shape of a cone. A conical buoy is one form of nun buoy. (17)

CONJUGATE IMPEDANCE. Two impedances having resis-

tive components which are equal and reactive components which are equal in magnitude but opposite in sign are known as conjugate impedances. (4)

CONSERVATIVE CONCENTRATIONS. Concentrations that are altered locally except at the boundaries, by processes of diffusion and advection only. Heat content and salinity are two outstanding examples of conservative concentration. (13)

CONSOL. Consol is a type of radio-navigational aid derived from the Sonne system developed by Germany.
Basically the system is a long-range circular radio-beacon offering the additional combined characteristics of a directional and rotating radiobeacon. The main components of a Consol station are a medium frequency transmitter and a directional antenna system consisting of three aligned vertical antennas, evenly spaced at a distance of three times the transmitter wavelength. (29)

CONSOLIDATED ICE. An area of the sea covered by ice of various origins consolidated, by wind and currents, into a solid mass. (24)

CONSTANT DISTANCE SPHERE. Given the concept of an effective center (SEE) the relative response of a projector may be said to refer to variations in acoustic intensity, or intensity per unit band, over the surface of a sphere concentric with its center. This is often described as a constant distance sphere. (4)

CONSTITUENT. One of the harmonic elements in a mathematical expression for the tide-producing force and in corresponding formulas for the tide or tidal current. Each constituent represents a periodic change or variation in the relative positions of the earth, moon, and sun. A single constituent is usually written in the form

$$y = A \cos (at + \alpha),$$

in which y is a function of time as expressed by the symbol t which is reckoned from a specified origin. The coefficient A called the amplitude of the constituent and is a measure of its relative importance. The angle (at $+\alpha$) changes uniformly and its value at any time is called the phase of the constituent. The speed of the constituent is the rate of change in its phase and is represented by the symbol a in the formula. The quantity α is the phase of the constituent at the initial instant from which the time is reckoned. The period of the constituent is the time required for the phase to change through 360° and is the cycle of the astronomical condition represented by the constituent. (14)

CONTINENTAL BORDERLAND. A PROVINCE adjacent to a continent, normally occupied by or bordering a CONTINENTAL SHELF that is highly irregular with depths well in excess of those typical of a continental shelf. (26)

CONTINENTAL DEPOSITS. Deposits laid down on land by rivers, winds, glaciers, etc., in contrast to deposits laid down in the ocean. (27)

CONTINENTAL RISE. A gentle slope with a generally smooth surface found at the base of a CONTINENTAL SLOPE. (26)

CONTINENTAL SHELF. The zone bordering a continent extending from the line of permanent immersion to the depth (usually about 100 fathoms) where there is a marked or rather steep descent toward the great depths. (11)

CONTINENTAL SLOPE. A declivity from the outer edge of a CONTINENTAL SHELF or CONTINENTAL BORDERLAND into greater depths. (26)

CONTINENTAL TALUS. See INSULAR TALUS.

CONTINENTAL TERRACE. The zone around the continents, extending from low water line to the base of the CONTINENTAL SLOPE. (27)

CONTINUOUS SPECTRUM. A continuous spectrum is the spectrum of a wave the components of which are continuously distributed over a frequency region. (2)

CONTOUR. 1. A line connecting the points, on a land or submarine surface, that have the same elevation.
2. In topographic or hydrographic work, a line connecting all points of equal elevation above or below a datum plane. (11)

CONTOUR LINE. See CONTOUR.

CONTOURING TEMPERATURE RECORDER. This device takes data from temperature sensors (thermistors) located in a chain towed behind a ship and plots on a continuous record the vertical distribution of isotherms. The thermistors are electronically scanned in sequence from the top to the bottom of the chain, with time intervals that may be adjusted from 2 to 20 seconds. The scan rate may be adjusted to the speed of the ship so that the information is taken from a vertical column in the water. Isotherms from -2 to $32^{\circ}C$ can be contoured along with all 0.1 and $0.05^{\circ}C$ isotherms between these limits. In addition, selection can be made so only the 1 and $0.1^{\circ}C$ or the $0.05^{\circ}C$ are contoured. Depth also is determined.
A Diesel hydraulic powered hoist is needed to transport 600 feet of chain. The chain itself consists of links about 11 inches long having a U-shaped cross section in the horizontal plane. (35)

CONTRA SOLEM. Against the sun; hence cyclonic, descriptive of motion turning to the left in the Northern Hemisphere and the right in the Southern Hemisphere; the reverse of cum sole. (These terms were introduced by V. W. Ekman in 1923) (24)

CONUS. Continental U. S.

CONVECTION. The transmission of heat by the movement of heated gas or fluid. If the diver were sitting in a tank of water in a cold room, he would lose heat to the surroundings not only by direct conduction through the water but also by movement of the water (called convection currents) produced in the following way: The water next to his body, warmed by conduction, would expand slightly and be lighter than the surrounding water. It would therefore rise; but on reaching the top and walls of the tank, it would lose heat to the room, contract, and sink to be warmed again. (37)

CONVECTION CELL. A vertical section of the isothermal mixed layer bounded by cool currents descending from a convergence and warm currents rising to a divergence.

CONVERGENCE. (1) In refraction phenomena, the decreasing of the distance between orthogonals in the direction of wave travel. This denotes an area of increasing wave height and energy concentration; (2) In wind set-up phenomena, the increase in set-up observed over that which would occur in an equivalent rectangular basin of uniform depth, caused by changes in planform or depth; also the decrease in basin width or depth causing such increase in set-up. (11)

CONVERGENT ZONE PATHS. The velocity structure of permanent deep sound channels which produces focusing regions at distant intervals from a shallow source.

COPEPODS. Small crustaceans, usually less than 1/4 inch in length, somewhat resembling tiny shrimp. Many species are bioluminescent, producing a bril-

liant sparkling light. Greatest concentrations occur in surface layers of temperate and subarctic waters. (15)

CORAL. 1. Biology - marine coelenterates, solitary or colonial which form a hard external covering of calcium compounds or other materials. The corals which form large reefs are limited to warm, shallow waters, while those forming solitary, minute growths may be found in colder waters to great depths.
2. Geology - the concretion of coral polyps, composed almost wholly of calcium carbonate, forming reefs, and treelike and globular masses. May also include calcareous algae and other organisms producing calcareous secretions, such as bryozoans and hydrozoans. (15)

CORAL HEAD. A mass of coral, usually forming a portion of a reef. Frequently, coral heads are large enough to be dangerous to navigation. On the basis of size, coral heads would be classed as rock, but are shown as coral on bottom sediment charts.

CORAL REEF. A calcareous structure built by large colonies of coral or shell-forming organisms. (27)

CORDILLERA. An entire mountain province, including all the subordinate ranges, interior PLATEAUS and BASINS. (27)

CORDONAZO. A tropical cyclone originating in the North Pacific Ocean, south and southwestward of Central America and Mexico. Sometimes called hurricane. (17)

CORE. That area within a layer of water where parameters such as temperature, salinity, velocity, etc., reach extreme values. (13)

CORE CATCHER. A mechanical device located near the bottom of a sediment corer barrel to prevent the loss of the sample during retrieval.

CORE OF THE EARTH. The earth is believed to consist of the following:
Inner Core, - Solid, - 860 mile radius.
Outer Core, - Liquid,- 1300 miles thick.
Mantle, - Solid, - 1800 miles thick.
Crust, - Solid, - 622 miles thick.
(27)

CORING DEVICES. Coring devices are essentially steel tubes that are driven into the ocean floor bottom for the purpose of obtaining and investigating a sediment sample or core from a particular topography.
PHLEGER, KULLENBERG, EWING, MOORE, EMERY DIETZ are some of the coring devices used for this purpose. (35)

CORIOLIS ACCELERATION. An acceleration of a parcel moving in a (moving) relative coordinate system. The total acceleration of the parcel, as measured in an inertial coordinate system, may be expressed as the sum of the acceleration within the relative system, the acceleration of the relative system itself, and the coriolis acceleration. In the case of the earth, moving with angular velocity Ω, a parcel moving relative to the earth with velocity V has the coriolis acceleration $2\Omega X V$. If Newton's laws are to be applied in the relative system, the coriolis acceleration and the acceleration of the relative system must be treated as forces. (24)

CORIOLIS (FERREL'S LAW). An apparent force acting on a body in motion, due to rotation of the earth, causing deflection to the right in the northern hemisphere and to the left in the southern hemisphere. It affects air (wind), water (current), etc., and introduces an error in bubble sextant observations made from a moving craft, the effect increasing with higher latitude and greater speed of the object. (17)

CORIOLIS FORCE. An apparent force on moving particles in a non-inertial coordinate system, i.e., the coriolis acceleration as seen in this (relative) system. Such a force is required if Newton's laws are to be applied in this system.

In meteorology the coriolis force per unit mass arises solely from the earth's rotation, and is equal to $-2\Omega \times V$, where Ω is the angular velocity of the earth, and V is the (relative) velocity of the particle. Thus the coriolis force acts as a "deflecting force", normal to the velocity, to the right of motion in the northern hemisphere and to the left in southern hemisphere. It cannot alter the speed of the particle. The three components toward east, north and zenith are, respectively, $2\Omega (v \sin \phi - w \cos \phi), -2\Omega u \sin \phi$,
and $2\Omega u \cos \phi$, where u, v, w are the component velocities and ϕ the latitude.

Since the coriolis force is in effect proportional to the speed, its importance duration of the motion. (24)

COROMELL. A night land breeze prevailing from November to May at La Paz, near the southern extremity of the Gulf of California. (17)

CORROSION. The destruction of a metal or alloy by chemical or electrochemical reaction with its environment. In ordinary marine environment, this reaction is electrochemical. (35)

CORROSION FATIGUE. The phenomenon in which a metallic structure subjected to the action of a corrosive environment and to repeated or alternating stresses, fails due to the development of a crack which increases in size as a function of time. (35)

CORROSION RATE. The rate which a metal or alloy is removed because of corrosion. This may be expressed in terms of loss in weight or loss of thickness in a given period of time.

(Corrosion rates in terms of thickness change refer to the loss of metal from one side only). (35)

COTIDAL HOUR. The average interval between the moon's transit over the meridian of Greenwich and the time of the following high water at any place. This interval may be expressed either in solar or lunar time. When expressed in solar time, it is the same as the Greenwich high-water interval. When expressed in lunar time, it is equal to the Greenwich high-water interval multiplied by the factor 0.966. (14)

COTIDAL LINE. A line on a map or chart passing through places having the same COTIDAL HOUR. (14)

COULOMB DAMPING (DRY FRICTION DAMPING). Coulomb damping is the dissipation of energy that occurs when a particle in a vibrating system is resisted by a force whose magnitude is a constant independent of displacement and velocity, and whose direction is opposite to the direction of the velocity of the particle. (2)

COUNTERCURRENT. A secondary current usually setting in a direction opposite to that of a main current. (14)

COUSTEAU'S DIVING SAUCER. Captain Jacques-Yves Cousteau's Diving Saucer, a research vehicle designed to operate at depths as great as 1,000 feet, weighs about 7,000 pounds, is approximately 10 feet in diameter and 6 feet high, and is propelled at a speed of about 1 knot by two water jets mounted on its sides. It holds two crew members -- a pilot and an observer -- who lie in a prone position and view their marine environment through two large windows. A hydraulically controlled arm and a specimen catch basket attached to the vehicle allow the crew to collect rock, vegetation, and some sea animals.

COVE. A small sheltered recess in a shore or coast, often inside a larger embayment. (11)

COWSHEE. See KAUS.

CPIEM. Counseil Permanent International pour L'Exploration de la Mer.

CPM. Critical Path Method (PERT).

CPR. Committee on Polar Research of the National Academy of Sciences - National Research Council.

CRACK. A fracture or narrow unnavigable rift in sea ice. A tide crack is one parallel to the shore, caused by the vertical movement of the water due to tides. A hinge or weight crack is one parallel and adjacent to a pressure ridge. A strain or tension crack is caused by stretching of the ice beyond its elastic limit. A torsion crack is produced by twisting of the ice beyond its elastic limit. A shear crack is caused by two different, simultaneous forces acting in parallel but opposite directions on adjacent portions of the ice. A concussion or shock crack is produced by the impact of one ice cake upon another. (17)

CRANE ROPE. See WIRE ROPE.

CREEP. The strain of a material subjected to prolonged constant stress or load for a specified time in a Creep Test or a Stress Rupture Test. Creep behavior is often presented in the form of graphs. The simplest graph is a plot of strain vs. log of time. For metals, strain may be either total measured strain, or where total strain is of the same order of magnitude as elastic strain, net strain due to plastic deformation only. This net strain is determined by obtaining the strain corresponding to the specified constant stress on the Stress-Strain Diagram for the specified temperature and subtracting it from total measured strain. For plastics, strain may be either total measured strain, in which case the graph also indicates strain of the corresponding control specimen, or net strain due to Creep only. This net strain is obtained by subtracting corresponding control specimen strain from total measured strain. A log-log plot is often preferred for plastics. For vulcanized rubber, total measured deformation (mm) is plotted against log of time (sec), and the magnitude of elastic deformation is indicated by drawing a tangent to the curve at 60 sec. From these graphs, Creep of metals or plastics is the total or net strain at the specified time, and Creep of vulcanized rubber is the difference between total deformation and 60 sec tangent deformation at the specified time. Creep of vulcanized rubber may also refer to the Yerzley Mechanical Oscillograph Test where it is the vertical

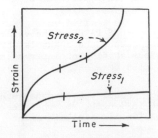

distance (in.) or reduction of thickness (%) represented by the difference between the beginning and end of the damped sinusoidal curve after a specified time. Creep of hard rubber is measured as Cold Flow. A Creep design chart may be constructed by plotting stress vs log of time for each of a series of limiting deformations. From such a chart, Creep Strength for various limiting deformations may be determined. Creep Rate and Creepocity may also be determined from Creep data.

CREO. Centre de Recherches et d'Études Océanographiques.

CREST LENGTH, WAVE. The length of a wave along its crest. Sometimes called crest width. (11)

CREST OF WAVE. 1. The highest part of a wave.
2. That part of the wave above STILL WATER LEVEL. (11)

CREST WIDTH. See CREST LENGTH, WAVE.

CREVICE CORROSION. Corrosion which occurs within or alongside a crevice formed by contact with another piece of the same or another metal or with a non-metallic material. (35)

CRITICAL DAMPING. Critical damping is the minimum viscous damping that will allow a displaced system to return to its initial position without oscillation. (2)

CRITICAL SPEED. Critical speed is a speed of a rotating system that corresponds to a resonance frequency of the system. (2)

CROMWELL CURRENT. An equatorial undercurrent in the Pacific Ocean, discovered in 1952 by Townsend Cromwell. The three other members of the Pacific Equatorial Current System (known for a century) are: the North Equatorial Current, Equatorial Countercurrent, and South Equatorial Current.

CROSS SEA. A series of waves or swell crossing another wave system at an angle. (17)

CROSS TIDE. A tidal current setting in a direction approximately 90° from the course of a vessel. One setting in a direction approximately 90° from the heading is called a beam tide. In common usage these two expressions are usually used synonymously. One setting in a direction approximately opposite to the heading is called a head tide. One setting in such a direction as to increase the speed of a vessel is called a fair tide. (17)

CRPAO. Commission Regionale des Peches pour L'Afrique de L'OUEST.

CRUDESPAC. Cruiser-Destroyer Forces, Pacific (USN).

CRULANT. Cruiser Forces, Atlantic (USN).

CRYOGENIC SWITCHING ELEMENTS. In information processing, logical switching information processing elements which utilize the variability of the transition to superconductivity as a function of magnetic field strength.

CRYSTAL. A natural substance, such as quartz or tourmaline, which is capable of producing a voltage stress when under pressure, or producing pressure when under an applied voltage. Under stress it has the property of responding only to a given frequency when cut to a given thickness. It is therefore a valuable medium to control the frequency of audio transmitters. (10)

CRYSTALLOGRAPHY. The study of the characteristics of crystals.

CSAGI. Special Committee for the Annual Geophysical International.

CSAGY. Special Committee for International Geophysical Year.

CSIRO. Commonwealth Scientific and Industrial Research Organization. (Australia)

CSK. Cooperative Study of the Kuroshio and Adjacent Regions.

CTCA. Commission for Technical Cooperation for Africa South of the Sahara.

CUBMARINE PC-3B. A manned submersible vehicle (US).

CUBMARINE PC-3X. A manned submersible vehicle (US).

CUM SOLE. See CONTRA SOLEM.

CUMULONIMBUS. A massive cloud with great vertical development, the summits of which rise in the form of mountains or towers, the upper parts having a fibrous texture and often spreading out in the shape of an anvil. Cumulonimbus generally produces showers of rain, snow, or hail, and often thunderstorms. Sometimes called thundercloud. (17)

CUMULUS. A dense cloud with vertical development, having a horizontal base and dome-shaped upper surface, exhibiting protuberances. When the cloud is opposite the sun, the edges appear darker than the center, while against the sun the opposite is true; when the light comes from the side, the cloud exhibits strong contrasts of light and dark. (17)

CURRENT. A horizontal movement of the water. Currents may be classified as tidal and nontidal. TIDAL CURRENTS are caused by the tide-producing forces of the moon and sun and are a part of the same general movement of the sea that is manifested in the vertical rise and fall of the tides. Nontidal currents include the permanent currents in the general circulatory systems of the sea as well as temporary currents arising from meteorological conditions. (14)

CURRENT, COASTAL. One of the offshore currents flowing generally parallel to the shore line with a relatively uniform velocity (as compared to the LITTORAL CURRENTS). They are not related genetically to waves and resulting surf but may be composed of currents related to distribution of mass in ocean waters (or local eddies), wind-driven currents and/or tidal currents. (11)

CURRENT DRIFT. A broad, shallow, slow-moving ocean or lake current. (11)

CURRENT, EBB. The movement of the tidal current away from shore or down a tidal stream. (11)

CURRENT, EDDY. A circular movement of water of comparatively limited area formed on the side of a main current. Eddies may be created at points where the main stream passes projecting obstructions. (11)

CURRENT ELLIPSE. A graphic representation of a ROTARY CURRENT in which the velocity and direction of the current at different hours of the tidal cycle are represented by radius vectors and vectorial angles. A line joining the extremities of the radius vectors will form a curve roughly approximating an ellipse. The cycle is completed in one-half tidal day or in a whole tidal day according to whether the current is of the semidiurnal or the diurnal type. A current of the mixed type will give a curve of two unequal loops each tidal day. (14)

CURRENT, FEEDER. The current which flows parallel to shore before converging and forming the neck of a rip current. See also RIP. (11)

CURRENT, FLOOD. The movement of the tidal current toward the shore or up a tidal stream. (11)

CURRENT HOUR. The mean interval between the transit of the moon over the meridian of Greenwich and the time of the strength of flood current modified by the times of slack water and strength of ebb. In computing the mean current hour an average is obtained of the intervals for the following phases: Flood strength, slack before flood increased by 3.10 hours (one-fourth of tidal cycle), slack after flood decreased by 3.10 hours, and ebb strength increased or decreased by 6.21 hours (one-half of tidal cycle). Before taking the average, the four phases are made comparable by the addition or rejection of such multiples of 12.42 hours as may be necessary. The current hours is usually expressed in solar time, but if the use of lunar time is desired, the solar hour should be multiplied by the factor 0.966. (14)

CURRENT, INSHORE. A current inside the BREAKER ZONE. (11)

CURRENT LINE (LOG LINE). A graduated line attached to a current pole and used in measuring the velocity of the current. The line is marked in such a manner that the velocity of the current expressed in knots and tenths is indicated directly by the length of line carried out by the current pole in a specified interval of time. When marked for a 60-second run, the principal divisions for the whole knots are spaced 101.33 feet and the subdivisions for tenths of knots are spaced at 10.13 feet. (14)

CURRENT, LITTORAL. The nearshore currents primarily due to wave action, e.g. LONGSHORE CURRENTS and RIP CURRENTS. (11)

CURRENT, LONGSHORE. The inshore current moving essentially parallel to the shore, usually generated by waves breaking at an angle to the shore line. (11)

CURRENT METER. An instrument for measuring the velocity of a current. It is usually operated by a wheel equipped with vanes or cups which is rotated by the action of the impinging current. A recording device is provided to indicate the speed of rotation which is correlated with the velocity of the current. See also EKMAN, PETTERSSON, PRICE, and RADIO CURRENT METERS. Other current meters include the Witting, Rauschelback, Sverdrup-Dahl, Fjeldstad, Roberts, Von Arx, Iwamiya, Nanniti, Ono, BBT-Neyrpic, Dunderque, Chausey, Ott, Bohnecke, Komatsu, Pegram, Winters, Carruthers, Idroc, Mosby, Hydrowerskstäten, Snodgrass, etc. (14)

CURRENT, OFFSHORE. (1) Any current in the offshore zone; (2) Any current flowing away from shore. (11)

CURRENT, PERMANENT. A current that runs continuously independent of the tides and temporary causes. Permanent currents include the fresh water discharge of a river and the currents that form the general circulatory systems of the oceans. (11)

CURRENT POLE. A pole used in observing the direction and velocity of the current. The standard pole used by the Coast and Geodetic Survey is about 3 inches in diameter and 15 feet long and is weighted at one end to float upright with the top about 1 foot out of water. Shorter poles are used when necessary for shallow water. In use, the pole is attached to the current line but is separated from the graduated portion by an ungraduated section of approximately 100 feet which is known as the stray line. As the pole is carried by the current out from an observing vessel, its direction and the amount of line passing over a fixed reference point during a specified time interval indicate the direction and velocity of the current. (14)

CURRENT, RIP (RIP SURF). A narrow current of water flowing seaward through the breaker zone. A rip current consists of three parts: (1) The "feeder currents" flowing parallel to the shore inside the breakers; (2) the "neck" - where the feeder currents converge and flow through the breakers in a narrow band or "rip"; and (3) the "head" - where the current widens and slackens outside the breaker line. (11)

CURRENT ROSE. A graphical representation of currents, usually by 1° quadrangles, using arrows for the cardinal and intercardinal compass points to show resultant drift and frequency of set for a given period of time. (15)

CURRENT, STREAM. A narrow, deep, and fast-moving ocean current. (11)

CURRENT SYSTEM, NEARSHORE. The current system caused primarily by wave action in and near the breaker zone and which consists of four parts: the shoreward mass transport of water; longshore currents; seaward return flow, including rip currents; and the longshore movement of the expanded heads of rip currents. (11)

CURRENT, TIDAL. A current, caused by the tide-producing forces of the moon and the sun, which is a part of the same general movement of the sea manifested in the vertical rise and fall of the tides. (11)

CUSP (BEACH CUSP). One of a series of naturally formed low mounds of beach material separated by crescent-shaped troughs spaced at more or less regular intervals along the beach face. (11)

CUSSI. Continental, Union, Shell and Superior Oil Companies barge and drill rig used during the first MOHOLE work in 1961.

CUW. Committee on Undersea Warfare of the National Academy of Sciences - National Research Council.

CV. U. S. Navy ship designation for an Aircraft Carrier.

CVA. U. S. Navy ship designation for an Attack Aircraft Carrier.

CVB. U. S. Navy ship designation for a Large Aircraft Carrier.

CVE. U. S. Navy ship designation for an Escort Aircraft Carrier.

CVHA. U. S. Navy designation for a Helicopter Assault Ship.

CVL. U. S. Navy ship designation for a Small Aircraft Carrier.

CVS. U. S. Navy ship designation for an ASW Support Aircraft Carrier.

CYCLE. A cycle is the complete sequence of values of a periodic quantity that occurs within one period. (9)

CYCLIC SALTS. Salts which have been introduced into the atmosphere from the sea surface by evaporation and bursting bubbles. They are carried inland by the atmosphere, deposited or carried down by rain and snow and are eventually carried back to the sea by streams.

CYCLOIDAL WAVE. A very steep, symmetrical wave whose crest forms an angle of 120 degrees. The wave form is that of a cycloid. A trochoidal wave of maximum steepness. See also TROCHOIDAL WAVE. (11)

CYCLONE. An atmospheric cyclonic circulation, a closed circulation. A cyclone's direction of rotation (counterclockwise in the Northern Hemisphere) is opposite to that of an anticyclone. While modern meteorology restricts the use of the term cyclone to the so-called cyclonic-scale circulations, it is popularly still applied to the more or less violent, small-scale circulations such as tornadoes, WATERSPOUTS, dust devils, etc. (which may in fact exhibit anticyclonic rotation), and even, very loosely, to any strong wind. The first use of this term was in the very general sense as the generic term for all circular or highly curved wind systems.

Because cyclonic circulation and relative low atmospheric pressure usually co-exist, in common practice the terms cyclone and low are used interchangeably. Also, because cyclones nearly always are accompanied by inclement (often destructive) weather, they are frequently referred to simply as storms. (24)

CYLINDRICAL WAVE. A cylindrical wave is a wave in which the wave fronts are coaxial cylinders. (1)

CYTOLOGY. The branch of the biological sciences that deals with the structure and processes of protoplasm and the cell. (18)

CYTOPLASM. That part of a cell outside the nucleus and within the cell membrane. (19)

D

DAILY RETARDATION (OF TIDES). The amount of time by which corresponding tidal phases grow later day by day (averages approximately 50 minutes). (11)

"DAILY WATER". See REFERENCE PLANE.

DALTON'S LAW. States that the total pressure exerted by a mixture of gases may be considered to be the sum of the pressures that would be exerted by each of the gases if it alone were present and occupied the total volume. (37)

DAMPING. Damping is the dissipation of energy with time or distance. (2)

DAMPING RATIO. The damping ratio for a system with viscous damping is the ratio of actual damping coefficient to the critical damping coefficient. (2)

DAN BUOY. A buoy consisting of a ballasted float carrying a staff which supports a flag or light. Dan buoys are used principally in minesweeping, and by British fishermen to mark the position of deep-sea fishing lines or the place for trawling. (17)

DANGER BUOY. A buoy marking an isolated danger to navigation, such as a rock, shoal, or sunken wreck. (17)

DASH. A drone antisubmarine helicopter for delivery of a weapon to an enemy submarine.

DATUM PLANE. A horizontal plane used as a reference from which to reckon heights or depths. See also REFERENCE PLANE. (27)

DAVIDSON CURRENT. A countercurrent of the Pacific Ocean running north along the west coast of the United States (from northern California to Washington to at least latitude 48°N) during the winter months. (24)

DD. U. S. Navy ship designation for a Destroyer.

DDC. Defense Documentation Center.

DDE. U. S. Navy ship designation for an Escort Destroyer.

DDG. U. S. Navy ship designation for a Guided Missile Destroyer.

DDI. Depth deviation indicator. (6)

DDK. U. S. Navy ship designation for a Hunter-Killer Destroyer.

DDR. U. S. Navy ship designation for a Radar Picket Destroyer.

DE. U. S. Navy designation for an Escort Vessel.

DEAD AHEAD. Bearing 000° relative. If the bearing is approximate, the term ahead should be used. (17)

DEAD ASTERN. Bearing 180° relative. If the bearing is approximate, the term astern should be used. Also called right astern. (17)

DEAD RECKONING. Determination of position by advancing a previous position for courses and distances. A position so determined is called a dead reckoning position. In air and land navigation, the best estimate of course and speed over the ground is used. In marine navigation, dead reckoning course and speed are generally reckoned without allowance for wind or current, although this practice is not universal. Dead reckoning performed automatically by a device which gives a continuous indication of position by double integration of accelerations since leaving a starting point is called inertial navigation, and when performed by integrating the speed derived from measurement of the Doppler effect of echoes from directed beams of radiant energy transmitted from the craft is called Doppler navigation. (17)

DEBRIS LINE. A line near the limit of storm wave uprush marking the landward limit of debris deposits. (11)

DEC. U. S. Navy designation for a Control Escort Vessel.

DECADE BAND. In accordance with accepted usage a decade band is one having a band width of $f_b - f_a = 10$. (4)

DECAY DISTANCE. The distance through which waves travel after leaving the generating area. (11)

DECAY OF WAVES. The change that waves undergo after they leave a generating area (FETCH) and pass through a calm, or region of lighter winds. In the process of decay, the significant wave height decreases and the significant wave length increases. (11)

DECCA. An electronic navigational system by which hyperbolic lines of position are determined by measuring the phase difference of continuous wave signals from synchronized transmitters. The system was developed by the British during World War II and is now being used for commercial navigation mostly in Europe. Decca has a range of 300 miles. In the present system the Decca Company has incorporated a lane identification system which operates automatically. Thus, the navigator can, at a glance, see which lane and fractional part of a lane he is in. (17)

DECIBEL (db). The decibel is one tenth of a bel. Thus, the decibel is a unit of level when the base of the logarithm is the tenth root of ten, and the quantities concerned are proportional to power. (1)

DECLINATION. 1. Angular distance north or south of the celestial equator, taken as positive (+) when north and negative (-) when south of the equator. The sun passes through its declinational cycle once a year, reaching its maximum north declination of 23 1/2° about June 21 and its maximum south declination of -23 1/2° about December 21. The moon has an average declinational cycle of 27 1/3 days which is called a tropical month. Tides or tidal currents occurring near the times of maximum north or south declination of the moon are called tropic tides or tropic currents and those occurring when the moon is over the equator are called equatorial tides or equatorial currents. The maximum declination which is reached by the moon in successive months depends upon the longitude of the moon's node and varies from 28 1/2° when the longitude of the ascending node is zero to 18 1/2° when the longitude of the node is 180°. The node cycle or time required for the node to complete a circuit of 360° of longitude is approximately 18.6 years. (14)
    2. In terrestrial magnetism: at any given location, the angle between the geographical meridian and the MAGNETIC MERIDIAN; that is, the angle between TRUE NORTH and MAGNETIC NORTH. Declination is either "east" or "west" according as the compass needle points to the east or west of the geographical meridian.
    Lines of constant declination are called ISOGONIC LINES and the one of zero declination is called the AGONIC LINE. (24)

DECLINATIONAL INEQUALITY. See DIURNAL INEQUALITY.

DECOMPRESSION. The degree of body saturation by various gases is dependent upon time of exposure, depth of dive and circulatory efficiency. In order to bring a diver safely to the surface, time for this gas to escape without bubble formation in the body tissues must be allowed. The escape of this gas is called decompression and the time required for the process is known as decompression time. (37)

DECOMPRESSION SICKNESS (OR BENDS). Dissolved nitrogen in the blood and tissues is only slowly gained or lost by the body, and tends to remain in solution except during rapid changes from greater to lesser pressures. The dissolved nitrogen will come out of solution and form bubbles in the blood and other tissues in the same way that bubbles are formed in carbonated beverages when they are decompressed by removal of the cork. Nitrogen which comes out of solution under these conditions may form sufficiently large and numerous bubbles to cause obstruction to blood flow in small vessels, painful distention of tendons, joint tissues, muscles, old scars, fractures, etc. If the ascent is sufficiently slow the excess nitrogen will be harmlessly eliminated by the lungs and bends will not occur. For each depth down to 130 feet there is a diving duration which can be accomplished without need for decompression other than that accomplished by normal ascent rate. The danger of bends during decompression is increased by exposure to greater depths, by exposure over longer periods of time, and by too rapid ascent. There

is little tendency for bends on dives less than 40 feet, even while breathing air; if deeper diving is to be performed using air, slow and regulated ascent must be carried out. This requires the swimmer to have a portable gas supply which will provide not only for the period of work at depth, but also for the period of slow decompression as he returns to the surface. Navy decompression tables should be strictly observed in regulating decompression. Pain evoked by too rapid ascent can be eliminated by redescent or recompression in a chamber if available. This increase in pressure will force the bubbles back into solution. (37)

DECTRA (TRUNK ROUTE DECCA). Dectra is a navigation position-fixing system intended for a specific route such as a long ocean crossing. The system is similar to the standard DECCA system. (35)

DEEP. A relatively small area of exceptional depth found in a depression. The term is generally restricted to depths greater than 3,000 fathoms. (27)

DEEP EASTERLIES. See EQUATORIAL EASTERLIES.

DEEPS. Those depths below 6000 m.

DEEP SCATTERING LAYER (DSL). Term applied to widespread strata in the ocean which scatter or return vertically directed sound such as in the case of echo sounding. These layers, which are evidently of biological origin, are located in depths ranging from 150 to 200 fathoms during the day with most of them migrating to or near the surface during the night.

DEEP-SEA CHANNEL. An elongate valley that cuts slightly below the surface of many of the deep-sea fans and may extend out to the basin floor. (27)

DEEP-SEA FLOOR ACCRETIONS. Materials on the deep-sea floor of possible economic interest, with rough estimates of total reserves are:

Material	Tonnage Estimates		Elements of Interest
Manganese nodules	-	10^{12}	- Mn, Cu, Co, Ni, Mo, V, Zn, Zr
Phosphorite nodules	-	10^{10}	- P, Zr
Globigerina Ooze	-	10^{14}	- $CaCO_3$
Diatomaceous Ooze	-	10^{13}	- SiO_2
Red Clay	-	10^{15}	- Cu, Al, Co, Ni
Barium sulfate concentrations	-	?	- $BaSO_4$
Magnetic Spherules	-	?	- Ni, Fe

DEEP SEA LEAD. A heavy sounding lead (about 30 to 100 pounds), usually having a line 100 fathoms or more in length. A light deep sea lead is sometimes called a coasting lead. Sometimes called dipsey lead. (17)

DEEP-SEA SYSTEM. See BENTHIC DIVISION.

DEEP-SEA TERRACE. A benchlike feature bordering an elevation of the deep-sea floor at depths generally greater than 300 fathoms. (27)

DEEP TRADES. See EQUATORIAL EASTERLIES.

DEEP WATER. Water of depth such that surface waves are little affected by conditions on the ocean bottom. It is customary to consider water deeper than one-half the surface wave length as deep water. (11)

DEEP-WATER WAVE (SHORT WAVE, STOKESIAN WAVE). A surface wave the length of which is less than twice the depth of the water. When this relationship exists the following approximation is valid:

$$c = \sqrt{\frac{gL}{2\pi}}$$

where c is the wave velocity, g is the acceleration of gravity, and L is the wave length. Thus, the velocity of deep-water waves is independent of the depth of the water. (24)

DEER. Directional Explosive Echo Ranging.

DEG. U. S. Navy ship designation for a Guided Missile Escort.

DELRAC. Delrac, a navigation system, resembles the standard DECCA Navigator. In Delrac, a network of hyperbolic lines are laid down in space from fixed transmitting stations. Instead of the star formation, however, the stations work in pairs, one master to each slave, on very long baselines (750 to 1000 miles). Present Decca Navigator transmissions are on different, but related frequencies, so that the receiver can discriminate between them, and the signals can be brought in the receiver to a common comparison frequency.

In Delrac, the necessary common frequency is produced at the source, by sending a short burst of the same frequency, first from the master and then from the slave. A memory circuit in the receiver stores these signals and enables their phase to be compared. This time sharing technique embraces two or three pairs of a group of stations.

Each pair of stations has an estimated range of 3000 miles even in regions of high atmospheric noise, and the overall accuracy of fixing is estimated at 10 miles or better over the entire coverage at the 95% level of probability. The use of the time-sharing process makes it possible to accomodate 21 pairs of Delrac stations (more than enough to cover the whole world) in the 10 to 14 kilocycles band. (29)

DELTA. An area of alluvial deposit, usually triangular in outline, near the mouth of a river. (27)

DELTAIC DEPOSITS. Sedimentary deposits laid down in a river delta. (27)

DENARY BAND. A band having a band ratio (See) of $f_b/f_a = 10$ is properly described as a denary band. This band is often spoken of, incorrectly, as a "frequency decade." (4)

DENSIGRAPH. An instrument that continuously measures density of sea water.

DENSITOMETER. An instrument for measuring fluid density.

DENSITY CURRENT. See TURBIDITY CURRENT.

DENSITY OF ICE. The density of fresh-water ice at its freezing point is 0.917. Newly-formed sea ice, due to its salt content, is more dense, 0.925 being a representative value. The density decreases as the ice freshens. By the time it has shed most of its salt, sea ice is less dense than fresh-water ice, because ice formed in the sea contains more air bubbles. Ice having no salt but containing air to the extent of eight per cent by volume (an approximately maximum value for sea ice) has a density of 0.845. (12)

DENSITY OF SEA WATER. The weight of a given volume of sea water at a specified temperature as compared with the weight of the same volume of fresh water at a temperature of 4°C. As the weight of a given volume of sea water will vary with its own temperature it is now the practice of the Coast and Geodetic Survey to adopt 15°C. as the standard temperature for sea water for the purpose of comparison and the hydrometers used for the observations are graduated accordingly. The average density of sea water is approximately 1.026 at a temperature of 15°C. (14)

DEPTH ANGLE. The angle between the horizontal and the bearing of the submerged target as seen from own ship. (7)

DEPTH, CONTROLLING. The least depth of water in the navigable parts of a waterway, which limits the allowable draft of vessels. (11)

DEPTH FACTOR. See SHOALING COEFFICIENT.

DEPTH RECORDER. This instrument is used to obtain a pictorial record of the ocean bottom. The device consists primarily of a projector, a hydrophone and a recorder. The recorder controls the keying of the transmitter and the gating of the receiver for precision drive. The recorder's primary function is to display sonic travel time intervals in a precise integrated fashion. A continuous record of the reflecting surface, which is the ocean bottom is thus obtained. (30)

DER. U. S. Navy designation for a Radar Picket Escort Vessel.

DERELICT. Any property abandoned at sea, often of sufficient size as to constitute a menace to navigation; especially an abandoned vessel. See JETTISON. (17)

DERRICK STONE. Stone of sufficient size as to require handling in individual pieces by mechanical means, generally 1 ton up. (11)

DESLANT. Destroyer Forces, Atlantic (USN).

DESMAS. See SPICULE.

DETRITUS. Particles worn from rocks by mechanical means; also broken organic material. (27)

DEVIATION LOSS. When relative response is considered as a function of bearing the transmission loss thus measured is known as the deviation loss of the transducer in question. (4)

DEW POINT. The temperature to which a given parcel of air must be cooled at constant pressure and constant water-vapor content in order for saturation to occur. When this temperature is below 0°C, it is sometimes called the frost point. The dew point may alternatively be defined as: the temperature at which the saturation vapor pressure of the parcel is equal to the actual vapor pressure of the contained water vapor.

Isobaric heating or cooling of an air parcel does not alter the value of that parcel's dew point, as long as no vapor is added or removed. Therefore, the dew point is a conservative property of air with respect to such processes. However, the dew point is non-conservative with respect to vertical ADIABATIC motions of air in the atmosphere. The dew point of ascending moist air decreases at a rate only about one-fifth as great as the dry-adiabatic lapse-rate.

The dew point of the atmosphere can be determined directly by any of several types of DEW-POINT HYGROMETERS, but it is more commonly determined with the aid of a psychrometric calculator or tables after the direct reading of a PSYCHROMETER. (14)

DEW-POINT HYGROMETER. An instrument for determining the DEW POINT; a type of hygrometer. It operates in the following manner. A parcel of air is cooled at constant pressure, usually by contact with a refrigerated polished metal surface. Condensation appears upon the metal surface at a temperature slightly below that of the thermodynamic dew point of the air. The observed dew point will differ from the thermodynamic dew point depending upon the nature of the condensing surface, the condensation nuclei, and the sensitivity of the condensate-detecting apparatus. (14)

DEZINCIFICATION. Corrosion of an alloy containing zinc in which the principal product of corrosion is metallic copper. The mechanism may involve overall corrosion of the alloy followed by re-deposition of the copper from the corrosion products or selective corrosion of zinc (or a high zinc phase) to leave a copper residue. Dezincifi-cation is commonly encountered in brasses that contain more than 15% zinc. (35)

DG. Directional Gyro. A gyroscopic device used to indicate a selected horizontal direction for a limited time, as during a turn. When used for an extended period, it is checked and reset at fre-quent intervals. (17)

DHI. Deutsches Hydrographisches Institute.

DIAPHONE. A device for producing a distinctive fog signal by means of a slotted reciprocating piston actuated by compressed air. Blasts may consist of two tones of different pitch, in which case the second tone is of lower pitch. Alternate pitch signals are called two tone. A diaphone is some-what similar to a siren, but the diaphone sound is lower and, if of a single tone, ends with an abrupt "grunt" at the end of the blast. (17)

DIAGENETIC DEPOSITS. Deposits consisting dominant-ly of minerals crystallized out of sea-water, such as manganese nodules. (27)

DIASTROPHISM. Refers to all processes of earth movement and rock deformation, many of which result in changes of relative position, both ver-tical and horizontal. (27)

DIATOM. A microscopic alga with an external skele-ton of silica, found in both fresh and salt water. Part of the ocean bed is composed of a sedimentary ooze consisting principally of large collections of the skeletal remains of diatoms. (17)

DIATOMIN (PHYCOXANTHIN). A yellow or yellowish brown pigment found in certain algae and diatoms. (20)

DIELECTRIC. An insulator. A term applied to the insulating material between the plates of a capacitor. (36)

DIFFERENTIAL SENSITIVITY. The 50 per cent detectable ratio between the sum of echo strength and background noise and the background noise. (5)

DIFFRACTED WAVE. A diffracted wave is one whose front has been changed in direction by an obstacle or other non-homogeneity in the medium other than by reflection or refraction. (9)

DIFFRACTION. Diffraction is the name given to that process which allows sound waves to bend around obstacles that are in their path. (9)

DIFFRACTION OF WATER WAVES. The phenomenon by which energy is transmitted laterally along a wave crest. When a portion of a train of waves is interrupted by a barrier such as a BREAKWATER, the effect of diffraction is manifested by propagation of waves into the sheltered region within the bar-rier's geometric shadow. (11)

DIGITAL MODULATION (DM). Digital modulation, a third method (AM, FM, DM) of radio transmission consisting of on-off pulses of radio energy coded into specific patterns. Among the claimed advan-tages of DM is the ability to collect, transmit and receive data in digitally-coded form without having to modify it for transmission over voice channels as with FM.

DIKE. An igneous intrusion that cuts across the bedding or other layered structure of the surround-ing rock. (27)

DIMORPHISM. Existing under two distinct forms. (19)

DIP. In geology, the angle at which the rock structure is inclined with a horizontal plane. In terrestrial magnetism, the angle formed by the lines of total magnetic force with the horizontal plane at the earth's surface; reckoned positive if downward. In mine warfare, the increase in depth of a moored mine case, due to current force against the case and cable. (27)

DIP EQUATOR. See ACLINIC LINE.

DIPLOID. Having two sets of chromosomes; the 2n number characteristic of the sporophyte generation. (18)

DIP POLE. See MAGNETIC POLE.

DIRECTIONAL GAIN (DIRECTIVITY INDEX). The direc-tional gain of a transducer, in decibels, is 10 times the logarithm to the base 10 of the direc-tivity factor. See DIRECTIVITY FACTOR. (1)

DIRECTIONAL HYDROPHONE. A directional hydrophone is a hydrophone the response of which varies sig-nificantly with the direction of sound incident. (1)

DIRECTIONAL RESPONSE PATTERN (BEAM PATTERN). The directional response pattern of a transducer used for sound emission or reception is a description, usually presented graphically of the response of the transducer as a function of the direction of the transmitted or incident sound waves in a specified plane and at a specified frequency. In general, the beam pattern will change with a change in the operating frequency. (9)

DIRECTIVITY FACTOR. (1) The directivity factor of a transducer used for sound emission is the ratio of the sound pressure squared, at some fixed dis-tance and specified direction, to the mean-square sound pressure at the same distance averaged over all directions from the transducer. The distance must be great enough so that the sound appears to diverge spherically from the effective acoustic center of the sources. Unless otherwise specified, the reference direction is understood to be that of maximum response. (2) The directivity factor of a transducer used for sound reception is the ratio of the square of the open-circuit voltage produced in response to sound waves arriving in a specified direction to the mean-square voltage that would be produced in a perfectly diffused sound field of the same frequency and mean-square sound pressure. (1)

DIRECTIVITY INDEX. A measure of the directional properties of a transducer. It is the ratio, in decibels, of the average intensity or response over the whole sphere surrounding the projector or hydrophone to the intensity or response on the acoustic axis. (5)

DIRECTIVITY PATTERN. A chart in which relative response is plotted as a function of bearing in some specified plane, either against rectangular coordinates or against polar coordinates, is known as a directivity pattern, or as a beam pattern. (4)

DIRECTIVITY RATIO. A measure of the directional properties of a transducer. It is the numerical ratio of the intensity, or response, on the acous-tic axis to the average intensity, or response, over the whole sphere surrounding the projector, or hydrophone. (7)

DISCONTINUOUS DISTRIBUTION. See BIPOLARITY.

DISPHOTIC ZONE. See EUPHOTIC ZONE.

DISSIPATION LOSS. The dissipation loss of a transducer connecting an energy source and an energy load is the transmission loss measured by the ratio of the input power of the transducer to its output power. (4)

DISSOLVED OXYGEN. Dissolved oxygen is measured on almost every oceanographic expedition because of its biological importance and for our understanding of the chemical processes in the sea, including the circulation of the ocean, and composition of bottom materials. Oxygen can be added to the sea only in the upper layers, by absorption of air, and in a layer strictly limited by the depth of light penetration, by photosynthesis. At the surface, oxygen can be lost from the sea by exchanges with the atmosphere, but at all depths it is consumed by the respiration of plants and animals, and during the decomposition of organic materials by bacteria. Reactions of oxygen with reduced materials such as sulphides, iron, manganese, other auto-oxidizable substances, and the consumption of oxygen actuated by enzymes, are of limited extent and largely confined to the surface and bottom layers. The oldest and most widely used technique for measuring oxygen is the Winkler method. (35)

DISTORTION. Distortion is an undesired change in waveform. Noise and certain desired changes in waveform, such as those resulting from modulation or detection, are not usually classed as distortion. (2)

DIURNAL. 1. Daily, recurring once each day. (e.g., lunar day or solar day). (11)
    2. Having a period or cycle of approximately one tidal day. Thus, the tide is said to be diurnal when only one high water and one low water occur during a tidal day, and the current is said to be diurnal when there is a single flood and a single ebb period in the tidal day. A rotary current is diurnal if it changes its direction through all points of the compass once each tidal day. A diurnal constituent is one which has a single period in the constituent day. The symbol for such a constituent is usually distinguished by the subscript 1. (14)

DIURNAL INEQUALITY. The difference in height of the two high waters or of the two low waters of each day; also the difference in velocity between the two flood currents or the two ebb currents of each day. The difference changes with the declination of the moon and to a lesser extent with the declination of the sun. In general the inequality tends to increase with an increasing declination, either north or south, and to diminish as the moon approaches the equator. Mean diurnal high water inequality (DHQ) is one-half the average difference between the two high waters of each day over a 19-year period. It is obtained by subtracting the mean of all high waters from the mean of the higher high waters. Mean diurnal low water inequality (DLQ) is one-half the average difference between the two low waters of each day over a 19-year period. It is obtained by subtracting the mean of the lower low waters from the mean of all low waters. Tropic high water inequality (HWQ) is the average difference between the two high waters of the day at the times of the TROPIC TIDES. Tropic low water inequality (LWQ) is the average difference between the two low waters of the day at the times of the tropic tides. Mean and tropic inequalities as defined above are applicable only when the type of tide is either semidiurnal or mixed. Diurnal inequality is sometimes called declinational inequality. (4)

DIVERGENCE. 1. In refraction phenomena, the spreading of orthogonals in the direction of wave travel. This denotes an area of decreasing wave height and energy concentration.
    2. In wind set-up phenomena, the decrease in set-up observed under that which would occur in an equivalent rectangular basin of uniform depth, caused by changes in plan-form or depth. Also the increase in basin width or depth causing such decrease. (11)

DIVERGENCE LOSS. Divergence loss is that part of the transmission loss which is due to the spreading of sound rays in accordance with the geometry of the situation. For example, in case of spherical waves emitted by a point source, the sound pressure at a point 20 yards distant from the source will be only one-half as great as the sound pressure 10 yards from the source. (9)

DIVING PHYSIOLOGY. Since Physiology covers the study of the functions and activities of the various organs and parts of living bodies, Diving Physiology may be described as the study of the physical and chemical functions of human beings while in the water environment.

DL. U. S. Navy ship designation for a Frigate.

DLG. U. S. Navy ship designation for a Guided Missile Frigate.

DM. U. S. Navy ship designation for a Minelayer, Destroyer.

DM RAYDIST. A range-elliptical measuring system used in navigational positioning.
    Four radio transmitters and frequencies are required to operate the system, the two distance measuring frequencies and two additional frequencies to transmit phase relationship information at each ground station back to the ship.
    DM Raydist is similar to the two range DECCA and the DECCA HI-FIX systems in that they are all circular plotting systems. (29)

DMS. U. S. Navy ship designation for a Minesweeper, Destroyer.

DOCK (SLIP). 1. The space between two piers. A PIER is sometimes erroneously called a dock.
    2. A basin or enclosure for reception of vessels, and provided with means for controlling the water level. A wet dock is one in which water can be maintained at any level by closing a gate when the water is at the desired level. A dry dock is a dock providing support for a vessel, and means for removing the water so that the bottom of the vessel can be exposed. A dry dock consisting of an artificial basin is called a graving dock; one consisting of a floating structure is called a floating dock. (17)

DOD. Department of Defense. (U.S.)

DOLDRUMS (EQUATORIAL CALMS). A nautical term for the EQUATORIAL TROUGH, with special reference to the light and variable nature of the winds. (24)

DOLPHIN. A post or group of posts, used for mooring or warping a vessel. The dolphin may be in the water, on a wharf, or on the beach. (17)

DOME. A transducer enclosure, usually streamlined, used with echo-ranging or listening devices to minimize turbulence and cavitation noises arising from the passage of the transducer through the water. (6)

DOME INSERTION LOSS. (See SONAR DOME INSERTION LOSS).

DOME LOSS PATTERN. (See SONAR DOME LOSS PATTERN).

DOME-SHAPED ICEBERG. An ICEBERG eroded in such a manner that its upper surface is well-rounded and smoothly contoured. This type iceberg is more common in the antarctic than the arctic. (25)

DOO. Director, Office of Oceanography. The proposed office to be established within the Natural Sciences Department of UNESCO.

DOPPLER CONSTANT. When the change in frequency is expressed in cycles per second, the source frequency in kilocycles per second, and the range rate in knots, the factor of proportionality is known as the Doppler constant for echo transmission. (4)

DOPPLER CURRENT METER. The Doppler Current Meter is an acoustic current meter based on the Doppler shift principle. With this device a collimated beam of ultrasonic energy is projected into the water and a volume reverberation signal received. The meter detects the difference between the transmitted and received frequencies, this difference being proportional to the speed of the water past the meter. The device can be made to indicate sense as well as flow rate. The current meter consists of an oscillator driving the transmitting crystal, an amplifier tuned to the oscillator frequency (10 mc) and driven by the receiving crystal, a detector, and an emitter follower as the output of an audio frequency stage. (30)

DOPPLER EFFECT. The Doppler effect is the phenomenon evidenced by the change in the observed frequency of a wave in a transmission system caused by a time rate of change in the effective length of the path of travel between the source and the point of observation. (2)

DOPPLER SHIFT. The Doppler shift is the change in the observed frequency of a wave, due to the Doppler effect. (2)

DORSAL. Toward or pertaining to the back, or upper surface. (19)

DOUBLE EBB. An ebb current having two maxima of velocity separated by a smaller ebb velocity. (14)

DOUBLE FLOOD. A flood current having two maxima of velocity separated by a smaller flood velocity. (14)

DOUBLE TIDE. A double-headed tide, that is, a high water consisting of two maxima of nearly the same height separated by a relatively small depression, or a low water consisting of two minima separated by a relatively small elevation. Sometimes called an agger. (14)

DOWNCOAST. In United States usage, the coastal direction generally trending towards the south. (11)

DOWN DOPPLER. (See UP DOPPLER).

DOWNDRIFT. The direction of predominant movement of littoral material. (11)

DRAFT. The depth to which a vessel is submerged. Draft is customarily indicated by numerals called draft marks at the bow and stern. It may also be determined by means of a DRAFT GAUGE. (17)

DRAFT GAUGE. A hydrostatic instrument installed in the side of a vessel, below the light load line, to indicate the depth to which a vessel is submerged. (17)

DRAG. See SEA ANCHOR

DRAI. Dead reckoning Analog Indicator.

DREDGING BUOY. A buoy marking the limit of an area where dredging is being performed. (17)

DRIFT. 1. The effect of the velocity of fluid flow upon the velocity (relative to a fixed external point) of an object moving within the fluid; the vector difference between the velocity of the object relative to the fluid and its velocity relative to the fixed reference.
2. The speed of an ocean current. In publications for the mariner, drifts are usually given in miles per day or in knots. (24)

DRIFT BOTTLE. A bottle, of one of various designs, which is released into the sea for use in studying currents. It contains a card, identifying the date and place of release, to be returned by the finder with the date and place of recovery. The bottle should be designed and ballasted as to minimize direct wind effects.
Since the path of a bottle can only be estimated between release point and recovery, and generally only a few per cent are returned, this is an inefficient, although inexpensive technique. (See also DRIFT METHODS.) (24)

DRIFT CARD. A card, such as is used in a DRIFT BOTTLE, encased in a buoyant, waterproof envelope and released in the same manner as a drift bottle.
Cheaper and lighter than bottles, drift cards are especially suited to dropping in large quantities from aircraft, and it is supposed that the card, having less freeboard than a bottle, is less affected by wind. (24)

DRIFT CURRENT. Slow-moving ocean current. Name is especially applied to the continuations of the GULF STREAM as it branches on leaving the American Continent to proceed across the Atlantic Ocean, and also to continuations of the KUROSHIO as it crosses the Pacific Ocean. (14)

DRIFT ICE. Any ice that has drifted from its place of origin.

DRIFT ICE FOOT. Same as RAMP. (17)

DRIFT LEAD. A lead placed on the bottom to indicate movement of a vessel. At anchor the lead line is usually secured to the rail with a little slack and if the ship drags anchor, the line tends forward. A drift lead is also used to indicate when a vessel coming to anchor is dead in the water or when it is moving astern. A drift lead can be used to indicate current if a ship is dead in the water. (17)

DRIFT METHODS. Accuracies obtainable by this method are determined by the navigational accuracy with which positions of the drifting device may be fixed, as well as by the ability of the device to be unaffected by influences other than the current under measurement. The primary advantage of this method is that anchoring of the ship is not required.
Drifting devices include woodchips, bottles, cards, confetti, dyes, etc., as well as more sophisticated devices such as drogues, telemetering buoys, and neutral buoyancy floats. Since all of the surface devices are at least partially exposed to the winds and extend to some depth below the water, they may not truly measure surface drift, and data must be viewed with caution. Another technique involving drift is the lowering of current meters from a drifting ship. Frequent, accurate positioning is necessary in this method to correct for the movement of the ship. A difficulty with freely-drifting devices is that instantaneous measurements are not possible, and only time-averaged currents may be obtained.
Subsurface currents may be measured by the drift method with drogues suspended at any given depth on a wire between a surface buoy and a weight. The complete device is made at negligible cost from a surplus parachute, piano wire, a weight and a float. (35)

DROGUE. A sea anchor or other parachute-shaped device for use in water. Drogues suspended at desired depths by buoys are used to determine the SET and DRIFT of currents at those depths, by following the motions that they give to the buoys at the surface. (24)

DROWNING. Asphyxial death due to submersion in water.

DRT. Dead Reckoning Tracer.

DRV. Deep Research Vehicle.

DRY-BULB THERMOMETER. A thermometer with an uncovered bulb, used with a wet-bulb thermometer to determine atmospheric humidity. The two thermometers constitute the essential parts of a PSYCHROMETER. (17)

DRY DOCK. See DOCK.

DRY SUIT. See RUBBER SUIT.

DSL. Deep Scattering Layer.

DSSP. Deep Submergence Systems Project.

DSSRG. Deep Submergence Systems Review Group.

DTMB. United States Navy David Taylor Model Basin.

DTMS. Department of Mines and Technical Surveys.

DUAL-FILTER HYDROPHOTOMETER. This instrument can be used to obtain in situ readings of two wave lengths within the visible part of the spectrum, and measurements can be made at day or night.
    The underwater unit consists of a 6- to 8-volt automobile-type sealed-beam spotlight mounted 15 cm from two GE-type PV-10 photocells. Blue, BG-12 and RG-(red) filters are mounted over each of the photocells. Daylight, which would interfere with transparency measurements, is filtered out by using a honeycomb of blackened drinking straws, placed between the photocells and the filters. The amount of light striking each photocell is measured on the deck of the ship and gives a measure of the transparency of the water. (35)

DUCTILITY. The extent to which a material, particularly a metal, can sustain plastic deformation without rupture. Bendability, Crushability, Elongation Reduction of Area and Wrapping Diameter, results of Cup Draw, Flattening, Kink, Repeated Bend and Twisting Tests are considered some indication of Ductility.

DUNC. Deep Underwater Nuclear Counting.

DURATION. In wave forecasting, the length of time the wind blows in essentially the same direction over the FETCH (generating area). (11)

DURATION, MINIMUM. The time necessary for steady state wave conditions to develop for a given wind velocity over a given FETCH LENGTH. (11)

DUTCHMAN'S LOG. A buoyant object thrown overboard to determine the speed of a vessel. The time required for a known length of the vessel to pass the object is measured. The time and distance being known, the speed can be computed. (17)

DVNIGMI. Far Eastern Scientific Hydrometeorological Institute.

DYKE. See DIKE.

DYNAMIC METER. A unit used to represent the work performed by lifting a unit mass nearly 1 meter.

DYNAMIC PRESSURE. 1. The pressure exerted by a fluid, such as air, by virtue of its motion.
2. The pressure exerted on a body, by virtue of its motion through a fluid, for example, the pressure exerted on a rocket moving through the atmosphere. (31)

DYSBARISM. A general term which includes a complex group of a wide variety of symptoms within the body caused by changes in ambient pressure, exclusive of HYPOXIA. (31)

DYSPNEA. Shortness of breath, difficult or labored respiration.

DYNAMIC MODULUS, EFFECTIVE. An indication of vibration absorption characteristics of rubber. A measure of dynamic stiffness of rubber deformed beyond the straight-line portion of the Load-Deflection Diagram in the Yerzley Mechanical Oscillograph Test. It is calculated as follows:

$$K_c = 210 \; If^2$$
$$K_s = 105 \; If^2$$

where
K_c = Effective Dynamic Modulus in compression, psi
K_s = Effective Dynamic Modulus in shear, psi
I = moment of inertia of beam and weights, slug ft^2
f = Frequency, cps

E

EAGER. See BORE.

EARTH TIDE. Periodic movement of the earth's crust caused by the tide-producing forces of the moon and sun. (14)

EAST AUSTRALIA CURRENT. A Pacific Ocean current flowing southward along the east coast of Australia, from the Coral Sea to a point northeast of Tasmania, where it curves eastward and northeastward, being influenced by water entering the Tasman Sea from the southwest. The east Australia current is a continuation of the southern branch of the SOUTH EQUATORIAL CURRENT, and forms the western part of the general counterclockwise oceanic circulation of the South Pacific Ocean. (17)

EAST AUSTRALIA CURRENT. The ocean current flowing southward along the east coast of Australia. It is formed by the division of part of the SOUTH EQUATORIAL CURRENT as it approaches the coast of Australia. Part of the east Australia Current joins the WEST WIND DRIFT flowing eastward toward South America.
    In the summer (Southern Hemisphere) part of this water flows westward along the south coast of Australia into the Indian Ocean. (14)

EAST GREENLAND CURRENT. An ocean current flowing south along the east coast of Greenland, carrying water of low salinity and low temperature. The east Greenland current is joined by most of the water of the IRMINGER CURRENT. The greater part of the current continues through Denmark Strait between Iceland and Greenland, but one branch turns to the east and forms a portion of the counterclockwise circulation in the southern part of the Norwegian Sea. Some of the east Greenland current curves to the right around the tip of

Greenland, flowing northward into Davis Strait as
the WEST GREENLAND CURRENT.

The main discharge of the Arctic Ocean is via
the east Greenland current. (24)

EASTROPIC. Eastern Tropical Pacific (Program).

EAU DE MER NORMALE. See NORMAL WATER.

EBB CURRENT. The movement of a tidal current away
from shore or down a tidal stream. In the semidiurnal type of reversing current, the terms
greater ebb and lesser ebb are applied respectively
to the ebb currents of greater and lesser velocity
of each day. The terms maximum ebb and minimum
ebb are applied to maximum and minimum velocities
of a current running continuously ebb, the velocity
alternately increasing and decreasing without coming to a slack or reversing. The expression maximum ebb is also applicable to any ebb current at
the time of greatest velocity. (14)

EBB TIDE. A non-technical term referring to that
period of the tide between a high water and the
succeeding low water; falling tide. (11)

EBULLISM. The formation of bubbles, with particular reference to water vapor bubbles in biological
fluids, caused by reduced ambient pressure. (31)

ECHO. An echo is a wave that has been reflected
or otherwise returned with sufficient magnitude and
delay to be detected as a wave distinct from that
directly transmitted. (1)

ECHO RANGING SONAR. (See ACTIVE SONAR).

ECHO REPEATER. Artificial target, used in sonar
calibration and training, which returns a synthetic
echo by receiving, amplifying, and retransmitting
an incident ping. (6)

ECHO SOUNDER (SOUNDING MACHINE). It is used for
measuring depth of water in open ocean areas. This
instrument consists of four parts; (1) A transmitter which generates an electrical impulse which is
transmitted to (2) a transducer, which translates
the electrical impulse into a sonic impulse at the
same frequency either by means of the piezoelectric effect of quartz or other crystals or the magnetostriction effect of a nickel alloy embedded in
a ceramic rod. The sonic impulse travels through
the water to the bottom, or any other reflecting
surface and an echo is returned to the transducer
where it is transformed again into an electrical
impulse and passed to (3) a regular radio frequency
receiver where the signal is detected, amplified,
and sent to (4) a recorder where the travel time
from the initial impulse to the return of the echo
is measured and displayed. Most American-built
instruments are calibrated for an assumed velocity
of sound in sea water of 4,800 feet per second.
The actual velocity varies with the temperature,
pressure, and salinity of the water in the column
being sounded. Echo sounding equipment can be
divided into three general classes of instruments;
general purpose, shallow water and deep water
instruments. (29)

ECM. Electronic Counter-Measures.

ECOLOGY. The relations of an organism to its
environment. (19)

ECPD. Engineer's Council for Professional
Development.

EDDY. 1. By analogy with a molecule, a "glob" of
fluid within the fluid mass that has a certain in-
tegrity and life history of its own; the activities
of the bulk fluid being the net result of the motion
of the eddies.

The concept is applied with varying results to
phenomena ranging from the momentary spasms of the
wind to storms and anticyclones.

2. Any circulation drawing its energy from a
flow of much larger scale, and brought about by
pressure irregularities as in the lee of a solid
obstacle. (24)

3. A circular movement of water. Eddies
may be formed where currents pass obstructions or
between two adjacent currents flowing counter to
each other. (15)

EDDY CONDUCTIVITY. The EXCHANGE COEFFICIENT for
Eddy Heat Conduction. (24)

EDDY DIFFUSIVITY. The EXCHANGE COEFFICIENT for the
diffusion of a conservative property by EDDIES in
a turbulent flow. (24)

EDDY FLUX. The rate of transport (or flux) of
fluid properties such as momentum, mass, heat, or
suspended matter by means of EDDIES in a turbulent
motion; the rate of turbulent exchange. (24)

EDDY KINETIC ENERGY. The kinetic energy of that
component of fluid flow which represents a departure from the average kinetic energy of the fluid,
the mode of averaging depending on the particular
problem. This eddy kinetic energy is represented
by $\rho \overline{u'^2}$ where ρ is the density, u' is the EDDY
VELOCITY, and the superior bar denotes an average.

In general circulation studies, for example,
the zonal average along a fixed latitude circle is
usually considered. As another example, in small-
scale turbulence studies it is frequently desirable
to consider the average with respect to time as a
fixed point in the fluid. (24)

EDDY SPECTRUM. The distribution of the frequency
of EDDIES of various sizes or scales in a turbulent
flow, or the distribution of kinetic energy among
eddies of various frequencies or sizes. (24)

EDDY VELOCITY. The difference between the mean
velocity of fluid flow and the instantaneous
velocity at a point. For example, $u' = u - \overline{u}$
where u' is the eddy velocity, u is instantaneous
velocity, and $\overline{u}$ is mean velocity.

Over the same interval which defines the mean
velocity, the average value of the eddy velocity
is necessarily zero. (24)

EDDY VISCOSITY. The turbulent transfer of momentum by EDDIES giving rise to an internal fluid
friction, in a manner analogous to the action of
molecular viscosity in LAMINAR FLOW, but taking
place on a much larger scale.

The value of the coefficient of eddy viscosity
(an exchange coefficient) is of the order of 10^4
cm^2/sec, or one hundred thousand times the molecular kinematic viscosity. (24)

EDGE WAVES. Widely spaced wave crests arranged at
right angles to the shore line. Such waves may be
excited by a wind shift associated with a passing
front.

EEG. Electro-Encephalograph.

EER. Explosive Echo Ranging.

EERC. Explosive Echo Ranging Charge.

EFFECTIVE ACOUSTIC CENTER. The effective acoustic
center of an acoustic generator is the point from
which the spherically divergent sound waves, observable at remote points, appear to diverge. (1)

EFFECTIVE BACK RADIATION. The difference between
the "temperature radiation" from the sea surface
and the long-wave radiation from the atmosphere.
This effective radiation depends mainly upon the

temperature of the sea surface and the water-vapor content of the atmosphere.

EFFECTIVE BAND WIDTH. The effective band width of a measuring system selectively responsive to energy distributed in a spectrum is given in terms of the band width of a hypothetical system which satisfies two requirements: (1) over its assigned frequency band it has a uniform response equal to the maximum response of the actual system; (2) the width of this uniform response band is such that, if frequency is plotted to a linear scale, the areas under the response-frequency characteristics of the hypothetical and of the actual systems will be equal. (4)

EFFECTIVE CENTER. The effective center of a sonar projector is defined as that point at which lines coincident with the direction of propagation, as observed at various points some distance from the projector, appear to intersect. If such a point of intersection exists it will correspond to the source at which acoustic energy, moving along any direction of propagation, appears to originate, as indicated by the variation of intensity with distance. For this reason the effective center is often spoken of as the apparent source. (4)

EFFECTIVE DIRECTIVITY FACTOR. The effective directivity factor of a hydrophone, at a specified frequency, may be defined as the ratio of the available power per unit band of the electric waves generated in the hydrophone when oriented in a specified manner in a specified location to the available power per unit band of the electric waves which would be generated, at the same location, in a hypothetical nondirectional hydrophone having a receiving response on any bearing equal to the maximum response of a given directional hydrophone. (4)

EFFECTIVE SOUND PRESSURE. The effective sound pressure at a point is the root-mean-square value of the instantaneous sound pressures, over a time interval at the point under consideration. In the case of periodic sound pressures, the interval must be an integral number of periods or an interval that is long compared to a period. In the case of non-periodic sound pressures, the interval should be long enough to make the value obtained essentially independent of small changes in the length of the interval. (2)

EFFICIENCY. The efficiency of a device with respect to a physical quantity which may be stored, transferred, or transformed by the device is the ratio of the useful output of the quantity to its total input. (1)

EFFICIENCY LOSS. The efficiency loss of a transducer connecting an energy source and an energy load is the transmission loss measured by the ratio of the input power of the transducer to the load power of the load. (4)

EKG. 1. Electrocardiogram
2. Electrocardiograph

EKMAN CURRENT METER. The Ekman current meter was developed by Dr. V. Walfrid Ekman, a Swedish scientist, whose original design, although modified, remains basically unchanged. The meter was designed to give speed and direction of the current at any depth. It consists of an impeller or screw, and shaft connected to a set of dials. The number of shaft revolutions per unit of time is read from the dials on the main body of the meter. A reservoir of bronze balls is connected by a narrow tube to a compass box containing a compass needle. Below the needle is the compass-ball receptacle which is divided into 36 chambers, each representing 10° of azimuth. As the impeller rotates, the balls fall, one at a time, onto the top of the compass needle which guides them into one or another of the chambers, depending on the heading of the current meter. This gives the direction toward which the current is flowing.

The current meter is lowered on either the oceanographic or bathythermograph wire. The impeller is locked while lowering or hoisting. A messenger is sent down the wire to unlock the impeller and set the meter in operation. A second messenger is sent down to lock the impeller and stop the meter before hoisting.

Valid measurements cannot be made with an Ekman current meter unless the ship or buoy from which it is suspended is anchored. (35)

EKMAN SPIRAL. A graphic representation of the way in which the theoretical wind-driven currents in the surface layers of the sea vary with depth. In an ocean which is assumed to be homogeneous, infinitely deep, unbounded and having a constant eddy viscosity, over which a uniform steady wind blows, Ekman has computed that the current induced in the surface layers by the wind will have the following characteristics: (a) At the very surface the water will move at an angle of 45° CUM SOLE from the wind direction. (b) In successively deeper layers the movement will be deflected farther and farther cum sole from the wind direction, and the speed will decrease. (c) A HODOGRAPH of the velocity vectors would form a spiral descending into the water and decreasing in amplitude exponentially with depth.

The depth at which the vector first points 180° from the wind vector is called the depth of frictional influence (or depth of frictional resistance). At this depth the speed is $e^{-\pi}$ times that at the surface. The layer from the surface to the depth of frictional influence is called the layer of frictional influence. If the velocity vectors from the surface to the depth of frictional influence be integrated, the resultant motion is 90° cum sole from the wind direction. (12)

ELASTIC LIMIT. In practice, the elastic limit is determined by subjecting a specimen carrying a strain-measuring device (extensometer) to a series of loading steps in which the maximum load applied is gradually increased, the load being released completely at each step. A load will finally be reached upon release of which the specimen will fail to return to its original length: this load is the elastic limit. The size of the load increments used and the sensitivity of the extensometer used will, of course, affect the value obtained, and, consequently, this property is not frequently determined.

ELASTIC LIMIT, APPARENT. An arbitrary approximation of Elastic Limit for a material that does not exhibit a significant Proportional Limit. It is obtained from a Stress-Strain Diagram and is equal

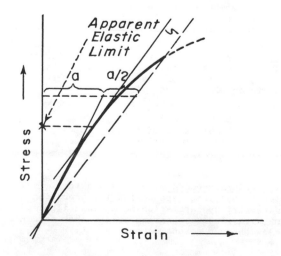

to the stress at which the rate of strain is 50% greater than at zero stress. It is determined as the stress at the point of tangency between the curve and a line having a slope with respect to the stress axis 50% greater than the slope of the curve at the origin.

ELECTRIC BATTERY. See GALVANIC CELL.

ELECTRIC WAVE STAFF. The Electric Wave Staff is an instrument designed to record wave heights and periods at sea. It consists of three 12-foot lengths of water-tight 3-inch aluminum tubing, a 3-foot circular steel damping disk, a Brush recorder, a transformer-rectifier circuit, electrical cables, floats, retrieving lines, and balancing weights. The upper section of tubing has 36 contact points set 4 inches apart, and is covered with black waterproofing material. It is called the step-resistance gage and has a connection for the electrical cable at the top. The remaining two sections of tubing provide proper buoyancy to the step-resistance gage so that it will float vertically in the water with one-half of its length exposed. Below the end of the lower tube is suspended the damping disk. Its function also is to provide weight to keep the staff vertical and to damp the tendency of the staff to rise and fall with the passing waves. As these waves pass, the water rises and falls along the step-resistance gage, thereby increasing and decreasing the resistance in the gage as it passes successive contact points. This variation in resistance is transmitted to the Brush recorder aboard ship by the electrical cable and transformer-rectifier circuit. A record of the wave height and period is thus recorded on a strip chart. The usual length of recording time is from 7 to 20 minutes. These observations are made when the ship is lying to and the wave-staff assembly put overboard to windward so that the normal drift of the ship will be away from the staff. (35)

ELECTRICAL FISHING. Fish respond to electric current by orienting themselves to face the anode and swimming toward that pole in a forced manner. By this means fish may be led into nets, traps or pumps and the method is termed electrical fishing. (34)

ELECTROACOUSTIC TRANSDUCERS. Hydrophones and projectors, together with microphones, telephone receivers, and loud speakers, are known generically as electroacoustic transducers. An electroacoustic transducer is a transducer for receiving waves from acoustic system, or vice versa. (1)

ELECTRODE. The conductor by which current enters and leaves an electrolyte when subjected to an externally impressed potential.

ELECTROLYTE. Any substance which, in solution or fused, exists as electrically charged ions that make the liquid capable of conducting a current. Sea water is an electrolyte. (35)

ELECTROLYSIS. The process of chemical decomposition of an electrolyte by the action of an electric current.

ELECTROKINETIC TRANSDUCER. An electrokinetic transducer is one that depends for its operation on the dielectric polarization in certain liquids resulting from viscous shearing stress that accompanies flow through porous materials. (1)

ELECTROLYTIC CELL. A voltaic cell to which an external electromotive force greater than the electromotive force developed by the voltaic cell is impressed across the electrodes.

ELECTROMECHANICAL TRANSDUCER. An electromechanical transducer is a transducer for receiving waves from an electric system and delivering waves to a mechanical system, or vice versa. (1)

ELECTROMOTIVE FORCE SERIES (EMF SERIES). The elements can be listed according to their standard electrode potentials. The more negative the potential the greater the tendency of the metals to corrode but not necessarily at higher rates. This series is useful in studies of thermodynamic properties. A hydrogen gas electrode is the standard reference and is placed equal to zero. All potentials are positive or negative with respect to the hydrogen electrode. (35)

ELECTRONIC LIQUID DENSITY INSTRUMENT. The instrument consists of a glass float on the end of a thin rod suspended in the liquid. The float-rod is supported by means of two flat springs so that it is constrained to precise vertical motion. The float-rod assembly carries a coil similar to the voice-coil of a dynamic loud speaker and a differential transformer core. Vertical movement of the float is detected by the electrical response of the differential transformer. The coil moves in a strong, radial, magnetic field and when the float is buoyed up by the liquid, the reaction force between the coil and the field is used to pull it down. Thus, balance is achieved at a null position by adjusting the coil current while observing the null indicator. (30)

ELECTRONIC POSITION INDICATOR (EPI). The Electronic Position Indicator is a pulse, time-measuring system similar to SHORAN and LORAN. It is similar to Loran in that it uses the same frequency (about 2 megacycles) and type of signal. It is similar to Shoran in that it is a 2-range circular system instead of a hyperbolic system like Loran.
The EPI measures the time it takes a radio signal to travel from the ship to the shore station and return. An internal variable delay is in the ship's read-out system. This delay is changed in time until it equals the round-trip time of the radio signal. Then the delay time is equal to the round trip time, and this value is converted into distance. For simplification, the arcs of distances are plotted directly as arcs of time on the hydrographic sheet. (29)

ELECTRONIC SEA-WAVE RECORDER. This instrument is a surface type of sea-wave recorder which is based upon the principle that the capacitance between sea water and an insulated wire placed vertically in it varies with changes in the level of the water. This change in capacitance is used to modulate the frequency of an oscillator. An electronic unit is used for recovering from the frequency modulated signal an electrical voltage which is an exact replica of the sea wave.
The advantages of this recorder are; (1) It is suitable for both laboratory studies and sea-wave recordings; (2) this type of recorder responds well to waves of all frequencies and can follow the rise and fall of the water surface with negligible error; and (3) the performance of the capacitance-wire electrode is fairly reliable and comparatively free from the action of the sea water. (35)

ELECTRONS. One of the three basic particles of atoms which has a negative charge and carries approximately 1/1837th of the weight of a proton. Electrons are the outermost parts of an atom and they revolve or circulate around the relatively heavy nucleus at terrific speeds so as to approximate shells. An atom in an electrically neutral state has as many electrons as protons (ATOMIC NUMBER). Chemical changes (e.g., burning coal, gasoline, dynamite and etc.) affect the electrons of an atom but not the nucleus. (39)

ELECTROSTATIC (CAPACITOR) (CONDENSER) TRANSDUCER. An electrostatic transducer is a transducer that consists of a capacitor and depends upon interaction between its electric field and the change of its electrostatic capacitance. (1)

ELECTROSTRICTION. Electrostriction is the phenomenon wherein some dielectric materials experience an elastic strain when subjected to an electric field, this strain being independent of the polarity of the field. (1)

ELECTROTAPE (MICRODIST). A phase comparison base line measuring system similar to TELLUROMETER and GEODIMETER. It is similar to Tellurometer in that radar frequencies are used whereas in the Geodimeter light waves are employed. All three systems use a 10 megacycle crystal as the basis of their measurement so one period or lane width is 15 meters in the electrotape and tellurometer and is 7.5 meters in the geodimeter due to the method of measuring. (29)

ELEPHANTA. A strong southerly or southeasterly wind which blows on the Malabar coast of India during the months of September and October and marks the end of the southwest monsoon. (17)

ELLIPTICALLY POLARIZED SOUND WAVE. An elliptically polarized sound wave is a transverse wave and hence each particle in the medium is moving at right angles to the direction of propagation of the wave. There is the additional requirement, however, that each point in the medium must be executing an ellipse, the plane of the ellipse being, of course, at right angles to the direction of propagation of the wave. (9)

EL NINO. A warm ocean current setting south along the coast of Ecuador, so called because it generally develops just after Christmas. In exceptional years, concurrently with a southerly shift in the tropical rain belt, the current may extend along the coast of Peru to 12°S. When this occurs, plankton and fish are killed in the coastal waters and a phenomenon somewhat like the RED TIDE of Florida results. (24)

ELONGATION. A term that is both general and specific. Generally, the extension of a material in the Tension Test at any specified point (e.g. Yield Point Elongation). Specifically, the extension of a material at rupture in the Tension Test. Generally, Elongation (%) is calculated by dividing total increase in gage length by original gage length and multiplying by 100. At rupture, Elongation (%) is usually calculated by dividing total permanent increase in gage length by original gage length and multiplying by 100. Total permanent strain can be measured by fitting the broken specimen together after rupture or by subtracting strain at the Elastic Limit from total strain indicated by a Stress-Strain Diagram. For any material with high Modulus of Elasticity and an important degree of Elongation, the error introduced by using total strain obtained from extensometer or Stress-Strain Diagram instead of total permanent strain is insignificant. Elongation of metals in short gage lengths is quite sensitive specimen, and gage length must therefore be specified. Elongation cannot be used to predict other mechanical properties but is considered an indicator of Ductility in metals. As such it is used to predict both formability and the extent to

which a metal can deform in service without rupture. However, Elongation may have little relation to the highly localized extension occurring in many forming operations, and Elongation specified for structural materials often has little relation to the much smaller extension actually permitted by service conditions. Elongation cannot be used to predict behavior of materials subjected to to the effects of localized extension occurring at the center of the "necked down" portion of the sudden or repeated loading. (41)

ELVEGUST (Also SNO). A cold descending squall in the upper parts of Norwegian fjords. (12)

EMERY-DIETZ GRAVITY CORER. In this corer an attempt was made to produce a cheap, sturdy and reliable instrument capable of working even under moderately adverse sea conditions. The corer weighs about 650 lbs. in air and consists essentially of a shaft, weights, and coring tube. The shaft is a standard 8-ft. pipe 2 1/2 in. in diameter with several small holes drilled in it to allow water to run off as it is lifted on board. On this shaft is mounted a set of removable lead weights, roughly streamlined, and varying in number depending upon the desired depth of penetration. The weights rest on a shoulder which is part of the valve housing. The valve is designed to prevent loss of the core by suction during withdrawal from the mud, to obviate any washing out of the relatively fluid upper part of the core during hauling, and to stop the weight of water in the shaft forcing out a short core as the device is lifted out of the sea. It consists of a rubber bung resting in guides and fitting loosely in a brass seating. The coring tube itself fits below this valve and consists of a standard pipe, 2 or 2 1/2 in. in diameter, thrust into a sleeve against a shoulder of the valve housing and clamped there with a set-screw. A removable plastic liner is fitted inside the coring tube so that the core may be readily removed, inspected and stored. Screwed to the bottom end of the tube is a nose-piece with a slightly smaller diameter than the coring tube itself. A core retainer is fitted in the nose-piece. This has strips of plastic pressed into a thin rubber sleeve and bent over towards the center. When the sample is passing up the coring tube they are pushed back against its wall, and if the core starts to slip, they close the opening. In use, the instrument is lowered on a 3/8-in. wire rope until about 300 ft. above the bottom when it is allowed to run almost free with only sufficient braking to insure a vertical descent. The device strikes the bottom with a velocity of 12 to 21 ft/sec. (35)

EMBATA. A local onshore southwest wind caused by the reversal of the northeast TRADE WINDS in the lee of the Canary Islands. (12)

EMISSARY SKY. A sky of cirrus clouds which are either isolated or in small, separated groups; so called because this formation often is one of the first indications of the approach of a cyclonic storm. (12)

EMIT. A Russian electromagnetic current meter which is similar to the American GEK. (35)

EMPHYSEMA. Refers to a swelling or inflation due to abnormal presence of air in the tissues. Subcutaneous emphysema is the presence of air in the tissues just under the skin. When seen in diving, it usually involves the skin of the neck and nearby areas. Mediastinal emphysema is the presence of air in the tissues in the vicinity of the heart and large blood vessels in the middle of the chest. Unless extreme, neither of these conditions is likely to cause serious difficulty. If emphysema is extreme, AIR EMBOLISM will usually be present also. (37)

EMR. Electromagnetic Radiation.

ENDOPHYTE. A plant living within another plant but not necessarily parasitic upon it. (20)

ENDOSKELETON. An internal supporting framework or structure. (19)

ENERGY. The capacity to perform work or the ability to make a certain force act through a distance. Potential energy is stored energy such as water behind a dam. Kinetic energy is energy which is being released such as light, x-ray, etc. There are various forms of kinetic energy, for instance chemical, mechanical, nuclear, etc. (39)

ENERGY ABSORPTION. A term that is both general and specific. Generally, it refers to the energy absorbed by any material subjected to loading. Specifically it is a measure of Toughness or Impact Strength of a material; the energy needed to fracture a specimen in an Impact Test. It is the difference in kinetic energy of the striker before and after impact, expressed as total energy (ft-lb or in-lb) for metals and ceramics, and energy per inch of notch for plastics and electrical insulating materials. A higher Energy Absorption indicates a greater Toughness. For notched specimens, Energy Absorption is an indication of the effect of internal multiaxial stress distribution on fracture behavior of the material. It is merely a qualitative index and cannot be used directly in design. Notch behavior of most metals can be deduced from results of the Tension Test, but notch behavior of ferritic steels is not predictable. Transition Temperature, derived from a series of Energy Absorption measurements, is commonly specified for such materials. Energy Absorption is quite sensitive to variations in materials and in test conditions, especially temperature, striking speed and energy, and specimen size and shape. Only results for identical specimens and notches may safely be compared. If a metal has reasonably high Energy Absorption at a specified temperature, it is assumed that it will exhibit ductile fracture at all higher temperatures.

ENERGY COEFFICIENT. The ratio of the energy in a wave per unit crest length transmitted forward with the wave at a point in shallow water to the energy in a wave per unit crest length transmitted forward with the wave in deep water. On refraction diagrams this is equal to the ratio of the distance between a pair of orthogonals at a selected point to the distance between the same pair of orthogonals in deep water. Also the square of the REFRACTION COEFFICIENT. (11)

ENTRANCE. The avenue of access or opening to a navigable channel. (11)

EOD. Explosive Ordnance Disposal.

EPIBENTHIC DREDGE. This bottom sampler developed by Scripps Institution consists of a pair of sheet-metal skis attached to a light framework for a silk or nylon net. A sheet of heavy canvas fastened beneath the net protects it from tearing. Removable rakers in front of the net stir up the bottom as the dredge advances, permitting the net to capture the creatures contained in the sediment. A bottom-walking wheel connected to a small veeder-root counter indicates the distance over the bottom the device travels during a haul. The EBD is lowered in the ocean with an ordinary hydrographic winch, and will go as far down as 4500 m. Collecting speed of the dredge is only 2 kt eliminating wire angle problems. (30)

EPICENTER. In Seismology, the point on the earth's surface directly over the focus or theoretical point of origin of an earthquake. (29)

EPILIMNION. The layer of water above the THERMOCLINE in a fresh water lake or pool; the opposite of HYPOLIMNION. In the ocean, the equivalent is the MIXED LAYER. (24)

EPIPHYTIC. A relationship in which one plant lives attached to or supported by another plant, but obtains food independently. (18)

EPITHECA. (1) An external calcareous layer investing the lower portion of the theca of many corals. (2) The outer or upper half or valve of the diatom frustule. The inner or bottom half or valve is called the HYPOTHECA. (20)

EPIZOIC. Dwelling upon the body of an animal (or plant). (20)

EPOC. Eastern Pacific Oceanic Conference.

EPPLEY PYRHELIOMETER. This instrument is designed to be used above water primarily for measurement of the intensity of solar radiation upon a horizontal plane and is calibrated at the Eppley Laboratory in sunshine against pyrheliometers which are standardized every year at the Weather Bureau, Washington, D. C. The probable error for the instrument, as compared with direct radiation, intensities ranging from 0.25 to 1.50 gm cal/ cm^2/min., is ± 1.5 per cent. The instrument is sensitive to the wavelength range between 3,000 and 50,000 Å.

EQUALANT I & II. Tropical Atlantic Investigation.

EQUAPAC. Equatorial Pacific (Project).

EQUATORIAL CALMS. See DOLDRUMS.

EQUATORIAL COUNTERCURRENT. An ocean current flowing eastward (counter to and between the westward-flowing NORTH EQUATORIAL CURRENT and SOUTH EQUATORIAL CURRENT) through all the oceans.
In the Atlantic Ocean, it flows east across the ocean between the north and south equatorial currents across the full width of the ocean in northern summer, and across the eastern half of the ocean in northern winter. It eventually becomes the GUINEA CURRENT.
In the Pacific Ocean, it is one of the swiftest of ocean currents; it flows east across the ocean between the latitudes 3°N and 10°N. East of the Philippines it is joined by the southern part of the north equatorial current.
In the Indian Ocean, it flows between the north and south equatorial currents, to the east; unlike the equatorial countercurrents of the Atlantic and Pacific Oceans, it lies south of the equator. In northern summer, when the southwest monsoon forms a continuation of the southeast trade winds, the countercurrent, along with the north equatorial current, is replaced by an easterly flowing monsoon current. (24)

EQUATORIAL CONVERGENCE ZONE. See INTERTROPICAL CONVERGENCE ZONE.

EQUATORIAL CURRENTS. (1) Ocean currents flowing westerly near the equator. There are two such currents in both the Atlantic and Pacific Oceans. The one to the north of the equator is called the NORTH EQUATORIAL CURRENT, and the one to the south of the equator is called the SOUTH EQUATORIAL CURRENT. Between these two currents there is an easterly flowing stream known as the EQUATORIAL COUNTER CURRENT. (2) Tidal currents occurring semimonthly as a result of the moon being over the equator. At these times the tendency of the moon to produce a DIURNAL INEQUALITY in the current is at a minimum. See also DECLINATION. (24)

EQUATORIAL EASTERLIES (DEEP TRADES, DEEP EASTERLIES). As used by some authors, the trade winds in the summer hemisphere when they are very deep, extending to at least 8 to 10 km altitude, and generally not topped by upper westerlies. If upper westerlies are present they are too weak and shallow to influence the weather.

In the winter hemisphere, these easterlies are restricted to a narrow belt along the equator. (24)

EQUATORIAL TIDES. Tides occurring semimonthly as the result of the moon being over the equator. At these times the tendency of the moon to produce a diurnal inequality in the tide is at a minimum. See also DECLINATION. (14)

EQUATORIAL TROUGH. 1. The quasi-continuous belt of low pressure lying between the SUBTROPICAL HIGH-PRESSURE BELTS of the Northern and Southern Hemisphere. This entire region is one of very homogeneous air, probably the most ideally BAROTROPIC region of the atmosphere. Yet, humidity is so high that slight variations in stability cause major variations in weather.

The position of the equatorial trough is fairly constant in the eastern portions of the Atlantic and Pacific; but it varies greatly with season in the western portions of those oceans and in southern Asia and the Indian Ocean. It moves into or toward the summer hemisphere.

It has been suggested that this name be adopted as the one general term for this region of the atmosphere. Thus, the equatorial trough would be said to contain regions of DOLDRUMS; portions of it could be described as INTERTROPICAL CONVERGENCE ZONES; and within it there might be detected INTERTROPICAL FRONTS. However, one weakness of this nomenclature is that it alludes specifically and only to the existence of a TROUGH of low pressure. Perhaps an even more general term might be preferable, for example, atmospheric equator.
2. Same as meteorological equator. (14)

EQUATORIAL WESTERLIES. The westerly winds occasionally found in the equatorial trough and separated from the mid-latitude westerlies by the broad belt of easterly trade winds.

As the air flow in the lower atmosphere is mostly easterly in and about the equatorial trough, the existence of westerlies on mean charts in some areas has been a subject of much interest and speculation. In some regions, this abnormality can be explained as the result of limited areas of west winds on the equatorward side of frequent westward-moving cyclones in the equatorial trough. Elsewhere (notably over the Indian Ocean during the Northern Hemisphere summer), the equatorial westerlies may result from the deflection of Southern Hemisphere air as it flows northward across the geographical equator as part of the monsoon. (24)

EQUILIBRIUM THEORY. A hypothesis under which it is assumed that the waters covering the face of the earth instantly respond to the tide-producing forces of the moon and sun and form a surface of equilibrium under the action of these forces. The theory disregards friction and inertia and the irregular distribution of land masses of the earth. The theoretical tide formed under these conditions is known as the equilibirum tide. (14)

EQUILIBRIUM TIDE. See EQUILIBRIUM THEORY. (14)

EQUIVALENT NOISE PRESSURE (INHERENT NOISE PRESSURE). The equivalent noise pressure of an electroacoustic transducer or system used for sound reception is the root-mean-square sound pressure of a sinusoidal plane progressive wave, which, if propagated parallel to the principal axis of the transducer, would produce an open-circuit signal voltage equal to the root-mean-square of the inherent open-circuit noise voltage of the transducer in a transmission band having a band width of 1 cycle per second and centered on the frequency of the plane sound wave. (1)

EQUIVALENT NOISE PRESSURE LEVEL. The equivalent noise pressure level, in decibels, of a transducer used for sound reception, is 20 times the logarithm to the base 10 of the ratio of the equivalent noise pressure to the stated reference pressure. (1)

EQUIVALENT VISCOUS DAMPING. Equivalent viscous damping is a value of viscous damping assumed for the purpose of analysis of a vibratory motion, such that the dissipation of energy per cycle at resonance is the same for either the assumed or actual damping force. (2)

EROSION. The phenomenon of wearing away the surface of a material by the hydraulic action of a moving stream of fluid.

EROSION, BASE LEVEL OF. The lowest level to which a river can erode its bed is called the base level. The sedimentary transporting power is minimal or has reached equilibrium at this level. (27)

EROSION-CORROSION. This is the combination of erosion phenomenon and corrosion phenomenon which produces a high rate of local attack of the base metal. Since many materials are corrosive resistant because of a protective oxide film adhering to their surface, when corrosive fluids strike this film it is eroded away leaving the base metal unprotected from corrosion. (35)

EROSION SURFACE. An area which has been flattened by subaerial or marine erosion to form an area of relatively low relief at an elevation close to the base-level (sea-level) existing at the time of its formation. Relics of such surfaces may now be found far above sea-level owing to the falling base-level... or below the present ocean surface. (27)

ERYSIPELOTHRIX. An organism of the sea which can cause skin lesions in humans.

ESCARPMENT (SCARP). A more or less continuous line of cliffs or steep slopes facing in one general direction which are caused by erosion or faulting. (27)

ESHP. Equivalent Shaft Horse Power.

ESTUARY. (1) That portion of a stream influenced by the tide of the body of water into which it flows; (2) A bay, as the mouth of a river, where the tide meets the river current. (11)

ETESIANS. The prevailing northerly winds in summer in the eastern Mediterranean and especially the Aegean Sea; basically similar to MONSOON and equivalent to the MAESTRO of the Adriatic Sea.

According to the ancient Greeks, the etesians blow for forty days beginning with the heliacal rising of Sirius. They are associated (along with the seistan and shamal) with the deep low pressure area which forms in summer over northwest India. They bring clear skies and dry, relatively cool weather.

In Greece the etesian wind is locally called the Sleeper. In Turkey it is the Meltem. The Romans used the word also for the southwest monsoon of the Arabian Sea. (12)

EULER VELOCITY FIELD. The Euler method assumes that the velocity of all particles of the fluid has been defined. On this assumption the velocity field is completely described if the components of the velocity can be represented as function of the coordinate and time.

EULERIAN COORDINATES. Any system of coordinates in which properties of a fluid are assigned to points in space at each given time, without attempt to identify individual fluid parcels from one time to the next. Since most observations in meteorology are made locally at specified time intervals, an Eulerian system is usually, though by no means always, more convenient. A sequence of synoptic charts is an Eulerian representation of the data.

Eulerian coordinates are to be distinguished from LAGRANGIAN COORDINATES. The particular coordinate system used to identify points in space (Cartesian, cylindrical, spherical, etc.) is quite independent of whether the representation is Eulerian or Lagrangian. (24)

EULITTORAL ZONE. See BENTHIC DIVISION.

EUPHOTIC ZONE. 1. For the purpose of biological investigations it is convenient to consider the sea as divided vertically into three zones with respect to the amount of light that is present. These are: (1) The euphotic zone, which is abundantly supplied with light sufficient for the photosynthetic processes of plants. This zone extends from the surface to 80 or more meters. (2) The disphotic zone, which is only dimly lighted and extends from about 80 to 200 or more meters. No effective plant production can take place in this zone, and the plants found here have mostly sunk from the layer above. (3) The aphotic zone, the lightless region below the disphotic zone. In the deep sea it is a very thick layer in which no plants are produced and the animal life consists only of carnivores and detritus feeders. (13)

2. The layer of a body of water which receives ample sunlight for the photosynthetic processes of plants. The depth of this layer varies with the water's extinction coefficient, the angle of incidence of the sunlight, length of day, and cloudiness; but it is usually 80 meters or more. The depth of compensation is the lower boundary of the euphotic zone. (24)

EURYHALINE. See STENOHALINE.

EURYTHERMIC. See STENOHALINE.

EUSTATISM. The fluctuations of sea-level due to the changing capacity of the ocean basins or the volume of ocean water. Glacio-eustatism causes variations of sea-level related to the changing volume of glacier ice; sedimento-eustatism is related to the rise of sea-level due to the filling of the ocean basin with sediment; and tectono-eustatism is due to changes in the capacity of the ocean basins resulting from earth movements, such as basin formation, which, by increasing the capacity of the ocean receptacles, lowers sea-level. (27)

EVAPORATION AND CONCENTRATION UNIT FOR DILUTE RADIOACTIVE AND NON-RADIOACTIVE SOLUTIONS. See RADIOACTIVITY METER FOR LIQUIDS.

EWING PISTON CORER. This corer, weighing approximately 1200 lbs. in air and measuring 20 ft. in length (1, 2 or 3 - 20 ft. sections of the coring tube can be coupled together to collect cores up to 60 ft. in length) is the largest used by the U. S. Navy Oceanographic Office. It has no tailfin for stability and employs no core liner--the cores either being extruded after each cast or stored in the coring tube itself. The operation of the trigger mechanism and piston is similar to those used on the KULLENBERG PISTON CORER and the counterweight or trigger weight is constructed similar to that of the PHLEGER CORER. It consists of a main tube with a cast lead drive weight of approximately 50 lbs., a short coring tube, plastic liner, core catcher, and cutting edge. (35)

EXCHANGE COEFFICIENTS (Also called AUSTAUSCH COEFFICIENTS, EDDY COEFFICIENTS, INTERCHANGE COEFFICIENTS). Coefficients of eddy flux (e.g., of momentum, heat, water vapor, etc.) in turbulent flow, defined in analogy to those of the kinetic theory of gases. The exchange-coefficient hypothesis states that the mean eddy flux per unit area of a conservative quantity (suitably expressed) is proportional to the gradient of the mean value of this quantity, that is,

$$\text{mean flux per unit area} = - A \frac{d\overline{E}}{dn'}$$

where A is the exchange coefficient, $\overline{E}$ the mean value of the quantity, and n the direction normal to the surface. In strict analogy to molecular properties A would be constant, for turbulent flow A turns out to depend on time and location. (24)

EXOSKELETON. An external supporting structure or covering. (19)

EXPENDABLE BT. The Expendable Bathythermograph (BT) has been successfully launched from destroyers at speeds of 30 knots. It requires no winch, it can be used in rough weather, and it is accurate, yet expendable. The BT system consists of four units: an expendable transducer unit, a surface float, a shipboard telemetry bale, and a recorder. Operating sequence is as follows; the float and transducer are launched from a moving vessel; the float unit remains essentially stationary in the water because the wire pays out readily from the shipboard telemetry bale; as the float hits the water it releases the BT transducer which falls freely and vertically, paying out wire from its bale at the rear; while falling, the transducer transmits an analog temperature signal through the telemetry wire to the shipboard recorder. The rate of descent is constant, so depth is a direct function of time. (35)

EXPENDABLE INSTRUMENTS. Expendable or "throw away" instruments are generally interpreted as a class of relatively inexpensive oceanographic research instruments which may be simply tossed overboard from a ship at sea to telemeter certain desired oceanographic information back to the ship. (35)

EXPIRATORY RESERVE VOLUME. The amount of air that can be expelled by forcible expiration at the end of a normal expiration. It normally amounts to about 1 liter during rest and becomes smaller as the tidal volume increases. Note that the sum of the tidal volume and inspiratory and expiratory reserve volumes equals the vital capacity. (37)

EXTERNAL WAVE. A wave in fluid motion having its maximum amplitude at an external boundary such as a free surface.

Any surface wave on the free surface of a homogeneous incompressible fluid is an external wave. (12)

EXTINCTION COEFFICIENT. A measure of the space rate of diminution, or extinction, of any transmitted light; thus, it is the attenuation coefficient applied to visible radiation. The extinction coefficient σ is identified in a form of Bouguer's law (or Beer's law): $dI = - \sigma I \, dx$ or $I = I_o e^{-\sigma x}$, where I is the illuminance (luminous flux density) at the selected point in space, I_o is the illuminance at the light source, and x is the distance from the source.

When so used, the extinction coefficient equals the sum of the medium's absorption coefficient and scattering coefficient, each computed as a weighted average over all wavelengths in the visible spectrum. As long as scattering effects are primary, as in the lower atmosphere, the value of the extinction coefficient is a function of the particle size of atmospheric suspensoids. It varies in order of magnitude from 10 km^{-1} with very low visibility to 0.01 km^{-1} in very clear air.

The extinction coefficient is related to the transmission coefficient τ as follows: $\tau = e^{-\sigma}$.

In oceanography, it is a measure of the attenuation of downward-directed radiation in the sea.

The coefficient K is defined by $K = 2.303 \log \frac{I\lambda_1}{I\lambda_2}$,

where $I\lambda_1$ is the intensity of radiation of a given wavelength λ on a horizontal surface and $I\lambda_2$ is the intensity on a horizontal surface 1 meter deeper. K varies with wavelength, with the nature of the scattering particles, and with the presence of dissolved colored substances. (24)

EYE OF THE STORM. The center of a tropical cyclone, marked by relatively light winds, confused seas, rising temperature, lowered relative humidity, and often by clear skies. The general area of lowest atmospheric pressure of a cyclone is called storm center. (17)

F

FACE PLATE. A glass or plastic window worn over the SCUBA or SKIN DIVERS face and designed to provide an air space between the diver's eyes and the water. The face plate permits both eyes to see in the same plane. A full face plate covers the eyes, mouth and nose while a regular face plate covers the eyes and nose only.

FACIES. See BIOTOPE.

FACSIMILE CHART (FAX CHART, FAX MAP). In meteorology, any graphic form of weather information, usually a type of synoptic chart, which has been reproduced by facsimile equipment. Master charts are plotted and analyzed at central weather stations, and these maps are transmitted by facsimile equipment via radio or wire to individual weather stations. (24)

FAC/SPC. Fisheries Advisory Committee of the South Pacific Commission.

FACULTATIVE BACTERIA. Bacteria which utilize free oxygen in respiration, but can also live in the total absence of free oxygen. (13)

FAGS. Federation of Astronomical and Geophysical Science.

FAIR TIDE. A tidal current setting in such a direction as to increase the speed of a vessel. One setting in a direction approximately opposite to the heading is called a head tide. One abeam is called a beam tide. One approximately 90° from the course is called a cross tide. (17)

FAIRWAY. The main traveled part of a waterway; a marine thoroughfare. (17)

FAIRWAY BUOY. A buoy marking a fairway, with safe water on both sides. (17)

FAIR WIND. A wind which aids a craft in making progress in a desired direction. Used chiefly in connection with sailing vessels, when it refers to a wind which permits the vessel to proceed in the desired direction without excessive changing of course. When applied to a power vessel or an aircraft, it refers to a wind which increases the speed of the craft. A wind which delays the progress of a craft is called an unfavorable wind. Also called favorable wind. (17)

FALKLAND CURRENT. A South Atlantic Ocean current flowing northeastward along the east coast of South America from Cape Horn to the Rio de la Plata, widening and curving eastward to continue as part of the SOUTH ATLANTIC CURRENT. The Falkland current is a continuation of the CAPE HORN CURRENT. (17)

FALLING TIDE. See EBB TIDE.

FALSE CIRRUS. Cirrus proceeding from cumulonimbus, and composed of the debris of the upper frozen parts of the cloud. (17)

FALSE ICE FOOT. Ice formed along a beach terrace and attached thereto just above the high water mark. It is derived from water originating from melting snow above the beach terrace. This formation is termed a false ice foot because, unlike a true ICE FOOT, it has its base above the low water mark. A false ice foot may be added to by accretions of SEA ICE resulting from waves, spray, and spring tides. (25)

FAN. A gently sloping, cone-shaped accumulation of material normally located at the mouth of a CANYON. (26)

FAO. Food and Agriculture Organization of the UN (United Nations).

FAREWELL BUOY. See SEA BUOY.

FASEB. Federation of American Societies for Experimental Biology.

FAST ICE (COASTAL ICE, COAST ICE, LANDFAST ICE). Ice which is held in position by contact with or attachment to the shore or bottom. It is called ICE FOOT if frozen to the shore, shore ice if cast onto the shore or beached, stranded ice if grounded, and BOTTOM ICE if frozen to the bottom. Ice which is not in contact with or attached to the shore or bottom is called floating ice. (17)

FAST RESPONSE CUP ANEMOMETER. This instrument is a standard device for the measurement of wind speed. The fast response Anemometer is used for accurate dynamic measurements in turbulent wind regimes. These wind measurements are important to oceanography due to the fact that winds generate waves and current systems. The instrument consists of cups which trap the wind and cause a shaft to rotate. A cap is locked to the shaft and acts as a light chopper. The light source is an incandescent bulb within a housing having a single slot. A photoelectric switch is placed in line with the slot. The chopper rotates between the lamp housing and the photo detector mount. Thus, as the shaft rotates, light passing the lamp housing slit is alternately interrupted and passed by the slots in the chopper causing the photoelectric switch to alternately open and close an electric circuit. The rate of switching depends on the wind speed. (30)

FATA MORGANA. A complex mirage that is characterized by multiple distortions of images, generally in the vertical, so that such objects as cliffs and cottages are distorted and magnified into fantastic castles. The name is due to Italian poets who related this type of mirage (often seen near the Strait of Messina) to a submarine crystal palace of Fata Morgana (Italian for Morgan le Fay).
     An unusual density stratification is required to produce this mirage, namely the joint occurrence, in vertically adjacent layers, of density gradients that would give an inferior mirage and a superior

mirage. A strong inversion over a relatively warm sea may satisfy this requirement. The instability of the air layer lying immediately over the sea may lead to sporadic breakdown of the stratification there, accompanied by rapid changes in the mirage characteristics, a circumstance that suggests the fairy-like features of the mirage forms. (Humphreys, W. J., in Physics of the Air, 3rd ed., 1940, pp. 474-475) (12)

FATHOM. The common unit of depth in the ocean, equal to six feet (or 1.83 meters). It is also sometimes used in expressing horizontal distances, in which case 100 fathoms make one CABLE or very nearly one-tenth nautical mile. (24)

FATHOMETER. An instrument used in measuring the depth of water by the time required for a sound wave to travel from surface to bottom and for its echo to be returned. It may be used also for measuring the rise and fall of the tides in off-shore localities. (14)

FATIGUE. A weakening or deterioration of metal or other material, or of a member, occurring under load, especially under repeated, cyclic, or continued loading. (31)

FATIGUE LIFE. A clue as to the length of useful life of a material subjected to repeated loading.

FAUDOE. Florida Atlantic University-Department of Ocean Engineering, Boca Raton, Florida.

FAULT. A break or shear in the earth's crust, with an observable displacement between the two sides of the break, and parallel to the plane of the break. (27)

FAX CHART. See FACSIMILE CHART.

FAX MAP. See FACSIMILE CHART.

FCC. Federal Communications Commission.

FCST. Federal Council of Science and Technology.

FEEDER BEACH. An artificially widened beach serving to nourish downdrift beaches by natural littoral currents or forces. (11)

FEEDER CURRENT. The current which flows parallel to shore before converging and forming the neck of a RIP CURRENT. (11)

FEEL THE BOTTOM. The action of a vessel proceeding in shoal water, when its speed is reduced and it sometimes becomes hard to steer. Also called smell the bottom. (17)

FERREL'S LAW. See CORIOLIS.

FETCH. 1. In wave forecasting, the continuous area of water over which the wind blows in essentially a constant direction. Sometimes used synonymously with FETCH LENGTH. Also, GENERATING AREA.
2. In wind set-up phenomena, for enclosed bodies of water, the distance between the points of maximum water surface elevations. This would usually coincide with the longest axis in the general wind direction. (11)

FETCH LENGTH. In wave forecasting, the horizontal distance (in the direction of the wind) over which the wind blows. (11)

FIGURE OF MERIT. Ratio, in decibels, of pressure in transmitted ping at a distance of 1 yard to pressure of the minimum detectable echo under prevailing conditions. (7)

FILAMENT WINDING. Basically filament winding is the technique of coating small filaments of materials, usually glass, with a resin, usually an epoxy.
Filament windings are used to especially impart higher compressive strengths and better corrosion resistance to sea structures.

FILTER. 1. In ocean-wave forecasting, a set of formulas that define the particular wave frequencies and directions in the fetch area which are of significance at the point of forecast. (24)
2. A combination of resistances, inductances, and capacitances, or any one or two of these, which allows the comparatively free flow of certain frequencies or of direct current while blocking the passage of other frequencies. An example is the filter used in a power supply, which allows the direct current to pass, but filters out the ripple. (20)

FILTERING EFFECT. The differential damping of pressures or of vertical oscillation of water particles with increasing depth, depending upon the wave period. Longer waves are damped less than shorter waves at a given depth. (15)

FILTER PHOTOMETER FOR USE AT SEA. This instrument determines the optical density of coloured solutions. It is suitable for the colorimetric analysis of nutrient salts. The device uses two similar photocells enclosed in cases which are light tight except for a circular aperture. Between the cells and equidistant is a lamp, the cells being so mounted that all light passing through the aperture falls on the active surface of the cathode. The two cells are arranged in a bridge circuit followed by an amplifier, the difference in the output of the cells being measured on a centre-zero meter. With the lamp at a fixed reference point, the aperture before one cell is adjusted until the meter reads zero. A suitable length of the solution, the optical density of which is to be measured is inserted between the lamp and one cell causing the meter to deflect. The lamp is moved toward the solution until the meter again reads zero. The distance the lamp has been moved is related to the optical density of the solution. (30)

FINAL ICE CLEARANCE, EARLIEST. Earliest reported date after breakup that open water (less than 1/10 coverage) was first observed over a specific area.

FINAL ICE CLEARANCE, LATEST. Latest reported date after breakup that open water (less than 1/10 coverage) was first observed over a specific area.

FIORD. See FJORD.

FIRN (Also called FIRN SNOW). Old snow that has become granular and compacted (dense) as the result of various surface metamorphosis, mainly melting and refreezing but also including sublimation. The resulting particles are generally spherical and rather uniform. Firnification, the process of firn formation, is the first step in the transformation of snow into land ice (usually GLACIER ICE). Some authorities restrict the use of firn to snow that has lasted through one summer, thereby distinguishing it from spring snow.
Originally the French term, "névé," was exactly equivalent to the German term, "firn", but there is a growing tendency, especially among British glaciologists, to use "névé" for an area of firn, i.e., generally for the accumulation area above or at the head of a GLACIER. (12)

FIRST APPEARANCE OF ICE, EARLIEST. The earliest re-reported date on which sea ice in any form was observed at a specific location.

FIRTH. A long, narrow arm of the sea. Also called frith. (17)

FISH LEAD. A type of sounding lead used without removal from the water between soundings. (17)

FISH NET BUOY. A buoy marking the limit of a fish net area. (17)

FISSION. 1. The division of a unicellular organism into two equal daughter cells. (18)
2. The disintegration of an atomic nucleus which may happen from spontaneous causes or more commonly when the nucleus itself is struck by sub-nuclear particles, such as a neutron. As the nucleus of an atom of uranium 235 is struck by a neutron it may be absorbed, then immediately or shortly after, the nucleus becomes unstable and breaks, usually into two fragments. This fission causes the release of other neutrons and of energy in the form of radiation and heat. (39)

FIXED ACOUSTIC BUOY (FAB). The Fixed Acoustic Buoy is a deep sea instrumentation device which measures acoustic data at a depth of 14,000 feet. It is controlled and powered from shore via a cable and has numerous modes of operation. Signal processing is accomplished in the deep sea unit to allow use of a single coaxial cable.
In FAB almost all of the signal processing is accomplished electronically in the deep sea portion. This results in a considerable cost saving because it allows use of a single coaxial cable with medium bandwidth requirements instead of 21 pair medium bandwidth cable or one high bandwidth coaxial cable with 21 channel multiplexing. (35)

FIXED TIDE STAFF. See TIDE STAFF.

FJORD (FIORD). A long narrow arm of the sea between highlands. (11)

FLAGELLUM. A long lash or threadlike extension capable of vibration; on flagellate protozoans and on collar cells of sponges. (19)

FLAT ROPE. See WIRE ROPE.

FLEXURAL MODULUS OF ELASTICITY. The Modulus of Elasticity of a material in the Flexure Test. It may be calculated from a Load-Deflection Diagram as follows:

$$E_F = \frac{L^3}{4bh^3}\left(\frac{P}{Y}\right) \text{ (for rectangular specimen)}$$

$$E_F = \frac{0.425\,L^3}{d^4}\left(\frac{P}{Y}\right) \text{ (for round specimen)}$$

where E_F = Flexural Modulus of Elasticity, psi

$\frac{P}{Y}$ = slope of initial straightline portion of curve on Load-Deflection Diagram, lb/in.

L = Span, in.
b = Specimen width, in. (41)

FLIP. A manned spar buoy, used free-floating with long axis vertical, but also capable of a horizontal, shallow-draft position used for berthing and towing to and from station. The general purpose of the structure is to provide a stable, acoustically quiet platform to support hydrophones and other instruments for making measurements under the sea surface, and at the same time to enable measurements at or above the surface.
The total length of the structure is 355 ft, of which 300 ft is normally submerged.
The circular cross-section has a maximum diameter of 20 ft, which diminishes to 12.5 ft in the range from 75 ft depth to 15 ft above the waterline, where the hull joins a superstructure having a further height of 40 ft. (35)

FLIPPERS. See SWIM FINS.

FLOATING ACCELEROMETER. This instrument for measuring waves in the open sea utilizes an accelerometer placed on a small raft which is connected with a ship by a conducting cable. The accelerometer supplies a signal which corresponds essentially to the vertical acceleration of the sea surface. This signal is integrated twice, and the integrated recording is made aboard ship. The frequency response is constant to periods as small as 1.5 seconds. The recorder has some of the disadvantages of the WAVE STAFF in that it is a floating instrument and thus tends to float away with the current. (35)

FLOATING DOCK. See DOCK.

FLOATING ICE. See FAST ICE.

FLOCCULENT DEPOSIT. An aggregate or precipitate of small lumps formed by precipitation. (27)

FLOE. Sea ice, either a single unbroken piece or many individual pieces, covering an area of water. A small floe is 30 feet to 600 feet across; a medium floe, 600 feet to 3,000 feet across; a giant floe, 3,000 feet to 5 miles across; an ice field, more than 5 miles across. A hummocky floe is composed of HUMMOCKED ICE. A land floe is thick fast ice which has broken adrift. Sludge hardened into a floe strong enough to bear the weight of a man is called sludge floe. See GLACON. (17)

FLOEBERG. A mass of thick, heavily-hummocked SEA ICE resembling an ICEBERG in appearance.
Floebergs may be from several feet to more than fifty feet in height. An iceberg in its last stages of disintegration may be mistaken for a floeberg. (25)

FLOOD CURRENT. The movement of a tidal current toward the shore or up a tidal stream. In the semidiurnal type of reversing current, the terms greater flood and lesser flood are applied respectively to the flood currents of greater and lesser velocity of each day. The terms maximum flood and minimum flood, are applied to the maximum and minimum velocities of a flood current the velocity of which alternately increases and decreases without coming to a slack or reversing. (14)

FLOOD INTERVAL. The interval between the transit of the moon over the meridian of a place and the time of the following strength of flood. (14)

FLOOR (OCEAN FLOOR). Used by some authors to designate the bottoms of the deeper parts of the oceans only, beyond the continental slope. Other authors use it to refer to any part of the ocean bottom. (27)

FLORESCENCE. The rapid reproduction of plankton. See PLANKTON BLOOM. (15)

FLORIDA CURRENT. All of the northward-moving water from the Straits of Florida to a point off Cape Hatteras where the current ceases to follow the continental slope. It is one of the swiftest of ocean currents (flowing at a rate of 2 to 5 knots).
The Florida current can be traced directly back to the Yucatan Channel because the greater part of the water flowing through that channel continues on the shortest route to the Straits of Florida and only a small amount sweeps into the Gulf of Mexico, later to join the Florida current. After passing the Straits of Florida the current is reinforced by the Antilles current, but the name Florida Current is retained as far as Cape Hatteras.
The Florida current is part of the Gulf Stream system. (24)

FLOTSAM. See JETTISON.

FLUOROMETER. The Fluorometer is an optical instrument which will determine the movements of a body of water by responding to the light emitted by a fluorescent dye previously injected in the body of water under consideration. (30)

FLUX-GATE MAGNETOMETER (SATURABLE REACTOR). The essential element of this instrument, which is used for detailed studies of the earth's magnetic field on a local basis, is the flux-gate. This consists of two identical saturable cores of high permeability, oppositely wound with identical coils. An alternating current in these coils magnetizes them first with one polarity, then in the opposite sense. If an additional field is present, such as the earth's field, it will add to the flux in one coil while decreasing that in the other. As a result, the voltage drop across the two coils will differ. The amount of this difference is proportional to the unvarying field, which can thus be measured by noting the average voltage difference between the two halves of the flux gate. This can be done to an accuracy of about ± 1 gamma. In use, a part of the earth's field is balanced out by an additional winding surrounding both cores and carrying direct current.

In airborne use, the recording flux gate is kept aligned with the magnetic field by the use of two additional flux gates. When these are at right angles to the earth's field, they generate no voltage, but if they depart from this position, they can be made to generate voltages which operate motors returning them to proper alignment. In this fashion the recording element is held always parallel to the total field. (35)

FLYBACK. The recycling period of the sawtooth-modulated FM oscillator. (5)

FMO. Frequency modulated oscillator. (5)

FOAM LINE. The front of a wave as it advances shoreward, after it has broken. (11)

FOG. A visible assemblage of numerous tiny droplets of water, or ice crystals formed by condensation of water vapor in the air, with the base at the surface of the earth. If this is primarily the result of movement of air over a surface of different temperature, it is called advection fog; if primarily the result of cooling of the surface of the earth and the adjacent layer of atmosphere by radiation, it is called radiation fog. California fog is fog peculiar to the coast of California and its coastal valleys. Monsoon fog is an advection fog occurring along a coast where monsoon winds are blowing, when the air has a high specific humidity and there is a large difference in the temperature of adjacent land and sea. Shallow and often dense radiation fog, through which the sky is visible, is called ground fog. Thin fog of relatively large particles, or very fine rain lighter than drizzle is called mist. Fog formed at sea, usually when air from a warm-water surface moves to a cold-water surface, is called sea fog. Fog produced by apparent steaming of a relatively warm sea in the presence of very cold air is called frost smoke, sea smoke, arctic sea smoke, water smoke, barber, or steam fog. Fog consisting of ice crystals is called ice fog. Frozen fog is called pogonip. A simulation of true fog by atmospheric refraction is called mock fog. Haze due to the presence of dust or smoke particles in the air is called dry fog. A mixture of smoke and fog is called smog. (17)

FOG BUOY. Position buoy. (17)

FOLD. A bend in a layer or layers of rock strata. (27)

FOLLOWING SEA. See BEAM SEA.

FOLLOWING WIND. In wave forecasting, wind blowing in the same direction that waves are travelling. (11)

FORAMINIFERA. Minute one-celled marine organisms which secrete a calcareous test (shell), or the test of such an organism. Foraminifera may be an important constituent of some deep sea deposits. If the foraminifera constitute 30 per cent or more of the samples, the sediment is referred to as foraminiferal ooze. On the basis of size, foraminiferal ooze usually is classified as mud-sand on bottom sediment charts. (16)

FORCED WAVE. A wave that is maintained by a periodic force, and the period of a forced wave must always coincide with the period of the force, regardless of the dimensions of the basin or of frictional influence.

FORDS. Floating Ocean Research and Development Station.

FOREDEEP. A deep, elongated oceanic depression fronting a mountainous land area. It is a trench if it has steep sides and a trough if it has gently sloping sides. (17)

FOREL SCALE. A basic means of determining water color. The Forel scale used on Navy surveys consists of a series of 11 small vials containing ammonical copper sulphate and neutral potassium chromate in such proportions that a different graduation of color is imparted to each vial. These vials are numerically designated and are compared directly with sea water samples. (29)

FORESHORE. The part of the shore, lying between the crest of the seaward berm (or the upper limit of wave wash at high tide) and the ordinary low water mark, that is ordinarily traversed by the uprush and backrush of the waves as the tides rise and fall. (11)

FORMATION. A stratum or a set of strata possessing a common suite of lithological and/or faunal characteristics. (27)

FOULING. The assemblage of marine organisms that attach to and grow upon underwater objects. (15)

FOULING PLATES. These are metal plates submerged to allow attachment of the fouling organisms and are analyzed on a monthly or seasonal schedule. Determination of species, growth rate, and growth pattern, as influenced by environmental conditions and time, are the aims of these programs. (35)

FOXBORO TIDE GAGE. This instrument is operated by the change of pressure caused by the change in water level above a pressure plate. The pressure change is converted to a pen deflection in a recorder, and the change in the level of the tide appears as a graph. The advantages of this gauge are its ease of installation and its capacity for transmitting measurements to one or more receivers as far as 500 feet from the sensing element. It can be used at any place where sufficient water is present to cover the element. No permanent installation of any type is required. It would appear that this type of instrument would prove useful in areas that do not readily permit the use of the standard automatic portable tide gage and/or in instances where data are to be collected for brief periods of time. It is also possible that the recording method may facilitate the data handling. (35)

FRACTURE ZONE. A zone of unusually irregular topography of the sea floor averaging 60 nautical miles in width and normally greater than 1000 nautical miles in length. This zone is characterized by large SEAMOUNTS, steep-sided or nonsymmetrical RIDGES, TROUGHS or ESCARPMENTS. (26)

FRAM (FLEET REHABILITATION AND MODERNIZATION PROGRAM. The purpose of the FRAM has been to arrest the downward trend of material readiness of the fleet, and to extend the life of certain Navy ships.

FRAUTSCHY BOTTLES. This water sampling device is messenger actuated. It is designed to allow free flow while in the cocked position on the downward traverse. When the desired sampling point has been reached, the closures are messenger actuated, resulting in isolation of the sample on the return traverse. Frautschy Bottles may be attached to the hydrographic wire at intervals and in such a manner that release of a single messenger from the surface will actuate the entire series. In this way samples from several depths may be obtained in a single operation. (30)

FRB. Fisheries Research Board.

FREE ASCENT. When a diver or swimmer's air supply fails or runs out, an emergency ascent becomes necessary. The ideal method for making an emergency ascent is accomplished by floating to the surface by means of natural buoyancy or assisted buoyancy from a lifejacket. While ascending with no life-jacket, air is exhaled continuously at such a rate that buoyancy is maintained, but the exhalation is sufficient to prevent overexpansion of the lungs. Free ascent, as this procedure is termed, is diffi-cult for the untrained individual.

Ascent assisted by an external source of buoyancy (now termed BUOYANT ASCENT) requires a slightly different technique. A fully inflated lifejacket will cause a much more rapid ascent through the water. The rate of ascent may be as much as 400 feet per minute. With this method, exhalation should start before ascent begins and must be rapid and continuous in order to prevent overexpansion of the lungs. (37)

FREE ADMITTANCE. The free admittance of a trans-ducer is the reciprocal of its blocked impedance. (4)

FREE FIELD. (See FREE SOUND FIELD).

FREE FIELD VOLTAGE RESPONSE. (See AS).

FREE IMPEDANCE. The free impedance of a transducer is its input impedance when its load terminals are short-circuited. (4)

FREE INSTRUMENTS. A catagory of instruments that are designed to initially sink to the bottom, re-lease their heavy ballast weights, and then float back to the surface where they can be retrieved with their acquired payload (e.g. a sediment core).

FREE PROGRESSIVE WAVE (FREE WAVE). A free progres-sive wave is a wave in a medium free from boundary effects. That is, there are no reflections from any nearby surfaces. A free wave can only be ap-proximated in practice. (9)

FREE-SOUND FIELD. A free-sound field is a field in a homogeneous, isotropic medium free from boundaries. In practice it is a field in which the effects of the boundaries are negligible over the region of interest. (1)

FREE WAVE. A wave representing one of the possible oscillations of a body of water if this body is set in motion by a sudden impulse. The period of a free wave depends on the dimensions of the basin and on the effect of friction.

FREEBOARD. The additional height of a structure above design high water level to prevent overflow. Also, at a given time the vertical distance between the water level and the top of the structure. On a ship, the distance from the water line to main deck or gunwale. (11)

FREQUENCY. The frequency of a periodic function is the reciprocal of the period. This is usually given in cycles per second, but not always. For example, the frequency of rotation of a propeller shaft is often given in revolutions per minute. (9)

FREQUENCY BAND. Those components of a complex wave, the frequencies of which are included between two points on a frequency scale. Such a limited group of components is said to occupy a frequency band. (4)

FRINGING REEF. A reef attached to an insular or continental shore. (11)

FRONT OF THE FETCH. In wave forecasting it is that end of the generating area toward which the wind is blowing. (11)

FROST SMOKE. A thick fog rising from the sea sur-face when relatively warm water is exposed to an air temperature much below freezing. Frost smoke frequently appears over newly-formed CRACKS and LEADS. If, however, the cold air moves across the sea surface with a rush - that is, as a strong wind - no fog is produced, as the vapor is distri-buted by the accompanying turbulence through too large a volume to produce saturation. (25)

FRUSTULE. (1) The siliceous shell of a diatom com-posed of two valves that overlap. (2) The sili-ceous shell of a diatom together with the proto-plast. (20)

FRV. Fisheries Research Vessel.

FSK. Frequency Shift Keyed.

FUCOXANTHIN. A brown crystalline carotenoid pig-ment $C_{40} H_{60} O_6$ occurring especially in the ova of brown algae. (20)

FUCUS (ROCKWEED). Any of a genus of olive-green or brown algae. Fucus grows attached to rocks; hence, the name rockweed. (16)

FULLS. See BEACH RIDGE.

FULLY-DEVELOPED SEA (FULLY-ARISEN SEA). The maxi-mum ocean waves that can be produced by a given wind force blowing over sufficient fetch, regard-less of DURATION. All possible wave components in the energy spectrum between f = 0 and f = ∞ are present with their maximum amount of spectral energy. (12)

FUMULUS. A very thin cloud veil at any level so delicate that it may be almost invisible. (17)

FUNDAMENTAL FREQUENCY. (1) The fundamental fre-quency of a periodic quantity is the frequency of a sinusoidal quantity which has the same period as the periodic quantity. (2) The fundamental fre-quency of an oscillating system is the lowest natural frequency. The normal mode of vibration associated with this frequency is known as the fun-damental mode. (2)

FUNDAMENTAL MODE OF VIBRATION. The fundamental mode of vibration of a system is that mode having the lowest natural frequency. (9)

FURROW. A fissure which penetrates into a conti-nental or insular shelf in a direction more or less perpendicular to a coast line. (17)

FWS. Fish and Wildlife Service (Department of Interior).

FY. Fiscal year.

G

GAIN. The ratio of the output power, voltage, or current to the input power, voltage, or current. (36)

GALE. Wind of a force exceeding a specified value, usually 30 miles per hour. In the United States, winds of force 7, 8, 9, and 10 on the Beaufort scale (32-63 miles per hour or 28-55 knots) are classed as gales. Wind of force 7 (32-38 miles per hour or 28-33 knots) is classified as a moderate gale; wind of force 8 (39-46 miles per hour or 34-40 knots) as a fresh gale; wind of force 9 (47-54 miles per hour or 41-47 knots) as a strong gale; and wind of force 10 (55-63 miles per hour or 48-55 knots) as a whole gale. (17)

GALOFARO. A whirlpool in the Strait of Messina; one time called "Charybdis." (14)

GALS. Measurements of gravity are expressed in gals (for Galileo) and milligals. One gal is equal to an acceleration of one centimeter per second per second. Values, of gravity on the earth's surface range approximately between 978.0490 gals at the equator to 983.2213 gals at the poles ($\pm$ 5200 milligals). A one foot change in elevation is equivalent to a .094 milligal change in gravity on land or a .068 milligal change under water. (35)

GALVANIC CELL (ELECTRIC BATTERY). An electrolytic cell in which a chemical reaction occurs that produces electrical energy.

GALVANIC CORROSION. The corrosion above normal corrosion of a metal that is associated with the flow of current to a less active metal in the same solution and in contact with the more active metal. (35)

GALVANIC SERIES. A list of metals and alloys arranged in order of their relative potentials in a given environment. The order of their arrangement in this list may be different in other environments. (35)

GALVANOMETER. An instrument used to measure small amounts of electric current or to detect its presence or direction by means of the deflections of a magnetic needle (or wire coil) placed in a magnetic field.

GAMETE. A protoplasmic body incapable of giving rise to another individual until after fusion with another gamete. (18)

GAMETOPHYTE. See ALTERNATION OF GENERATIONS.

GAMMA. 1. High energy electromagnetic radiation emitted during the fission process, nuclear decay and/or Bremsstrahling.

2. A gamma is a unit of magnetic force equal to 10^{-5} oersteds.

GAP. A steep-sided depression cutting transversly across a RIDGE or RISE. (26)

GARUA. A thick, damp fog on the coasts of Ecuador, Peru, and Chile. Also called camanchaca. (17)

GAS BUOY. A buoy having a gas light. (17)

GAT. A natural or artificial passage or channel extending inland through shoals or steep banks. (17)

GCT. GREENWICH CIVIL TIME.

GEBCO. General Bathymetric Chart of the Oceans.

GEE. A VHF (very high frequency) Radio Navigation system transmitting synchronized pulses, similarly to LORAN. The hyperbolic lines of position are determined by the measurement of the differences in the time of arrival of the pulses which is again also similar to Loran. (29)

GEIR AND DUNKLE RADIOMETER. The response of the Geir and Dunkle Radiometer is independent of the wave length of the incident energy. For this reason this instrument has an advantage over a pyrheliometer in that it can be used to measure long wave radiation as well as solar radiation and can be used both for daytime and nighttime measurements. It also can be used as a net exchange radiometer to measure the net heat transfer through a surface.

The radiometer is essentially a heat flow meter. It consists of three bakelite plates 4 1/2 inches square and 1/64 inch thick. The thermopile is constructed by winding 40 gauge constant wire onto the center plate at approximately 88 turns per inch. The wire is then silver-coated on one side of the plate, giving in effect a series of thermocouple junctions on opposite sides of the plate.

Aluminum cover plates are mounted on both sides of the thermopile. These plates increase the thermal capacity without appreciably increasing the thermal resistance, therby damping out minor variations in heat flow caused by fluctuations in the air stream. The cover plates also give additional strength and weather resistance. The upper aluminum plate is painted black to absorb the incident radiation, and the lower aluminum plate is highly polished to reduce the emissivity and absorbtivity to the lowest possible values. When the instrument is used as a net exchange radiometer, both the upper and lower aluminum plates are painted black.

Since long wave radiation will not penetrate glass, no protective coverings are put over the sensitive surfaces. The sensing unit is mounted in the air stream from a small blower to maintain uniform values of the unit thermal resistance from both meter surfaces. The air stream also prevents the deposit of dust or dew on the meter surface. (35)

GEK. See GEOMAGNETIC ELECTROKINETOGRAPH.

GEM. Ground Effects Machine.

GENERATING AREA. In wave forecasting, the continuous area of water surface over which the wind blows in essentially a constant direction. Sometimes used synonymously with FETCH LENGTH. (11)

GENERATION OF WAVES. 1. The creation of waves by natural or mechanical means.
2. In wave forecasting, the creation and growth of waves caused by a wind blowing over a water surface for a certain period of time. The area involved is called the GENERATING AREA or FETCH. (11)

GEODESY. The science which deals mathematically with the size and shape of the earth, usually after accurate measurements of large areas of the surface of the earth; and with surveys in which the size and shape must be considered. (17)

GEODIMETER. The Geodimeter is an instrument which employs an electronic method of measuring distance by measuring the time it takes a modulated light wave to travel from the master unit to a mirror and to return.

In the Geodimeter a 10 megacycle signal operates a Kerr cell which interrupts the light beam at this frequency. A Kerr cell has the property or rotating the plane of the polarized light beam when under the influence of a strong electrical field. A second polarized lens on the output of the Kerr cell is so adjusted as to pass the light beam after its plane has been rotated. Thus, the Kerr cell has the effect of pulsing (or modulating) the light beam at a rate dependent upon the frequency of the applied voltage. Since the applied frequency is 10 megacycles, the Kerr cell will permit the light to pass on the positive alternation of the 10 megacycle signal and also on the negative alternation.

The modulated (or pulsed) light beam is directed towards a distant mirror and reflected back to the Geodimeter, which is focused on a phototube (a tube sensitive to light variations). Also, a portion of the outgoing light is passed to a variable delay line which can delay the light beam over the distance of one phase at 20 megacycle. This distance is 7.5 meters instead of 15 meters as in the Tellurometer and Electrotape. Thus the Geodimeter is capable of being read more closely since the "lanes" are one-half the width of the Tellurometer "lanes". (29)

GEOGRAPHIC MILE. Same as NAUTICAL MILE.

GEOID. The particular geopotential surface which most nearly coincides with the mean level of the oceans of the earth. For mapping purposes it is customary to use an ellipsoid of revolution as an adequate and convenient approximation to the geoid. The dimensions and orientation of the assumed ellipsoid may represent an attempt to find the ellipsoid that most nearly fits the geoid as a whole, or they may represent an attempt to fit only a particular part of the geoid without regard to the remainder of it. When mention is made of the dimensions of the earth, reference is usually made to the dimensions of the ellipsoid most nearly representing the geoid as a whole. (24)

GEOLOGIC ERA. The primary and largest division of geologic time. Limits are rather arbitrary, but each begins and ends with a time of major crustal, climatic, and volcanic upheaval in some part of the earth, with a great world-wide withdrawal of the sea from land masses.

Five geologic eras are recognized: Archeozoic, Proterozoic, Paleozoic, Mesozoic, and Cenozoic. Some authorities regard the Cenozoic as actually two eras, the Tertiary and Quaternary. All eras are divided into at least two geologic periods and a number of geologic epochs. (24)

GEOLOGIC EPOCH. The third-order division of GEO-LOGIC TIME, delimited by partial withdrawal of the sea from land masses and by gentle crustal distur-bances in localized areas.

Two or more epochs are required to make up a GEOLOGIC PERIOD; and, in turn, two or more periods are needed to constitute a GEOLOGIC ERA. (12)

GEOLOGIC ERA. The primary and largest division of GEOLOGIC TIME. Limits are rather arbitrary, but each begins and ends with a time of major crustal, climatic, and volcanic upheaval in some part of the earth, with a great world-wide withdrawal of the sea from land masses.

Five geologic eras are recognized: Archeozoic, Proterozoic, Paleozoic, Mesozoic, and Cenozoic. Some authorities regard the Cenozoic as actually two eras, the Tertiary and Quaternary. All eras are divided into at least two GEOLOGIC PERIODS and a number of GEOLOGIC EPOCHS. (12)

GEOLOGIC PERIOD. The secondary division of GEO-LOGIC TIME, delimited by full-scale withdrawal of the sea from land masses and by limited crustal, climatic and volcanic upheaval in a localized area.

Two or more periods are required to make up a GEOLOGIC ERA, and each period is comprised of two or more GEOLOGIC EPOCHS. (12)

GEOLOGIC TIME. Time as considered in terms of the vast geologic past, and basically divided into GEOLOGIC ERAS, PERIODS, and EPOCHS. Seldom is geo-logic time expressed in increments as small as 10,000 years, but frequently it is expressed in millions of years. (12)

GEOMAGNETIC ELECTROKINETOGRAPH (GEK). The GEK is a shipboard surface-current measuring device de-signed to record the electrical potential developed by the movement of an electrolyte (ocean current) through a magnetic field (the earth's) in depths of more than 100 fathoms.

The essential physical equipment constituting the instrument is:

1. A matched pair of electrodes mounted 100 meters apart on a 2-conductor cable long enough (ordinarily 3 times the length of the ship) to stream them astern, away from the magnetic in-fluences of the ship.

2. A recording potentiometer assembly to which the cable is connected.

3. A gyrocompass repeater, mounted above or close to the recorder assembly.

With the above equipment, observations of the potential difference between the electrodes along the ship's course and at right angles to it are made underway. These potential differences are due to the motion of the water through the earth's magnetic field. They are rigidly related to the set and drift of the ship and to the electrodes. The potential difference changes sign when currents set the ship to port or starboard. The magnitude of the potential difference depends on the rate of drift normal to the course, the length of cable between electrodes, the local strength of the ver-tical component of the earth's magnetic field, and to some extent on the vertical distribution of water velocities in the vicinity. Through measure-ments of the potential differences on 2 courses nearly at right angles, the drift or component velocities in these 2 directions are known. The vector sum or resultant of these velocities is the surface current vector for that locality. (35)

GEOMAGNETIC MERIDIAN. See MAGNETIC MERIDIAN.

GEOMETRIC MEAN DIAMETER. The diameter equivalent of the arithmetic mean of the logarithm frequency distribution. In the analysis of beach sands it is taken as that grain diameter determined graphi-cally by the intersection of a straight line through selected boundary sizes (generally points on the distribution curve where 16 and 84 per cent of the sample by weight is coarser) and a vertical line through the median diameter of the sample. (11)

GEOMETRIC SHADOW. In wave diffraction theory, the area outlined by drawing straight lines paralleling the direction of wave approach through the ex-tremities of the protective structure. It differs from the actual protecting area to the extent that the diffraction and refraction effects modify the wave pattern. (11)

GEOMORPHOLOGY. (1) That branch of physical geo-graphy which deals with the form of the Earth, the general configuration of its surface, the distri-bution of the land, water, etc. (2) The investi-gation of the history of geologic changes through the interpretation of topographic forms. (27)

GEON. Gyro Erected Optical Navigation. A celes-trial navigation system utilizing a meridian gyro compass as the level reference plane.

GEOPHONE. A transducer used in seismic work. When it is placed in the ground it responds to any displacements of the ground caused by the passage of elastic waves arising from earthquakes, seismic shots, explosions, etc.

GEOPHYSICS. The study of the physical characteristics and properties of the Earth. (27)

GEOPOTENTIAL. The potential energy of a unit mass relative to sea level, numerically equal to the work that would be done in lifting the unit mass from sea level to the height at which the mass is located; commonly expressed in terms of dynamic height or geopotential height. The geopotential Φ at height z is given mathematically by the expression,

$$\Phi = \int_0^z g\,dz,$$

where g is the acceleration of gravity. (24)

GEOSPHERE. The "solid" portion of the earth, including water masses; the LITHOSPHERE plus the HYDROSPHERE.

Above the geosphere lies the ATMOSPHERE and at the interface between these two regions is found almost all of the BIOSPHERE, or zone of life. (12)

GEOSTROPHIC. Referring to the balance, in the atmosphere, between the horizontal coriolis forces and the horizontal pressure forces. (24)

GEOSTROPHIC WIND. A wind that blows parallel to straight isobars, with no tendency to curve, because of a balance of forces. These forces are the pressure force (high to low) and Coriolis (apparent deflecting force due to the rotation of the earth). Such a wind blows along a great circle. A GRADIENT WIND blows parallel to curved isobars. (17)

GEOSYNCLINE. An elongated trough in which sediments accumulate to considerable thickness (up to 40,000 ft.) where they are available from neighbouring land masses by erosion. Such geosynclinal areas, for example the southern North Sea, have a tendency to prolonged subsidence. (27)

GFCI. Gulf and Caribbean Fisheries Institute.

GFCM. General Fisheries Council for the Mediterranean.

GHARBI. A fresh westerly wind of oceanic origin in Morocco. (12)

GIANT FLOE. See FLOE.

GLACIAL DRIFT (GLACIAL ALLUVIUM). Rock debris which has been transported by glaciers and deposited either in place as the ice melts, or carried some distance by accompanying melt water before deposition. (27)

GLACIER. A mass of land ice, formed by the further recrystallization of FIRN, flowing slowly (at present or in the past) from an accumulation area to an area of ablation.

This term covers all such ice accumulations from the extensive continental glaciers of prehistoric ice ages, to tiny snowdrift glaciers. Nearly all glaciers are classified according to the topographical features with which they are associated, for example, highland glacier, plateau glacier, piedmont glacier, valley glacier, cirque glacier. They are also classed according to their seasonal temperatures, or melting characteristics as temperate glaciers, or polar glaciers. If a glacier is flowing it is active or living; but an active glacier may be advancing or retreating depending upon the rate of flow compared to the rate of abla-

tion at the terminus. A glacier which has ceased to flow is termed stagnant or dead. (12)

GLACIER ICE. Any ice that is or was once a part of a GLACIER. It has been consolidated from FIRN by further melting and refreezing, and by static pressure. Glacier ice may be found in the sea as an ICEBERG. (12)

GLACIER ICEBERG. An iceberg derived from a glacier, piedmont ice, or confluent ice. It is usually much smaller than a tabular iceberg and is bluish or greenish in color, with little or no snow covering. It often contains many crevasses. (17)

GLACIER TONGUE. See ICE TONGUE.

GLACIO-EUSTATISM. See EUSTATISM.

GLACON. A fragment of SEA ICE ranging in size from BRASH to a MEDIUM FLOE. (25)

GLASS-RANGES OF PROPERTIES.

Specific Gravity	2.18 and up
Specific Heat (cal/gm - $^{\circ}$C)	0.17
Thermal Conductivity (cal/sec-cm -$^{\circ}$C)	0.0025
Coefficient of Expansion (10-7/$^{\circ}$C)	8 to 127
Refractive Index	1.47 and up
Photoelastic Fringe Constant (5461 A)	1150 lbs/in. order
Light Transmission	up to 90%
Dielectric Constant	3.8 and up
Dielectric Strength (volts/mil) (0."25)	250
Volume Resistivity (ohm-cm)	10^{12} to 10^{17}
Poissons Ratio	0.18 to 0.24
Young's Modulus of Elasticity (10^6 psi)	8 to 17
Compressive Yield Stress (10^6 psi)	0.8 to 1.25
Flexural Strengths (treated) (psi) experimental	120,000
guaranteed minimum	35,000
Delayed Elastic Recovery (% of unit strain)	0.5
Creep After 10 Years at 200,000 psi	zero
Creep After 168 Hours at 800,000 psi	zero
Maximum Temp. for No Creep (500 hrs.) ($^{\circ}$C)	330 to 710
Anneal Point ($^{\circ}$C)	350 to 1200
Softening Point ($^{\circ}$C)	400 to 1500
Working Point ($^{\circ}$C)	750 to 1700
Toxicity	none

GLIMMER ICE. Newly-formed ice within CRACKS or holes of older ice, or in the puddles upon older ice. (25)

GLITTER. The spots of light reflected from a point source by the surface of the sea. Statistical analysis of glitter patterns has revealed relationships from which the roughness of the sea can be determined by the study of photographs of the glitter. (12)

GLOBAL SEA. The concept of all of the sea-waters of the earth as being but parts of one global ocean, constantly intermixing. (27)

GLOBIGERINA. A very small marine animal of the foraminifera order, with a chambered shell; or the shell of such an animal. In large areas of the ocean the calcareous shells of these animals are very numerous, being the principal constituent of a soft mud or globigerina ooze forming the ocean bed. (17)

GLOBIGERINA OOZE. See GLOBIGERINA.

GMT. See GREENWICH MEAN TIME.

GNP. Gross National Product.

GOIN. State Institute of Oceanography (USSR).

GONG BUOY. A buoy with one or more gongs. In the United States a gong buoy is a flat-topped float with a skeleton superstructure supporting a series of three or four gongs of varied tone. (17)

GONIMOBLAST. One of the sporogenous filaments which arise from the fertilized CARPOGONIUM in most red algae. (20)

GPRC. Geophysical and Polar Research Center.

GRAB-CAMERA. An ocean floor sampling system incorporating a large sediment grab with a deep sea camera. (35)

GRADED BEDDING. Beds whose grain size of particles decreases systematically upward; the finer material overlies the coarser, owing to the more rapid settling out of coarse material from a mixture of grain sizes. (27)

GRADIENT. 1. The space rate of decrease of a function. The gradient of a function in three space dimensions is the vector normal to surfaces of constant value of the function and directed toward decreasing values, with magnitude equal to the rate of decrease of the function in this direction. The ascendent is the negative of the gradient.
2. Often loosely used to denote the magnitude of the gradient or ascendant (i.e. without regard to sign) of a horizontal pressure field. See SLOPE. (24)

GRADIENT HYDROPHONE. (See PRESSURE GRADIENT HYDROPHONE).

GRADIENT WIND. A wind that blows parallel to curved isobars because of a balance of forces. These forces are the pressure force (high to low). Coriolis (apparent deflecting force due to the rotation of the earth), and the centrifugal force. A GEOSTROPHIC WIND blows parallel to straight isobars. (17)

GRAF SEA GRAVIMETER. A balance type gravity meter (heavily overdamped to attenuate shipboard vertical accelerations) which consists of a mass at the end of a horizontal arm that is supported by a torsion spring rotational axis. The mass rises and falls with gravity variation but is restored to near its null position by a horizontal reading spring, tensioned with a micrometer screw. Difference between actual beam position and null position gives an indication of gravity value after micrometer screw position has been taken into account. (37)

GRAVEL. Loose detrital material which consists of fragments ranging in size from approximately 0.08 to 10.08 inches (2 to 256 millimeters) (16)

GRAVIMETER (GRAVITY METER). An instrument to measure the value of gravity or for measuring variations in the magnitude of the earth's gravitational field.
Measurements of gravity are accomplished generally by one of three methods; dropped ball, pendulum or spring gravimeter. The latter type of gravimeter based upon the principle of the weighted spring and where the length or measured variations in the length of this spring are a function of the gravitational field at different locations are the type widely used today. See GRAF SEA GRAVIMETER. (35)

GRAVING DOCK. See DOCK.

GRAVITY POTENTIAL. The work required or gained in moving a unit mass from sea level to a point above or below sea level. The unit in m.t.s. system is one dynamic decimeter.

GRAVITY WAVE. (Also called gravitational wave.) A wave disturbance in which buoyancy (or reduced gravity) acts as the restoring force on parcels displaced from hydrostatic equilibrium. There is a direct oscillatory conversion between potential and kinetic energy in the wave motion.
Pure gravity waves are stable for fluid systems which have static stability. This static stability may be (a) concentrated in an interface or (b) continuously distributed along the axis of gravity. The following remarks apply to the two types, respectively.
(a) A wave generated at an interface is similar to a surface wave, having maximum amplitude at the interface. A plane gravity wave is characteristically composed of a pair of waves, the two moving in opposite directions with equal speed relative to the fluid itself. In the case where the upper fluid has zero density, the interface is a free surface and the two gravity waves move with speeds

$$c = U \pm \left[\frac{gL}{2\pi} \tanh \frac{2\pi H}{L} \right]^{1/2},$$

where U is the current speed of the fluid, g the acceleration of gravity, L the wave length, and H the depth of the fluid. For deep-water waves (or Stokesian waves or short waves), $H \gg L$ and the wave speed reduces to

$$c = U \pm \sqrt{\frac{gL}{2\pi}}.$$

For shallow-water waves (or Lagrangian waves or long waves), $H \ll L$, and

$$c = U \pm \sqrt{gH}.$$

All waves of consequence on the ocean surface or interfaces are gravity waves, for the surface tension of the water becomes negligible at wave lengths of greater than about one inch.
(b) Heterogeneous fluids, such as the atmosphere, have static stability arising from a stratification in which the environmental lapse rate is less than the process lapse rate. The atmosphere can support short internal gravity waves and long external gravity waves. The short waves (of the order of 10 km) have been associated, for example, with lee waves and billow waves. Such waves have vertical accelerations which cannot be neglected in the vertical equation of perturbation motion. The long gravity waves, moving relative to the atmosphere with speed $\pm\sqrt{gH}$, where H is the height of the corresponding homogeneous atmosphere, have small vertical accelerations, and are therefore, consistent with the quasi-hydrostatic approximation. In neither type of gravity wave, however, is the horizontal divergence negligible. For meteorological purposes in which neither type is desired as a solution, e.g., numerical forecasting, they may be eliminated by some restriction on the magnitude of the horizontal divergence.
The above discussion is based upon the method of small perturbations. In certain special cases of water waves, e.g., the Gerstner wave, or the solitary wave, a theory of finite-amplitude disturbances exists. (24)

GREASE ICE. A kind of SLUSH formed from the congelation of ice crystals in the early stages of freezing. It gives the sea surface a greasy appearance. (25)

GREAT DIURNAL RANGE (Gt). The difference in height between mean higher high water and mean lower low water. The expression may also be used in its contracted form - diurnal range. (14)

GREAT TROPIC RANGE (Gc). The difference in height between tropic higher high water and tropic lower low water. The expression may also be used in its contracted form - tropic range. (14)

GRB. Geophysics Research Board of the NAS/NRC (National Academy of Sciences - National Research Council).

GREATER FLOOD. See FLOOD CURRENT.

GRECO. An Italian name for the northeast wind. It was given by Roman sailors to the northeast wind in the Gulf of Lions because it came from the direction of the Greek colony of Marsala (Marseilles). (12)

GREEN FLASH. A brilliant green coloring of the upper edge of the sun as it appears at sunrise or disappears at sunset when there is a clear, distinct horizon. It is due to refraction by the atmosphere, which disperses the first (or last) spot of light into a spectrum and causes the colors to appear (or disappear) in the order of refrangibility. The green is bent more than red or yellow and hence is visible sooner at sunrise and later at sunset. (17)

GREEN MUD. A deep-sea TERRIGENOUS deposit, characterized by a considerable proportion of glauconite; calcium carbonate present in variable amounts up to 50 per cent. (27)

GREEN SKY. A greenish tinge to part of the sky, supposed by seamen to herald wind or rain, or, in some cases, a tropical cyclone. (12)

GREENHOUSE EFFECT. The heating effect exerted by the atmosphere upon the earth by virtue of the fact that the atmosphere (mainly, its water vapor) absorbs and reemits infrared radiation. In detail: the shorter wavelengths of insolation are transmitted rather freely through the atmosphere to be absorbed at the earth's surface. The earth then reemits this as long-wave (infrared) terrestrial radiation, a portion of which is absorbed by the atmosphere and again emitted. Some of this is emitted downward back to the earth's surface (counterradiation).
The mean surface temperature for the entire world, $14^{\circ}C$, is almost $40^{\circ}C$ higher than the mean temperature required for radiative equilibrium of a black body at the earth's mean distance from the sun. It is essential, in understanding the concept of the greenhouse effect, to note that the important additional warming is due to the counterradiation from the atmosphere. The glass panes of a greenhouse function in this manner exactly analogously to the atmosphere in maintaining high greenhouse temperatures, hence the name. (24)

GREENLAND CURRENT. Ocean currents flowing clockwise around the southern part of Greenland. The EAST GREENLAND CURRENT flows southward and southwestward along the eastern and southeastern coasts, and the WEST GREENLAND CURRENT flows northwestward and northward along the southwest and west coasts. (17)

GREENWICH CIVIL TIME. See GREENWICH MEAN TIME.

GREENWICH MEAN TIME. Local mean time at the Greenwich meridian; the arc of the celestial equator, or the angle at the celestial pole, between the lower branch of the Greenwich celestial meridian and the hour circle of the mean sun, measured westward from the lower branch of the Greenwich celestial meridian through 24 hours. Mean time reckoned from the upper branch of the Greenwich meridian is called Greenwich Astronomical time. Called Greenwich Civil Time in United States terminology from 1925 through 1952. Also called Universal Time. (17)

GREGALE. A strong northeast wind of the central Mediterranean. (17)

GROIN (Brit. GROYNE). A shore protective structure (built usually perpendicular to the shore line) to trap littoral drift or retard erosion of the shore. It is narrow in width (measured parallel to the shore line), and its length may vary from less than one hundred to several hundred feet (extending from a point landward of the shore line out into the water). Groins may be classified as permeable or impermeable; impermeable groins having a solid or nearly solid structure, permeable groins having openings through them of sufficient size to permit passage of appreciable quantities of littoral drift. (11)

GROUND LOG. A device for determining the course and speed made good over the ground in shallow water, consisting of a lead or weight attached to a line. The lead is thrown overboard and allowed to rest on the bottom. The course being made good is indicated by the direction the line tends and the speed by the amount of line paid out in unit time. (17)

GROUND SWELL. A long high ocean swell; also, this swell as it rises to prominent height in shallow water, however, usually not so high or dangerous as BLIND ROLLERS. (11)

GROUND WATER. Subsurface water occupying the zone of saturation. In a strict sense the term is applied only to water below the water table. (11)

GROUP VELOCITY. The velocity of a wave disturbance as a whole, i.e., of an entire group of component simple harmonic waves. The group velocity G is related to the phase speed C of the individual harmonic waves of length L by the frequency equation

$$G = C - L \frac{dC}{dL} ;$$

the phase speed C is thus equal to the group velocity only in the case of nondispersive waves, i.e., when dC/dL = zero.
The significance of the concept of group velocity lies in the fact that the energy of the disturbed flow is, in a sense, propagated at this speed. The group velocity of several simple atmospheric models has been studied by T. C. Yeh ("On energy dispersion in the atmosphere.")
For water-surface waves, the group velocity of deep-water waves is equal to one-half the velocity of individual waves in the group; for shallow-water waves, it is the same as their velocity. (24)

GROWLER. A small fragment of ice awash, smaller than a BERGY BIT, usually of glacial origin, and generally greenish in color. (25)

GROWLER ICE. An accumulation of GROWLERS. (25)

GSMFC. Gulf States Marine Fisheries Commission.

GTS. Guinean Trawling Survey.

GUINEA CURRENT. A North Atlantic Ocean current flowing southeastward and eastward along the Atlantic coast of Africa, from the vicinity of the Cape Verde Islands to the Gulf of Guinea, flowing for some distance in close proximity but in the opposite direction to the SOUTH EQUATORIAL CURRENT before curving southward and westward to merge with that current. The Guinea current is the continuation of the eastern branch of the CANARY CURRENT, augmented by the EQUATORIAL COUNTERCURRENT. (17)

GULDER. A double low water occurring on the south coast of England. (17)

GULF. A relatively large portion of the sea which

penetrates into the interior of the land. In general, the entrance is wider than the length. (17)

GULF ICE. WINTER ICE formed in a GULF or BAY. (25)

GULF STREAM. In the Western Atlantic much of the waters of the North and South Equatorial Current combine and flow northward through various passages between the Windward Islands and into the Carribbean Sea. Upon reaching the Yucatan peninsula some of the water curves toward the right, flowing some distance off the shore of the Gulf of Mexico, and part of it curves more sharply toward the east and flows directly toward the north coast of Cuba. These two parts reunite in the Straits of Florida to form the Gulf Stream. Off the southeast coast of Florida this current is augmented by a current flowing along the northern coasts of Puerto Rico, Hispaniola, and Cuba. Another current flowing eastward of the Bahamas joins the stream north of these islands.

The Gulf Stream follows generally along the east coast of North America, flowing around Florida, northward and then northeastward towards Cape Hatteras, and then curving toward the east and becoming broader and slower. After passing the Grand Banks, it turns more toward the north and becomes a broad drift current flowing across the North Atlantic. In a stricter sense that segment of the current popularly called the "Gulf Stream" which lies between the Straits of Florida and Cape Hatteras is called the FLORIDA CURRENT. That segment lying between the continental slope off Cape Hatteras and the region to the east of the Grand Banks (about long. 45°W) is called the Gulf Stream. All the easterly and northerly currents of the North Atlantic from the region to the east of the Grand Banks where the Gulf Stream divides are usually placed under the general term NORTH ATLANTIC CURRENT. (12-13)

GULF STREAM SYSTEM. The FLORIDA CURRENT, GULF STREAM and NORTH ATLANTIC CURRENT, collectively. (12)

GULLY-SQUALL. A nautical term for a violent squall of wind from mountain ravines on the Pacific side of Central America. (12)

GUT. (1) A narrow passage such as a strait or inlet. (2) A channel in otherwise shallower water, generally formed by water in motion. (11)

GUYOT. A flat-topped submarine mountain, rising at least 1 killometer above the surrounding ocean floor. (27)

GUY ROPE. See WIRE ROPE.

GYROCOMPASS. A compass that is actuated by a rapidly spinning rotor which tends to place its axis of rotation parallel to the earth's axis of rotation. It indicates direction relative to the true north. (14)

H

HAAR. A name applied to a wet sea fog or very fine drizzle which drifts in from the sea in coastal districts of eastern Scotland and northeast England. It occurs most frequently in summer. (12)

HALF LIFE. Each radioactive material has an inherent characteristic that during a certain determinable time one-half of the atoms of that substance will have decayed or lost their original radiation; during the next period of time identical in length with the first period, one-half of the remaining atoms will have also decayed. The half-life period varies in radioisotopes from less than a second to many billions of years. (39)

HALF-TIDE LEVEL (MEAN TIDE LEVEL). A plane midway between mean high water and mean low water. (14)

HAND LEAD. A light sounding lead (7 to 14 pounds), usually having a line of not more than 25 fathoms. (17)

HAPLOID. The reduced, or n, chromosome number, characteristic of the gametophyte generation. (18)

HARBOR (British - HARBOUR). A protected part of a sea, lake, or other body of water used by vessels as a place of safety and/or the transfer of passengers and cargo between water and land carriers. (11)

HARBOUR. See HARBOR.

HARDY CONTINUOUS PLANKTON RECORDER. This device can be towed for long distances behind any ship at speeds up to 15 knots. It is fitted with fixed planes which enable it to be towed at constant depths which are determined by the amount of towing cable payed out. Water enters a small hole in the front and passes through a tunnel and out the back. The plankton are sieved out by a continuously moving band of silk gauze which is slowly wound across the tunnel and into a storage tank of formalin by a system of rollers geared to a propeller on the outside of the instrument. The propeller is turned as it moves through the water, and the gauze is moved in direct proportion to the distance the recorder travels through the water. Sections of the gauze are marked to correspond with previously determined distances, depending on the size or pitch of the propeller. For most collections, two inches of gauze for each mile sampled are recommended. The spools hold as much as 500 inches of gauze which allow nearly 250 miles of continuous data collection. As the gauze leaves the tunnel, it is at once joined by a second gauze strip which winds with it onto the storage spool in the formalin tank. This second strip prevents the plankton from being rubbed from one part of the roll to another.

This sampler has the advantage of being able to sample continuously for over two hundred miles and will indicate horizontal distribution or "patchiness" in plankton populations.

However, this instrument has an even smaller aperture than the CLARKE-BUMPUS sampler, and consequently most macroplankton will avoid capture. It is restricted to near-surface sampling and crushes some of the larger zooplankton. (35)

HARMATTAN. The dry, dusty trade wind blowing off the Sahara Desert across the Gulf of Guinea and the Cape Verde Islands. Sometimes called the doctor, because of its supposed healthful properties. (17)

HARMONIC. A harmonic is a sinusoidal quantity having a frequency that is an integral multiple of the frequency of a periodic quantity to which it is related. (2)

HARMONIC PREDICTION. Method of predicting tides and tidal currents by combining the harmonic constituents into a single tide curve. The work is usually done mechanically by means of a machine designed for the purpose. (14)

HARMONIC TIDE PLANE. See INDIAN SPRING LOW WATER.

HARPOON LOG. A log which consists essentially of a rotator and distance registering device combined in a single unit, which is towed through the water. It has been largely replaced by the taffrail log, which is similar except that the registering device is located at the taffrail, with only the rotator in the water. (17)

HAULAGE ROPE. See WIRE ROPE.

HAWSER. See WIRE ROPE.

HAYCOCK. An isolated ice cone rising above the surface of LAND ICE or SHELF ICE as a result of pressure or ice movement. (25)

HEAD SEA. A sea in which the waves move in a direction approximately opposite to the heading. The opposite is FOLLOWING SEA. Those moving in a direction approximately 90° from the heading are called BEAM SEA, and those moving in a direction approximately 45° from the heading (striking the quarter) are called QUARTERING SEA. See CROSS SEA. (17)

HEADLAND. A point or portion of land jutting out into the sea, a lake, or other body of water; a CAPE or PROMONTORY; now, usually specifically, a promontory especially bold and cliff-like. (11)

HEAVE. 1. The motion imparted to a floating body by wave action. It includes both the vertical rise and fall, and the horizontal transport.
2. The up and down motion of the center of gravity of a ship. (12)

HEAVY FLOE. A FLOE that is more than 10 feet thick. (25)

HEAVY ICE. Any SEA ICE more than 10 feet thick. (25)

HETERODYNE. The action between two alternating currents of different frequencies in the same circuit; they are alternately additive and subtractive, thus producing two beat frequencies which are the sum of, and difference between, the two original frequencies. (20)

HI-FIX DECCA. Hi-Fix is a short range navigational survey system which uses the 2 to 3 megacycle band.
Some of the outstanding features of the Hi-Fix system are:
It uses one frequency. If lane identification is desired, then a second frequency is needed, which does not have to be harmonically related to the first.
The signals are not modulated, and therefore give very little interference to other services.
The system can be arranged either as a two-range (for single party operation) or hyperbolic (for unlimited parties), without any additional equipment. If the Master is placed on the ship, it becomes a two-range system.
Regardless of what frequency is used, the lane width in a two-range system remains fixed. Any prearranged unit (feet, yards, or meters) may be chosen. This is important as all boat sheets can be prepared with the same lane widths regardless of frequencies.
If the ground stations are duplicated at separate frequencies the system is then capable of lane identification. The duplicate systems may be run simultaneously and fixes can be had from both systems to check one against the other. This

guards against the failure of one system. There are no signals transmitted between ground stations. Ground stations can be located without regard to the lane in between the two stations. (29)

HIGH-PASS FILTER. A high-pass filter is a wave filter having a single transmission band extending from some critical or cutoff frequency, not zero, up to very large or infinite frequencies. (9)

HIGH TIDE. See HIGH WATER.

HIGH WATER (HW) (HIGH TIDE). The maximum height reached by a rising tide. The height may be due solely to the periodic tidal forces or it may have superimposed upon it the effects of prevailing meteorological conditions. (14)

HIGH WATER LINE. In strictness, the intersection of the plane of mean high water with the shore. The shore line delineated on the nautical charts of the Coast and Geodetic Survey is an approximation to the high water line. (14)

HIGH WATER OF ORDINARY SPRING TIDES (HWOST). A tidal datum appearing in some British publications, based on high water of ordinary spring tides. (11)

HIGHER HIGH WATER (HHW). The higher of the two high waters of any tidal day. The single high water occurring daily during periods when the tide is diurnal is considered to be a higher high water. (14)

HIGHER LOW WATER (HLW). The higher of the two low waters of any tidal day. (14)

HINDCASTING, WAVE. The calculation from historic synoptic wind charts of the wave characteristics that probably occurred at some past time. (11)

HINTERLAND. The region inland from the coast. (11)

HIRAN. See SHORAN.

HMMFC. House Merchant Marine and Fisheries Committee -- Subcommittee on Oceanography.

HO. Hydrographic Office. (Now officially designated U.S. Naval Oceanographic Office)

HODOGRAPH. In general (mathematics), the locus of one end of a variable vector as the other end remains fixed. A common hodograph in meteorology represents the vertical distribution of the horizontal wind. (12)

HODS. Hydrographic Oceanographic Data Sheets.

HOLDFAST. (1) Flattened disklike tip of a tendril, used in attachment; (2) basal part of an algal THALLUS, which attaches it to a solid object; may be unicellular or composed of a mass of tissue. (18)

HOLDING GROUND. The condition of the bottom of an anchorage area; called good or bad according to whether or not the material of which the bottom is composed will prevent a ship's anchor from dragging. (27)

HOLME SUCTION GRAB. In this device the force required to suck in a sample of the sediment is provided by a "vacuum" chamber (containing air at atmospheric pressure) which is mounted above the collecting tube. On striking the bottom the chamber is put into communication with the outside and the water pressure forces the sample into the collecting tube. The pressure chamber itself is a strong brass tube closed at the upper end by a lid and held firmly in position by a clamp. A sampling tube is fixed below the chamber and extends upwards into it. Between the upper and

lower parts of the central tube is a plug held in
position by retaining hooks through slots in the
wall of the lower tube. When the device strikes
the bottom a mouth tube rises, disengaging the
plug, which flies up the tube. The water pressure
then forces material up into the collecting tube.
(35)

HOLME (SUCTION GRAB)

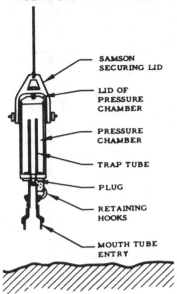

- SAMSON SECURING LID
- LID OF PRESSURE CHAMBER
- PRESSURE CHAMBER
- TRAP TUBE
- PLUG
- RETAINING HOOKS
- MOUTH TUBE ENTRY

HOLME MUD SAMPLER. With this device the sample is
taken by a scoop rotating on an axle mounted on a
heavy frame that rests firmly on the bottom. The
device is lowered open with the entire weight
being taken by a shackle on a balanced arm. Closure
is not effected on touching bottom. On hoisting,
the pressure of water on a vane attached to the
balanced arm tips a lever and allows a pin to slip
out and release the shackle. The weight is then
transferred to a rope rotating round a large drum.
This in turn rotates a small pulley and drags the
sampling hemisphere through the bottom via a second
pulley to which it is attached by a light wire. The
maximum volume of the sample is 5 1/2 liters, and
in practice, usually about 3-4 liters are collected.
(35)

HOLOPHYTIC. Obtaining food after the manner of a
green plant. (20)

HOLOPLANKTON. See MARINE LIFE.

HOLOZOIC. Obtaining food after the manner of most
animals by ingesting complex organic matter. (20)

HOMOIOTHERMOUS. Warm-blooded animals having regulated body temperatures. Seals, whales and other
marine mammals have deep layers of fat (blubber)
under the skin that insulates their bodies from
heat loss in the water. (19)

HOMOLOGY. Fundamental similarity; structural like-
ness of an organ or part in one kind of animal with
the comparable unit in another resulting from descent from a common ancestry. (19)

HOOK. A spit or narrow cape, turned landward at
the outer end, resembling a hook in form. (11)

HOOKAH. In free diving-apparatus consisting of a
demand regulator worn by the diver and a hose connected to a compressed air supply at the surface.

HORN BUOY. A buoy provided with a horn. (17)

HORSE LATITUDES. The regions of calms and variable
winds coinciding with the subtropical high pressure
belts on the poleward sides of the trade winds.
The expression is generally applied only to the
northern of these two regions in the North Atlantic
Ocean, or to the portion of it near Bermuda. (17)

HOT-WIRE INSTRUMENT FOR MEASURING LOW VELOCITIES.
The probe incorporates a thermocouple to measure
the temperature, made from two metals which form a
tubular thermojunction. The hot wire, a nichrome
resistance wire is mounted in a small metal tube at
the tip of the probe. The wire is heated by an
electric current which is passed through it from
the adjustable current supply. The temperature
difference between the probe and the water is
measured by a pair of thermojunctions. A sleeve
joint in the tube made from copper and constan-
tan, forms the hot junction and gives a voltage
dependant on the temperature of the tube. The cold
junction is placed clear of the probe, but in the
water, giving a voltage dependent on the temperature of the water. The difference between the voltages from the junctions is proportional to the temperature difference between them: $E_o = K_1 \Delta t$

The cooling effect of the flowing water is
most marked at low velocities, becoming less effective as the velocity increases.

The output voltage is observed on a galvanometer. For more accurate measurements a D.C.
slide wire potentiometer employed in conjunction
with the galvanometer is used. (30)

HOT-WIRE INSTRUMENT FOR OCEAN TURBULENCE
MEASUREMENTS. In this system the temperature of
the wire is maintained as nearly constant as is
possible by increasing the power to the hot-wire
when it attempts to cool off and decreasing the
power when it attempts to become hotter. If the
temperature of the wire is kept constant by means
of a negative feedback amplifier which compensates
for the cooling effect of the turbulent flow, the
wire resistance will remain constant and the heating current in the wire will vary. This variation
in the heating current can be used to measure the
turbulent fluctuations. The changes in temperature
and resistance of the wire are detected by means of
a bridge in which the hot-wire forms one of the
arms. The wire is made of platinum-coated tungsten
one inch long.

The turbulence signals from the hot-wire are
recorded on tape using a frequency modulation system. A carrier frequency of 10kc is used and the
signal from the hot-wire is superimposed on the
carrier. The tapes are played back and analyzed
on an audio frequency spectrum analyser to obtain
the frequency spectrum. (30)

HOVERCRAFT AND GEMS (GROUND EFFECT MACHINES).
Ships designed to hover above water and supported
by air trapped between the bottom of the ship and
the water. The supporting air cushion is augmented
at high speeds (i.e., 100 knots) by the forward
motion of the craft. (Note: Various types of ground
effect machines are: Air Curtain, Plenum, Ram Wing,
Diffuser-Recirculation, Water Curtain, and Skegs.)

HUK. Hunter-Killer Naval Force or Unit.

HUKFORLANT. Hunter-Killer Forces, Atlantic (USN).

HUMBOLDT CURRENT. See PERU CURRENT.

HUMMOCKED ICE. Ice piled haphazardly into mounds
or hillocks. At the time of formation hummocked
ice is similar to RAFTED ICE except that the former requires a greater degree of pressure and heap-
ing than the latter. After hummocked ice and
rafted ice have been repeatedly covered with snow
and weathered, no distinction is then made between
the two terms and hummocked ice is the term applied
to both types.

HUMMOCKY FLOE. See FLOE.

HURRICANE SURGE. See HURRICANE WAVE.

HURRICANE TIDE. See HURRICANE WAVE.

HURRICANE WAVE (HURRICANE SURGE, HURRICANE TIDE).
As experienced on islands and along a shore,
a sudden rise in the level of the sea associated
with a hurricane.
In low latitudes, the hurricane wave appears
to occur in the proximity of the storm's center.
As the hurricane moves into higher latitudes,
however, the maximum wave appears to become associated more and more with only the dangerous
semicircle. (12)

HUYGENS'S PRINCIPLE. A very general principle applying to all forms of wave motion which states
that every point on the instantaneous position of
an advancing phase front (wave front) may be regarded as a source of secondary spherical "wavelets." The position of the phase front a moment
later is then determined as the envelope of all of
the secondary wavelets (ad infinitum).
This principle, stated by the Dutch physicist
Christian Huygens (1629-1695), is extremely useful
in understanding effects due to refraction, reflection, diffraction, and scattering, of all types
radiation, including sonic radiation as well as
electromagnetic radiation and applying even to
ocean wave propagation. (24)

HYALINE. Glassy or semitransparent. Hyaline animals in the sea, living from the surface to more
than 300m, are extremely abundant. (19,13)

HYDRAULIC CURRENT. A current in a channel that
results from a difference in the surface level at
the two ends. Such a current may be expected in a
strait connecting two bodies of water in which the
tides differ in time or range. The current in the
East River, New York, connecting Long Island Sound
and New York Harbor, is an example. (14)

HYDRAULIC GRADIENT. The slope of the profile of
the static level for a hydraulic system. In open
channel flow the hydraulic gradient is the slope
of the water surface taken parallel to the flow;
in unconfined ground water flow it is the slope of
the water table taken normal to its contours; and
for artesian ground water it is the slope of the
PIEZOMETRIC surface taken normal to its contours.
(24)

HYDRAULIC JUMP. In fluid flow, a change in flow
conditions accompanied by a stationary, abrupt turbulent rise in water level in the direction of
flow. A type of STATIONARY WAVE. (11)

HYDRAULIC RADIUS. The ratio of the area of a cross
section of a stream to its wetted perimeter. (14)

HYDRO. Hydrographic Office. (Now officially
designated Navy Oceanographic Office).

HYDRODIST. A navigation positioning system which
is actually a modification of the TELLUROMETER system. In Hydrodist, two separate tellurometer mas-
ters are mounted side by side on board a vessel
and these aimed to their respective remote units.
The Hydrodist system is used for hydrographic
control. (29)

HYDROGRAPHIC WIRE SLOPE AND AZIMUTH INDICATOR.
This mechanical instrument enables determination
of the positioning of hydrographic instruments
attached to a hydro wire, by furnishing information
concerning the wire slope and set. In this indicator, a vertically orienting and magnetic north-
seeking unit of practically neutral buoyancy is
housed spherically to allow the inner unit to
preserve its northward and vertical orientation,
while magnetic needles attached to this unit cause
it to seek magnetic north. The spherical shape

of the inner member permits its being locked
accurately, relative to the wire orientation. (30)

HYDROGRAPHY. The science which deals with the
measurement of the physical features of the oceans,
seas, lakes, rivers, and other waters, and their
marginal land areas, with special reference to the
elements that affect safe navigation, and the publication of such information in a suitable form for
use of navigators. (17)

HYDROLOGY. The scientific study of the waters of
the earth, especially with relation to the effects
of precipitation and evaporation upon the occurrence and character of water in streams, lakes and
on or below the land surface. In terms of the
hydrologic cycle, the scope of hydrology may be
defined as that portion of the cycle from precipitation to re-evaporation or return of the water to
the seas.
Applied hydrology utilizes scientific findings
to predict rates and amounts of runoff (river forecasting), estimate required spillway and reservoir
capacities, study soil-water-plant relationships
in agriculture, estimate available water supply,
and for other applications necessary to the manage-
ment of water resources. (12)

HYDROMETER. An instrument used to determine the
density or specific gravity of a liquid.

HYDROPHONE. The hydrophone is an electro-acoustic
transducer that responds to water borne sound
waves and delivers essentially equivalent electric
waves. The conversion from sound energy to electrical energy is achieved through the use of either
the piezoelectric or magnetostrictive effect. The
varying potential generated across a piezoelectric
material when it is subjected to a varying mechanical force can be coupled to an amplifier as an
electric signal with the same frequency characteristics as those of the mechanical vibration that
excited the material. (30)

HYDROPHONE LOSS. The hydrophone loss of a sonar
transducer, used for the reception of acoustic
energy, at a specified frequency, may be defined
as the transmission loss measured by the ratio of
(1) the source power of the free-field acoustic
energy available as plane sinusoidal waves from a
water surface having an area of one square centimeter and lying perpendicular to the direction of
the maximum response reference axis of the transducer at the point to be occupied by its effective
center to (2) the resulting output power of the
electric energy available from the transducer. (4)

HYDROPHOTOMETER. A sensitive instrument used in
water transparency and light absorption measurements at sea. The instrument, which contains its
own light source, can measure fine graduations of
transparency of an individual water mass. (35)

HYDROSPHERE. The water portion of the earth as
distinguished from the solid part, called the
LITHOSPHERE, and from the gaseous outer envelope,
called the ATMOSPHERE. (12)

HYGROMETER. An instrument which measures the water
vapor content of the atmosphere. There are six
basically different means of transduction used in
measuring this quantity and hence an equal number
of types of hygrometers. These are: (a) the
psychrometer, which utilizes the thermodynamic
method; (b) the class of instruments which depends
upon a change of physical dimensions due to the
absorption of moisture (hair hygrometer, torsion
hygrometer, goldbeater's-skin hygrometer, carbon-
film hygrometer element); (c) those which depend
upon condensation of moisture (DEW-POINT HYGROMETER);
(d) the class of instruments which depend upon the
change of chemical or electrical properties due to
the absorption of moisture (absorption hygrometer,
electrical hygrometer, carbon-film hygrometer

element); (e) the class of instruments which depend upon the diffusion of water vapor through a porous membrane (diffusion hygrometer); and (f) the class of instruments which depend upon measurements of the absorption spectra of water vapor (spectral hygrometer). (Middleton, W. E. K., and Spilhaus, A. F., Meteorological Instruments, 3rd ed., rev., 1953, pp. 105-116) (12)

HYPERPNEA. Abnormally rapid or deep breathing.

HYPERVENTILATION. Hyperventilation is the term applied to breathing more than is necessary to keep the body's carbon dioxide tensions at the proper level. If carried to an extreme, hyperventilation can be as undesirable and dangerous as conditions involving interference with breathing. UNINTENTIONAL HYPERVENTILATION is most often triggered by nervous tension and can be experienced by otherwise normal individuals in stress situations anywhere. It is also brought on by ANOXIA and is a common and serious problem in aviators. Divers using self-contained equipment for the first few times are likely to hyperventilate to some extent largely because of anxiety. Hyperventila-

tion has little effect on the body's oxygen levels, but it can reduce carbon dioxide tensions to the point of producing serious symptoms.
Symptoms of abnormally low carbon dioxide tension (hypocapnia) can be produced by voluntary hyperventilation - taking a number of deep breaths over a short period of time as in preparation for a BREATH-HOLD dive. (37)

HYPOLIMNION. The layer of water below the THERMOCLINE in a fresh water lake or pool; the opposite of EPILIMNION. (12)

HYPOPLANKTON. See MARINE LIFE.

HYPOTHECA. See EPITHECA.

HY STEELS. High yield strength steels (e.g. HY80 = yield strength of 80,000 psi, HY100 = yield strength 100,000 psi, HY150 and HY185 = 150,000 and 185,000 psi yield strength respectively). These are present and candidate steels for pressure vessels including subs and research submersibles. Mild steel in the way of contrast has a yield of about 30,000 psi.

I

IAC. International Advisory Committee on Research in the Natural Sciences (Programme of UNESCO).

IACOMS. International Advisory Committee on Marine Sciences.

IAG. International Association of Geodesy.

IAGA. International Association on Geomagnetism and Aeronomy.

IAHR. International Association of Hydraulic Research.

IAL. International Association of Limnology.

IALA. International Union of Lighthouse Authorities.

IAMAP. International Association of Meteorology and Atmospheric Physics.

IAPO. International Association of Physical Oceanography. One of the associations constituting the International Union of Geodesy and Geophysics (IUGG).

IASH. International Association of Scientific Hydrology.

IASPEI. International Association of Seismology and Physics of Earth's Interior.

IATTC. Inter-American Tropical Tuna Commission.
Established by treaty between the United States and Costa Rica March 1950, providing for the scientific investigation of the tuna fishery of the east Pacific Ocean.
Headquarters of the Commission is at the Scripps Institution of Oceanography, La Jolla, California, with branch laboratories at Panama and San Jose, Costa Rica.
Activities: The IATTC investigates the abundance, biology and ecology of tunas and tuna-bait fishes, and the effects of natural factors and human activities on the abundance and catch; col-

lects and interprets statistics and other information regarding past and present operations and results of the fishing; determines the past and present conditions of the fish stocks, and publishes reports on its findings.
Members and Financing: United States, Costa Rica and Panama share expenses in proportion to their utilization of the tuna fisheries catch. U. S. Share: 99.8%.

IAV. International Association of Volcanology.

IBP. International Biological Program.

IBRD. International Bank of Reconstruction and Development.

IBY. International Biological Year.

ICA. 1. International Co-operative Administration.
     2. International Cartographic Association.

ICAS. Interdepartmental Committee for Atmospheric Sciences (FCST).

ICE. The solid state of water formed either by freezing or SUBLIMATION.
Ice encountered at sea consists for the most part either of ICEBERGS or other LAND ICE originating from CONTINENTAL ICE sheets and GLACIERS, or of SEA ICE formed by the freezing of the top layers of the sea itself. Sea ice proper accounts for probably 95 per cent of the area of ice encountered at sea, but ICEBERGS are important because of the manner in which they drift far from their place of origin, constituting grave menaces to navigation. A certain amount of ice also may originate in rivers or estuaries as fresh-water ice, but it is in a state of decay by the time it reaches the open sea and is of local importance only. (25)

ICEBERG. A mass of land ice that has broken away from land and floats in the sea, or becomes stranded in shallow water; to be distinguished from FLOEBERG. The unmodified term "iceberg" usually refers to the irregular masses of ice formed by the calving of GLACIERS along on orographically rough coast; whereas TABULAR ICEBERGS and ICE ISLANDS are calved from an ICE SHELF, and floebergs are formed from sea ice. (12)

ICEBLINK. A yellowish-white glare on the underside of extensive cloud areas created by light reflected from ice-covered surfaces. (25)

ICE CAKE. An individual piece of ice of any size, particularly a relatively flat one. A collection of ice cakes is called cake ice. (17)

ICE CLEARING. See POLYNYA.

ICE FOOT. A class of FAST ICE consisting of ice formed along and attached to the shore. The base of the ice is at or below low water mark. The action of tide, waves, and sea spray causes the development of the ice foot during the freezing season. Differences in the causative factors are reflected in the differences in the ice foot. Types of ice foot formations are: TIDAL PLATFORM ICE FOOT, STORM ICE FOOT, DRIFT ICE FOOT, STRANDED ICE FOOT, FALSE ICE FOOT, AND WASH AND STRAIN ICE FOOT. (25)

ICE-FREE PORT. A port in which ice formations sufficient to interfere with navigation in the harbor or the terminals have not been recorded.

ICE ISLAND. One of the many, large TABULAR ICE-BERGS found in the Arctic Ocean.
    Nearly one hundred were identified in a few years following discovery of the first one in 1946. All have level, slightly undulating surfaces 10 to 25 feet above water, and appear to have calved from an ICE SHELF such as that which fringes northern Ellesmere Island. Ice islands are smaller than the largest tabular icebergs of the Antarctic. The area of the largest one known is about 300 square miles; they are about 150 feet thick over all; and, unlike the surrounding PACK ICE, they drift with the ocean currents rather than with the wind.
    Their occupation by semipermanent research stations has provided much new information on the meteorology, oceanography, and other aspects of the Arctic. (12)

ICE ISLAND ICEBERG. A conical or dome-shaped ICEBERG. Under various lighting conditions an ice island iceberg will resemble an island in color and shape. (25)

ICE PACK. Any large area of FLOATING ICE driven closely together.
    The entire area of ice in the polar seas and the seas surrounding Antarctica. (25)

ICE PERIOD(Season). The time between first appearance and final clearance of ice during any year.

ICE POLE. The center around which is located the more consolidated portion of the arctic ICE PACK. The ice pole, or Pole of Inaccessibility as it is sometimes called, lies in the vicinity of latitude 83 degrees to 84 degrees N. and longitude 160 degrees W. (25)

ICEQUAKE. The crash or concussion attending the breaking up of masses of ice, often due to contraction from extreme cold. (25)

ICEREC. Aerial Ice Reconnaissance and Ice Advisory Sciences.

ICES. International Council for the Exploration of the Sea.
    ICES was founded in Copenhagen July 1902 to carry out a series of oceanographic research programs previously adopted at an international conference held in Stockholm in 1899.
    Headquarters are near Copenhagen at Charlottenlund Slot.
    Brief history: ICES is the oldest international oceanographic organization.
    Activities: Encourages marine research, promotes cooperation between the member governments and recommends regulations for fisheries management.

The work of the Council is conducted by various "subject" committees on salmon and trout, statistics, plankton, hydrography; and "area" committees on the Baltic Area, the Transition Area, the North-eastern Area, Northwestern Area and the Southern North Sea. One of the largest oceanographic libraries in existence (15,000 volumes) is located at ICES headquarters.
    Annual scientific conferences are held. The Council collects and collates fisheries statistics and hydrographic information and publishes the results of investigations. Publications include the Bulletin Hydrographique, Annales Biologiques, the Bulletin Statistique, Plankton Identification Sheets and the Journal du Council (3 issues per year). Sponsors production of standard C^{14} for marine productivity measurements.

ICE SHEET. See SHEET ICE.

ICE SHELF (SHELF ICE). A thick ice formation with a fairly level surface, formed along a polar coast and in shallow bays and inlets, where it is fastened to the shore and often reaches bottom. It may grow hundreds of miles out to sea. It is usually an extension of land ice, and the seaward edge floats freely in deep water. The calving of an ice shelf forms TABULAR ICEBERGS and ICE ISLANDS. (12)

ICE TONGUE. A narrow peninsula of ice such as a glacier or a steep narrow cliff of ice rising high above glacial neve. An extension of a glacier into the sea is called a GLACIER TONGUE, and if the end is afloat it is called an ICE TONGUE AFLOAT. (17)

ICE TONGUE AFLOAT. A floating extension of a glacier into the sea. See also ICE TONGUE. (17)

ICITA. International Co-operative Investigation of the Tropical Atlantic.

ICNAF. International Commission for the North American Fisheries.

ICNOBF. International Committee on the Nomenclature of Ocean Bottom Features.

ICO. Interagency Committee on Oceanography.

ICRD. Interior Committee on Research and Development.

ICSEMS. International Commission for the Scientific Exploration of the Mediterranean Sea.

ICSU. International Council of Scientific Unions.

IDA. 1. International Development Association.
    2. Institute Defense Analysis.

IDEAL SEA LEVEL. A sea surface which is everywhere normal to the plumb line. In the open ocean the deviations from the ideal sea level rarely exceed 1 or 2 meters. (13)

IDEAL TRANSDUCER. Any transducer connecting an energy source with an energy load for which the transition and dissipation losses are zero is said to be an ideal transducer. (4)

IDPC. International Data Processing Conference.

IEEE. Institute of Electrical and Electronics Engineers (formerly AIEE and IRE).

IES. International Exchange Service.

IFF. Abbreviation meaning identification friend or foe.

IFIP. International Federation for Information Processing.

IFM. Institut für Meereskunde.

IFS. U. S. Navy designation for an Inshore Fire Support Ship.

IGC. International Geographical Congress.

IGIPAS. Interagency Group on International Programs in Atmospheric Science.

IGN. Institut Geographique Nationale.

IGNEOUS ROCK. Rock formed by solidification from a molten state. (27)

IGPP. Institute of Geophysics and Planetary Physics.

IGU. 1. International Geophysical Union.
2. International Geographical Union.

IGY. International Geophysical Year.

IHB (BHI). International Hydrographic Bureau (Monaco).

IHP. International Hydrographic Program.

IIOE. International Indian Ocean Expedition.

IIP. International Ice Patrol.
A treaty organization of North Atlantic maritime nations organized in 1914 to improve safety of navigation in the vicinity of the Grand Banks and along the transatlantic steamship lanes where icebergs are a menace to shipping. Makes oceanographic observations during iceberg season and computes dynamic currents to predict location of icebergs.
Financing: A share of the cost of the Patrol is charged to member nations at the end of each year, based on their proportionate share of the gross tonnage passing through the iceberg area.

IMCO. International Maritime Consultative Organization.

IMPEDANCE. If we apply a sinusoidal force at a particular frequency to a system, we can expect some sort of motion to ensue. If the velocity which is produced as a result of the excitation is small, we say that the impedance of the system at the point of application of the force is high; conversely, if the velocity is high, we say that the impedance at the point is low. In order to make this idea quantitative, we include two notions in the specification of impedance. The first is the ratio of the magnitude of the exciting force to the magnitude of the resulting velocity. The second is the phase difference between the excitation and resulting motion. These two aspects of impedance are usually represented in the form of a complex number. In general, the impedance will change with a change in frequency of the excitation. (9)

IMPINGEMENT ATTACK. This is a form of erosion-corrosion in which aerated water strikes the surface of a metal causing removal of protective films making small anodic areas with respect to adjacent areas. The adjacent areas are depolarized cathodes causing ideal electrochemical circuits. (35)

IMPULSE. Impulse is the product of a force and the time during which the force is applied; more specifically, the impulse if $\int_{t_1}^{t_2} F dt$ where the force F is time dependent and equal to zero before time t_1 and after t_2. (2)

INAFC. International North American Fisheries Commission.

INCLINATION. In terrestrial magnetism, the angle through which a freely suspended magnet would dip below the horizon in the magnetic north-south meridional plane; one of the MAGNETIC ELEMENTS.

At the ACLINIC LINE the inclination is zero; at either MAGNETIC POLE the inclination is 90°. (24)

INDEX LEVEL. The index level of a sound is defined as the level which that sound would have at a point one yard from the point of its apparent origin, assuming such a point to exist, if it were generated at this apparent source point but produced the same effects at distant points as the effects it actually does produce. (4)

INDIAN SPRING LOW WATER (INDIAN TIDE PLANE, HARMONIC TIDE PLANE). A datum originated by Prof. G. H. Darwin when investigating the tides of India. It is a plane depressed below mean sea level by an amount equal to the sum of the amplitudes of the harmonic CONSTITUENTS M_2, S_2, K_1, and O_1. (14)

INDIAN TIDE PLANE. See INDIAN SPRING LOW WATER.

INDUCTION-CONDUCTIVITY-TEMPERATURE INDICATOR. This device operates through the inductive measurement of an electric current which has been induced in a sea water path. The sensing head consists of two iron-core toroidal windings potted in an insulating resin. One winding is excited by a 115-volt, 60-c.p.s. electrical signal; the sea water path through the hole in the center of this toroid acts as a one-turn secondary of a transformer and, consequently, has about 0.2 volt induced in it. The amount of current flowing depends primarily upon the length and diameter of the hole and upon the conductivity of the water in the hole. The current flowing in the sea water is measured by means of the second toroid which is mounted adjacent to and coaxially with the existing toroid. No sea-water-to metal contact exists in this system, so the problems inherent to electrodes are eliminated. This system is essentially independent of line frequency variations over a moderate range of several cycles per second. Stability of the instrument depends wholly upon the dimensional stability of the resin "doughnut" and the stability of the electrical components.
Laboratory tests have shown this device to be capable of measuring conductivity to ± 0.02 millimho (± 0.02% of salinity) over the entire ranges of temperature and salinity encountered in estuarine and marine environments. (35)

INDURATED. Hardened; rocks hardened by heat, pressure, or the addition of some ingredient not commonly contained in the rock referred to; for example, sand indurated by limonite. (27)

INERTIAL GUIDANCE. Guidance by means of accelerations measured and integrated within the craft. (17)

INERTIAL NAVIGATION. Dead reckoning performed automatically by a device which gives a continuous indication of position by double integration of accelerations since leaving a starting point. (17)

INFRA-GRAVITY WAVES. Those waves with periods from 30 seconds to 5 minutes.

INFRARED DETECTORS. Sea surface temperatures have been taken from aircraft by measuring black-body radiation from the surface. Infrared detectors (thermopiles or bolometers) are used in chopped optical systems so that they "look" alternately at the sea surface and a reference black-body in the instrument. (35)

INFRASONIC FREQUENCY. An infrasonic frequency is a frequency lying below the audio frequency range. Vibrations in this frequency range can be felt but not heard. (9)

INJECTION SIGNAL. The sawtooth frequency-modulated

signal introduced into the first detector circuit for heterodyning with the incoming echo signal. (5)

INLET. Short narrow waterway connecting a bay, lagoon, or similar body of water with a large parent body of water. An arm of the sea (or other body of water), that is long compared to its width, and that may extend a considerable distance inland. (11)

INPFC. International North Pacific Fisheries Commission.

INPUT CURRENT. The input current of a transducer connecting a given source and given load is the rms current through the terminals connecting that transducer and that source. (4)

INPUT IMPEDANCE. The input impedance of a transducer connected to a given load is the impedance which would be measured at its source terminals if they were not connected to a source. (4)

INPUT POWER. The input power of a transducer connecting a given source and a given load is the average rate of flow of energy through the terminals connecting that transducer and that source. (4)

INPUT VOLTAGE. The input voltage of a transducer connecting a given source and a given load is the rms voltage between the terminals connecting that transducer and that source. (4)

INSERTION LOSS. The insertion loss in DECIBELS resulting from the insertion of a transducer into a transmission system is ten times the logarithm to the base ten of the ratio of the power delivered to that part of the system that follows the transducer, before the insertion of the transducer, to the power delivered to that same part of the system after insertion of the transducer. In short, this term is intended to give an idea of how much the output of a system is changed by the insertion of a transducer. (9)

INSHORE. See SHOREFACE.

INSHORE (Zone). In beach terminology, the zone of variable width extending from the shore face through the breaker zone. (11)

IN SITU. In the natural or original position.

INSOLATION. The absorption of solar energy by the ocean. (15)

INSPIRATORY RESERVE VOLUME. The amount of air that can be brought in by forcible inspiration after completion of a normal inspiration. It averages about 2 1/2 liters at rest and becomes smaller as the tidal volume increases. (37)

INSULAR. (1) Of or pertaining to an island or islands. (2) Detached; standing alone. (27)

INSULAR SHELF. The zone surrounding an island extending from the line of permanent immersion to the depth (usually about 100 fathoms) where there is a marked or rather steep descent toward the great depths. (11)

INSULAR SHOULDER. See INSULAR TALUS.

INSULAR SLOPE. A declivity from the outer edge of an INSULAR SHELF into greater depths. See also INSULAR TALUS.

INSULAR TALUS (INSULAR SHOULDER, INSULAR SLOPE). The slope from the lower edge of an insular shelf into deeper water. A similar slope from the lower edge of a continental shelf is called CONTINENTAL TALUS. (17)

INTEGRATING WATER SAMPLER. This device consists of a plastic cylinder containing a free piston whose movement is controlled by the evacuation of a charge of fresh water. Sea water enters the sampler following the piston. As the device moves through the sea a rotor-driven pump evacuates the fresh water, thereby moving the piston at a rate directly determined by the sampler's travel through the water. Sea water enters the projecting mouth of the sampler. Thus, a sample representative of a horizontal column of water several miles long can be collected in a short time. Several samplers can be attached to a hydrographic cable to sample at different depths at one time. (30)

INTENSITY LEVEL (SOUND ENERGY FLUX DENSITY LEVEL). The intensity level, in decibels, of a sound is 10 times the logarithm to the base 10 of the ratio of the intensity of this sound to the reference intensity. The reference intensity shall be stated explicitly. (2)

INTERFERENCE. Any wave which would interfere with an attempted observation of a signal is known as interference. (4)

INTERMEDIATE WAVES. Waves under conditions where the relative depth (water depth/wave length) lies between 0.5 and 0.05.

INTERNAL WAVES (BOUNDARY WAVES). Internal waves or boundary waves are created below the surface, at the boundaries between water strata of different densities. Since the density differences between adjacent water strata in the sea are considerably less than that between sea and air, internal waves are much more easily formed than surface waves, and they are often much larger. The maximum height of wind waves on the surface is about 60 feet, but internal wave heights as great as 300 feet have been encountered.

Internal waves are detected by a number of observations of the vertical temperature distribution, using recording devices such as the BATHY-THERMOGRAPH. They have periods as short as a few minutes, and as long as 12 or 24 hours, these greater periods being associated with the tides.

The full significance of internal waves has not been determined, but it is known that they may cause submarines to rise and fall like a ship at the surface, and they may also affect sound transmission in the sea. (12)

INTERNATIONAL ATOMIC ENERGY AGENCY (IAEA). Headquarters in Vienna. Established October, 1956 in New York. An autonomous international organization under the aegis of the United Nations.

Activities: Sponsors symposia and provides a mechanism for international discussion and agreement on many topics including safe procedures for handling and disposal of radioactive wastes.

INTERNATIONAL LOW WATER. A hydrographic datum originally suggested for international use at the International Hydrographic Conference in London in 1919 and later discussed at the Monaco Conference in 1926. The proposed datum, which has not yet been generally adopted, was to be "a plane so low that the tide will but seldom fall below it." This datum was the subject of International Hydrographic Bureau's Special Publication No. 5 (March 1925) and No. 10 (January 1926), these publications were afterwards reproduced in the Hydrographic Reviews for May 1925 and July 1926. (14)

INTERTIDAL ZONE. Generally considered to be the zone between mean high water and mean low water levels. (27)

INTERTROPICAL CONVERGENCE ZONE (EQUATORIAL CONVERGENCE ZONE). 1. The axis, or a portion thereof, of the broad TRADE-WIND current of the tropics. This axis is the dividing line between the southeast trades and the northeast trades (of the Southern and Northern Hemispheres, respectively).

At one time it was held that this was a convergence line along its entire extent. It is now recognized that actual convergence occurs only along portions of the line.

    2. Same as METEOROLOGICAL EQUATOR. (14)

INVERTED ECHO SOUNDER. This instrument is primarily designed to provide a continuous and precise measurement of the depth of other instruments, such as the velocimeter being lowered along with it into the sea. The device is also used for detailed survey of the ocean bottom in deep water and by simple alteration of its suspension can be used for high powered short pulse echo ranging.

The device consists of a high powered "pinger" as a short pulse transmitting unit mounted alongside a sensitive fixed tuned receiver. Both units are connected to a common transducer which is used both as a projector and as a receiving hydrophone. The apparatus is self-contained and battery operated. (30)

IN VITRO. In Glass or in a test tube, beaker etc.

IN VIVO. In a living organism - man, plant or animal.

IOAN. Institute of Oceanology (Academy of Sciences USSR).

IOBC. Indian Ocean Biological Center.

IOC. Intergovernmental Oceanographic Commission of the United Nations Education, Scientific and Cultural Organization (UNESCO).

IOE. Indian Ocean Expedition.

IOF. International Oceanographic Foundation -
    Institute of Marine Sciences
    1 Rickenbacker Causeway - Virginia Key
    Miami, Florida.
This organization publishes the "SEA FRONTIERS" and "SEA SECRETS" magazines and provides active support for scientific research and education regarding the oceans.

IOMS. International Organization on Marine Sciences.

ION. An atom which has lost or gained one or more electrons and is therefore positively or negatively charged. (36)

IONIZATION. The breaking up of atoms into ions. (36)

IPCEESP. International Permanent Commission for the Exploration and Exploitation of the South Pacific.

IPFC. The Indo-Pacific Fisheries Council, a 17 country intergovernmental organization sponsored by the Food and Agriculture Organization of the United Nations, was established as a result of a meeting held at Baguio, Republic of the Philippines, in February 1948.

IPHC. International Pacific Halibut Commission.

IPMS. International Polar Motion Service.

IPSE. International Pool of Scientific Equipment.

IPSFC. International Pacific Salmon Fisheries Commission.

IPY. Inches penetration per year. Usually used in corrosion studies as a means of expressing the loss in thickness in a given period of time. M_{py} = mils penetration per year and M_{dd} = milligrams per square decimeter per day loss in weight are also terms used. (35)

IRMINGER CURRENT. An ocean current that is one of the terminal branches of the Gulf Stream system (part of the northern branch of the NORTH ATLANTIC CURRENT); it flows toward the west off the south coast of Iceland.

A small portion of the water of the Irminger Current bends around the west coast of Iceland but the greater amount turns south and becomes more or less mixed with the water of the EAST GREENLAND CURRENT. (24)

IRREGULAR ICEBERG. See PINNACLED ICEBERG.

ISA. Instrument Society of America.

ISAACS HIGH-SPEED SAMPLER. This is a streamlined tube containing a net and a depth registering flow meter. Water enters the sampler through a one-inch opening, is filtered by the net, passes around and activates the meter, and is ejected astern. The sampler has been constructed so that it precedes the cable by about a third of its length, thereby more readily capturing everything in its path. A depressor-vane is used to sample at depth.

This instrument is reputed to capture macro-plankton, be useful at depths to 60 meters, perform well at high speeds (8 to 12 knots), give a record of both depth and flow, be useful over considerable distances, and be used in series alignment. (35)

ISAACS-KIDD WATER SAMPLER. The sampler consists essentially of a plastic tube closed off at one end by a plastic disc containing an "o" ring in its inner face. A stainless steel rod orients another plastic disc (the induction plunger), which seals off, when in closed position, the hole through which the rod enters, and positions a plastic plug, containing an "o" ring in its periphery, which closes off the open end of the plastic tube. A stainless steel framework supports the tube. Stainless steel springs which operate the closure plug and induction plunger, are attached to the framework at one end. The sampler is activated when the inverting frame is tripped to the upright position. A steel pressure-tight chamber for protecting reversing thermometers at very great depths may be mounted on the inverting frame in place of the water sampler. (30)

ISABNORMAL. A line connecting points having the same difference from normal, usually temperature, or indicating the same difference between actual and calculated values at different parallels. (17)

ISALLOBAR. A line connecting points having the same change of atmospheric pressure in a specified period. (17)

ISALLOTHERM. A line connecting points having the same change of temperature in a specified period. (17)

ISANOMAL. A line connecting points having the same anomalies of temperature, pressure, etc. (17)

ISLAND SHELF. See INSULAR SHELF.

ISLAND SLOPE. See INSULAR SLOPE.

ISOBAR. A line connecting points having the same atmospheric pressure reduced to a common datum, usually sea level. (17)

ISOBATH. Depth contour. (17)

ISOBATHIC. Having equal depth. (17)

ISOBATHYTHERM. A line or surface showing the depths in oceans or lakes at which points have the same temperature. Isobathytherms are usually drawn to show cross sections of the water-mass. (24)

ISOBRONT. A line connecting points at which some specified phase of a thunderstorm occurs at the same time. (17)

ISOCERAUNIC (ISOKERAUNIC). Indicating or having equal frequency or intensity of thunderstorms. (17)

ISOCHASM. A line connecting points having the same average frequency of auroras. (17)

ISOCHEIM. See ISOTHERE.

ISOCLINIC LINE. A line drawn through all points on the earth's surface having the same magnetic INCLINATION. The particular isoclinic line drawn through points of zero inclination is given the special name of ACLINIC LINE. (24)

ISODEE. A line connecting points of equal difference between pressure altitude and absolute altitude above sea level. (17)

ISODYNAMIC LINE. A line connecting points of equal magnetic intensity, either the total or any component. (17)

ISOGONIC LINE. In the study of terrestrial magnetism, a line drawn through all points on the earth's surface having the same magnetic DECLINATION; not to be confused with MAGNETIC MERIDIAN. The particular isogonic line drawn through all points having zero declination is called the agonic line. (24)

ISOHALINE. Having no change in salt content along a given reference plane. (15)

ISOHEL. A line connecting points having the same amount of sunshine during any specified period. (17)

ISOHYET. A line connecting points having the same amount of precipitation for any specified period. (17)

ISOKERAUNIC. See ISOCERAUNIC.

ISONEPH. A line connecting points having the same amount of cloudiness. (17)

ISOPAG. A line connecting points where ice is present for the same number of days per year. (17)

ISOPECTIC. A line connecting points at which ice begins to form at the same time of the winter. A line connecting points at which ice melts at the same time of the spring is called an isotac. (17)

ISOPLETH. An isogram indicating the variation of an element with respect to two variables, one of which is usually the time of year. The other may be time of day, altitude, or some other variable. (17)

ISOPYCNIC (ISOPYCNIC LINE). A line connecting points of equal density, particularly of ocean water. A line connecting points of equal atmospheric density may be called an ISOSTERE. (17)

ISOPYCNIC LINE. See ISOPYCNIC.

ISOSTASY. A supposed equality existing in vertical sections of the earth, whereby the weight of any column from the surface of the earth to a constant depth is approximately the same as that of any other column of equal area, the equilibrium being maintained by plastic flow of material from one part of the earth to another. (17)

ISOSTERE. See ISOPYCNIC.

ISOTAC. See ISOPECTIC.

ISOTHERE. A line connecting points having the same mean summer temperature. A line connecting points having the same mean winter temperature is called an isocheim. (17)

ISOTHERM. A line connecting points of equal temperature. (17)

ISOTHERMAL. Having no change in temperature along a given reference plane. (15)

ISOTHERM FOLLOWER. This device directly measures the temperature of internal waves and automatically traces isothermal vertical oscillations with reference to time. This instrument is comprised of (1) a sea sensing unit; (2) an electric winch containing a cable to which the sea sensing unit is attached; (3) electronic components (servo-mechanism, amplifiers, etc.) and (4) two recorders (depth and temperature). The sea sensing unit contains a thermistor head balanced bridge circuit with a resistance corresponding to the desired isothermal temperature. If the bridge becomes unbalanced, a thyratron tube is fired. This activates a winch and causes it either to wind in or let out the sea unit, "locking it" onto the desired isotherm. The isotherm depth is continuously recorded on the ship by means of a pressure sensor in the sea unit. The net result is a trace of the given isotherm depth. (30)

ISOTHERMOBATH. A line connecting points of equal temperature in a verticle plane in the ocean. (17)

ISOTOPE. A member of an element family which differs from the other members only by its weight. Isotopes of the same element have no chemical difference - they have the same number of electrons and protons but differ in their number of neutrons which accounts for the difference in weight. Sometimes this excess or deficiency causes the atom to be unstable or radioactive, the atom is then a radioisotope. There are over 300 stable isotopes in nature. A few elements exist in only one isotopic form, for instance, aluminum. Others such as the element tin, exists in 10 isotopic forms, one of which is a radioisotope. (39)

ISOTOPE POWER GENERATORS. See SNAP.

ISOTROPIC. Having the same physical properties in all directions; isotropous. (17)

ISRU. International Scientific Radio Union.

ISS. International Seismological Summary.

ISTHMUS. A narrow strip of land connecting two larger portions of land. A submarine elevation joining two land areas separating two basins or depressions by a depth less than that of the basins is called a submarine isthmus. (17)

ITTC. Inter-American Tropical Tuna Commission.

ITU. International Telecommunications Union.

IUB. International Union of Biochemistry.

IUBS. International Union of Biological Sciences.

IUG. International Union of Geography.

IUGG. International Union of Geodesy and Geophysics.

IUGS. International Union on Geological Sciences.

IUPAC. International Union of Pure and Applied Chemistry.

IUPAP. International Union of Pure and Applied Physics.

IUPS. International Union of Physiological Science.

IURS. International Union of Radio Sciences.

IWC. International Whaling Commission.
Established December 1946 under the International Whaling Convention of November 1948.
Activities: Conserves the remaining world whale stocks, encourages studies of whale populations, collects statistical information, studies methods of maintaining and increasing the whale population. The Commission meets annually to carry out its functions of reviewing reports and issuing such regulations as seem necessary. Annual reports are published and there is some participation in whale tagging studies and research programs. Most of the research activity is supported directly by member countries.
Membership: Australia, Brazil, Canada, Denmark, France, Iceland, Japan, Mexico, Netherlands, New Zealand, Norway, Panama, Sweden, Union of South Africa, United Kingdom, U.S.S.R., United States.

J

JAN. Joint Army-Navy.

JAPAN CURRENT. See KUROSHIO CURRENT. (24)

JCAR. Joint Commission of Applied Radioactivity.

JELLYFISH. Common name for medusoid coelenterates; they are semitransparent, pelagic, tentacled invertebrates. Some species have venom cells in their tentacles; some species are capable of producing a glowing-ball type of bioluminescence. (15)

JETTISON. The throwing overboard of objects, especially to lighten a craft in distress. Jettisoned objects that float are termed flotsam; objects that sink, jetsam; and heavy articles that are buoyed for future recovery, lagan. (17)

JETSAM. See JETTISON.

JETTY. United States terminology. A structure, such as a wharf or pier, so located as to influence current or protect the entrance to a harbor or river. A jetty extending into the sea to protect the coast from erosion is called a GROIN. A jetty which breaks the force of the sea at any place is called a BREAKWATER. A jetty wall, or bank, often submerged, built to direct or confine the flow of a river or tidal current is called a training wall. A wall or embankment along a waterfront, to resist encroachments of the sea, is called a sea wall. British Terminology. A pier, usually of solid construction, intended as a berthing place for vessels. See DOCK, LANDING, WHARF. (17)

JHO. Japan Hydrographic Office.

JMA. Japan Meteorological Agency.

JUNCTION BUOY. A buoy marking the junction of two channels or two parts of a channel when proceeding from seaward. The opposite is bifurcation buoy. (17)

JURY RIG. Any temporary or makeshift device, rig, or piece of equipment.

K

KALEMA. A very heavy surf breaking on the Guinea coast during the winter, even when there is no wind. (17)

KASPNIRO. Caspian Institute of Marine Fisheries and Oceanography (USSR).

KAUS (Also spelled QUAS; Also called COWSHEE, SHARKI). A moderate to gale-force southeasterly wind in the Persian Gulf; it is accompanied by gloomy weather, rain and squalls. The Kaus is most frequent between December and April. It is associated with the passage of a winter depression, and is often followed by a strong southwesterly wind, the Suahili. (12)

KEDGE. To move, as a vessel, by carrying out an anchor, letting it go, and hauling the ship up to the anchor. (17)

KEG BUOY. A buoy consisting of a keg to which is attached a small pole with a flag, used by fishermen to mark the position of a trawl line. (17)

KELP. Brown algae of the order Laminariales, including the largest known algae. Kelp typically grow on rock or stone bottom. They attain their greatest size in cold waters, with length as great as 100 feet and blades 4 or more feet in width. (15)

Kev. In nuclear physics: A unit of energy: 1 Kev = 1.6×10^{-9} ergs. A unit of temperature: 1 Kev = 11.6×10^{6} °K

KEY (CAY). A low insular bank of sand, coral, etc., as one of the islets off the southern coast of Florida. (11)

KINETIC ENERGY (OF WAVES). In a progressive oscillatory wave, a summation of the energy of motion of the particles within the wave. This energy does not advance with the wave form. (11)

KNAPP BOTTOM PRESSURE GAUGE. This instrument was designed for studying harbor surging. A strain-gauge unit, used in connection with a pressure-sensitive bellows, comprises the transducer of the pressure head. The four strain-gauges in the unit are connected to form a bridge circuit that is linked to the recorder by an electrical cable. A d.c. voltage is applied to the bridge, and the record is obtained by recording photographically the unbalanced current from a magnetic OSCILLOGRAPH. Any standard strain-gauge recorder can be used for the recording system.
The gauge differs from other pressure gauges in that no slow leak is provided to eliminate tides and long period waves. In place of the slow leak, a solenoid valve is installed which is held open while the instrument is being lowered or raised to prevent damage to the pressure-sensing element. Once the instrument is in place, the valve is closed electrically to seal the reference chamber at an average pressure corresponding to the depth of the water. (35)

KNOLL. An elevation rising less than 500 fathoms from the sea floor, having a nearly equidimensional plan less than 60 nautical miles across the summit. (27)

KNOT. (Abbreviation kt. or kts.) The unit of speed used in navigation. It is equal to 1 NAUTICAL MILE per hour. (11)

KNUDSEN'S TABLES. Tables published by Martin Knudsen in 1901 ("Hydrographical Tables"), to facilitate the computation of results of sea-water CHLORINITY titrations and HYDROMETER readings, and their conversion to SALINITY, density, and SIGMA-T. (12)

KONA STORM. A storm over the Hawaiian Islands, characterized by strong southerly or southwesterly winds and heavy rains. (17)

KULLENBERG PISTON CORER. The Oceanographic Office model of this sediment sampler weighs approximately 400 lbs. and consists of a hard steel coring tube either 5 1/2 or 11 1/2 ft. in length (the original model is 70 ft. or greater in length and is made up of 15 ft. sections) which employs a 5 ft. 9 3/4 in. or 11 ft. 9 3/4 in. (depending upon length of coring tube used) plastic liner having a 2-in. outside diameter for containment and subsequent storage of cores. Added weight for greater penetration is provided by 50 lb. removable lead weights. A tail-fin is not used for increased stability. The coring tube is provided with a piston which is connected directly to the suspension cable and rests just above the core catcher in the set position. The coring assembly is suspended from the short arm of a balanced lever, and a counterweight which hangs approximately 12 ft. below the nose-piece in order to provide a 4-6 ft. free fall for the coring tube is suspended from the longer arm. In practice, contact with the bottom by the counterweight releases the coring tube which has sufficient slack line for a 4-6 ft. free fall before striking the bottom. Contact with the bottom by the counterweight is registered on the ship by slack in the suspension cable or by a dynamometer and the winch is stopped, thus bringing the piston to rest at or near the water-bottom interface. The coring tube slips over the piston and into the sediment a distance which depends on its initial velocity and the character of the sediment. The purpose of the piston is to provide a partial vacuum ahead of the core and to decrease wall friction. A core catcher, usually consisting of overlapping metal leaves, prevents the core from being lost as the corer is raised to the surface. (35)

KUROSHIO COUNTERCURRENT. Part of the KUROSHIO SYSTEM. Between longitudes 155° and 160°E, considerable water turns south and southwest forming part of the Kuroshio countercurrent. It runs at a distance of approximately 700 km from the coast as the eastern branch of a large whirl on the right-hand side of the Kuroshio. (24)

KUROSHIO CURRENT (BLACK STREAM, JAPAN STREAM). A North Pacific Ocean current flowing northeastward along the coast of Formosa, the Nansei Shoto, and Japan, the main part flowing along their southeast coasts, and then widening, part curving southward and part continuing eastward as the NORTH PACIFIC CURRENT. Part of the Kuroshio, called the TSUSHIMA CURRENT, flows northeastward through Korea Strait and the Sea of Japan, following the northwest coast of Japan and then curving southeastward to rejoin the main part of the Kuroshio. The Kuroshio is a continuation of the NORTH EQUATORIAL CURRENT, and forms the western and northwestern part of the general clockwise oceanic circulation of the North Pacific Ocean. (17)

KUROSHIO EXTENSION. The warm, eastward-flowing ocean current that represents the direct continuation of the KUROSHIO (in latitude 35°N where the Kuroshio leaves the coast of Japan), and flows eastward in two branches.

The major branch of the Kuroshio extension turns due east; it retains its character as a well-defined flow approximately as far as longitude 160°E (eventually becoming the NORTH PACIFIC CURRENT). The minor branch, to the north, continues toward the northeast as far as latitude 40°N where it bends east (eventually becoming the ALEUTIAN CURRENT). This northern branch becomes rapidly mixed with the cold waters of the OYASHIO. (24)

KUROSHIO (JAPAN CURRENT). An ocean current flowing northeastward from Formosa to Riukiu and then close to the coast of Japan as far as latitude 35°N; part of the Kuroshio system. It is a density-distribution type current, and one of the swiftest of all ocean currents.

The Kuroshio is the northward flowing part of the NORTH EQUATORIAL CURRENT (which divides east of the Philippines). Beyond latitude 35°N, where it leaves the coast of Japan, it branches to form two sections of the KUROSHIO EXTENSION.

The current is similar to the FLORIDA CURRENT of the Atlantic Ocean. (24)

KUROSHIO SYSTEM. A system of ocean currents including the KUROSHIO, KUROSHIO EXTENSION, NORTH PACIFIC CURRENT, and the lesser TSUSHIMA CURRENT and KUROSHIO COUNTERCURRENT. (12)

L

LABRADOR CURRENT (ARCTIC CURRENT). An ocean current that flows southward from Baffin Bay, through the Davis Strait, thence southeastward past Labrador and Newfoundland. East of the Grand Banks, the Labrador current meets the GULF STREAM, and the two flow east separated by the COLD WALL. (24)

LACROSSE. A military system of measuring distances. Lacrosse uses pulsed light ranging equipment for the accurate measurement of enemy targets, for station keeping of ships, fire control, military surveying under war time conditions and for landing aircraft. (35)

LAFOND'S TABLES. A set of tables and associated information for correcting REVERSING THERMOMETERS and computing DYNAMIC HEIGHT ANOMALIES, compiled by E. C. Lafond and published by the U. S. Navy Hydrographic Office as H. O. Pub. No. 617. (12)

LAGAN. See JETTISON.

LAGOON. A shallow body of water, as a pond or lake which usually has a shallow, restricted outlet to the sea. (11)

LAGRANGIAN COORDINATES (MATERIAL COORDINATES).
1. A system of coordinates by which fluid parcels are identified for all time by assigning them coordinates which do not vary with time. Examples of such coordinates are (a) the values of any properties of the fluid conserved in the motion; or (b) more generally, the positions in space of the parcels at some arbitrarily selected moment. Subsequent positions in space of the parcels are then the dependent variables, functions of time and of the Lagrangian coordinates.

Few observations in meteorology are Lagrangian: this would require successive observations in time of the same air parcel. Exceptions are the constant-pressure balloon observation, which attempts to follow a parcel under the assumption that its pressure is conserved, and certain small-scale observations of diffusing particles.
2. Same as generalized coordinates. (24)

LAGRANGIAN WAVE. See SHALLOW-WATER WAVE.

LAMBDA. Lambda is a low-ambiguity, accurate position-fixing system used in Oceanography and Hydrography. It is quite similar to two-range DECCA, but with two additional features. The first feature is Lane Identification while the second is the use of Phase Locked Oscillators at both ship and ground stations.

The technique of lane identification does not require an extra ground station. Also, it only requires one additional radio frequency which is used only for a fraction of a second during lane identification. When the lane identification button is pressed, the ships' transmitter shifts to a new frequency. This operates relays at the ground station which shift their frequency by about 14 kc. On the ship is a phase-locked oscillator locked to the ground station transmitter. Since it continues on the same frequency during lane identification, it differs from ground station transmitter by 14 kc. Special phase meters read the ship's position within lanes of 14 kc, each lane being about six miles wide. (29)

LAMINAR FLOW (LAMINARY FLOW, SHEET FLOW, STREAMLINE FLOW). A flow in which the fluid moves smoothly in streamlines in parallel layers or sheets; a nonturbulent flow. (24)

LAMINARY FLOW. See LAMINAR FLOW.

LAND BREEZE. A light wind blowing from the land caused by unequal cooling of land and water masses. (11)

LANDFAST ICE. See FAST ICE.

LAND FLOE. See FLOE.

LAND ICE. All ice formed on land. It may be classified according to its source as continental, island, highland, cirque, or snowdrift ice; according to its movement as wall-sided or valley glacier; according to its deposition as piedmont, confluent, avalanche, or expanded-foot ice, or as ice tongue afloat; or according to dissolution as iceberg, bergy bit, or growler. Shelf ice is usually considered a form of land ice, but may be partly sea ice. (17)

LANDING. 1. A place where boats receive or discharge passengers, freight, etc.
2. Bringing of a vessel to a landing.
3. Bringing of an aircraft to earth.
Called alighting in British and Canadian terminology. (17)

LANDLOCKED. An area of water enclosed, or nearly enclosed, by land, as a bay, a harbor, etc., (thus, protected from the sea). (11)

LAND-SEA BREEZE. The combination of a land breeze and a sea breeze as a diurnal phenomenon. (11)

LAND SKY. Dark streaks, patches, or a grayness on the underside of extensive cloud areas caused by the absence of reflected light from the bare ground. Land sky is not as dark as WATER SKY. (25)

LANG LAY. See WIRE ROPE.

LARVIPAROUS. See OVIPAROUS.

LASER. Light Amplification by Stimulated Emission of Radiation.

LATENT HEAT. Heat resulting in a change in state but no temperature change. (33)

LATITUDE. The latitude of any point is the angle between the local plumb line and the equatorial plane. Because the earth can be considered as having the form of a spheroid, and as the plumb line, for all practical purposes, is perpendicular to the surface of the spheroid, any plane parallel to the Equator cuts the surface of the spheroid in a circle, and all points on this circle have the same latitude. These circles are called PARALLELS OF LATITUDE. Latitude is measured in degrees, minutes, and seconds north and south of the Equator. Since the earth is not a sphere the distance represented by a unit of latitude increases by about 1 per cent between the Equator and the Poles. At the Equator, 1 degree of latitude is equivalent to 110,567.2 meters, and at the Poles it is 111,699.3 meters. (13)

LAYER DEPTH. In oceanography, the thickness of the MIXED LAYER; or the depth to the top of the THERMOCLINE. (12)

LAYER EFFECT. Reduction in the echo and listening ranges on a target located within or beneath a thermocline.

LAYER OF NO MOTION. A layer, assumed to be at rest, at some depth in the ocean. This implies that the isobaric surfaces within the layer are level, and hence they may be used as reference surfaces for the computation of absolute gradient currents.
     This same concept can define a level of no motion or a surface of no motion. (12)

LCU. U. S. Navy designation for a Utility Landing Craft.

LEAD. A long narrow but navigable water passage in PACK ICE. A lead may be covered by thin ice. (25)

LEAD LINE. See SOUNDING LINE.

LEAGUE. A unit of distance of indefinite value, varying from 2.4 to 4.6 miles. In the U.S. it is approximately 3 miles, either statute or nautical. (17)

LEDGE. A rocky formation continuous with and fringing the shore. (27)

LEE. (1) Shelter, or the part or side sheltered or turned away from the wind or waves. (2) (Chiefly nautical) The quarter or region toward which the wind blows. (11)

LEEWARD. The direction toward which the wind is blowing; the direction toward which the waves are travelling. (11)

LEEWARD TIDE. A tidal current setting in the same direction the wind is blowing. A tidal current setting in the opposite direction is called a windward tide. Also called lee tide. (17)

LEFT LAY. See WIRE ROPE.

LENGTH OF WAVE. The horizontal distance between similar points on two successive waves measured perpendicularly to the crest. (11)

LESSER FLOOD. See FLOOD CURRENT.

LEVEE. An embankment bordering one or both sides of a CANYON or SEACHANNEL. (27)

LEVEL. In acoustics, the level of a quantity is the logarithm of the ratio of that quantity to a reference quantity of the same kind. The base of the logarithm, the reference quantity, and kind of level must be specified. (2)

LEVEL SURFACE. An imaginary surface along which no component of gravity acts.

LGO. Lamont Geological Observatory.

LIGHTED BUOY. A buoy with a light having definite characteristics for detection and identification during darkness. If the light is produced by gas, it may be called a gas buoy. (17)

LIGHTED SOUND BUOY. A lighted buoy provided with a sound signal. This is one type of combination buoy. (17)

LILY-PAD ICE. Pancake ice when the cakes are not more than about 18 inches in diameter. (17)

LIMESTONE. A sedimentary rock consisting essentially of the mineral calcite (calcium carbonate). (27)

LIMITING RAY. Any ray which is tangent to a plane at which the velocity of propagation has a maximum value, either at a boundary of the medium or at a level where the velocity gradient changes sign, is known as a limiting ray. (4)

LIMIT OF BACKRUSH. See BACKRUSH.

LINEAR TRANSDUCER. A linear transducer is a transducer for which the pertinent measure of all the waves concerned are linearly related. (1)

LINE HYDROPHONE. A line hydrophone is a directional hydrophone consisting of a single, straight-line element, or any array of contiguous or spaced electroacoustic transducing elements, disposed on a straight line, or the acoustic equivalent of such an array. (1)

LINE OF CENTERS. When considering the paths of rays in a vertical plane crossing a region of constant vertical velocity gradient the intersection of the vertical plane with the horizontal level of zero velocity is known as the line of centers. (4)

LINE SPECTRUM. 1. If the frequencies of the sinusoidal components making up a complex wave are separated by intervals on the frequency scale of such magnitude that the magnitude of each component may be independently evaluated, the wave is said to have a line spectrum. (4)
          2. A line spectrum is a spectrum whose components occur at a number of discrete frequencies. (1)

LINE SQUALL. See SQUALL.

LIPPER. 1. Slight ruffling or roughness on a water surface.
          2. Light spray from small waves. (17)

LISTENING SONAR.   See PASSIVE SONAR

LITHOLOGY. (1) Study of the characteristics of rocks.
          (2) Study of the composition of rocks. (27)

LITHOPHYTE. A plant or plantlike organism that grows on the surface of rocks. (20)

LITHOSPHERE. The solid crust of the earth. (27)

LITRE. The 12th General Conference on Weights and Measures (Oct. 1964) abolished the 1901 definition of the litre based on the volume occupied by 1 kilogramme of water. This decision was accompanied by a declaration that the word "litre" can be used as a special name given to the cubic decimetre and by a recommendation that the name "litre" shall not be used to express the results of volume measurements of high precision. The litre of 1901 has been experimentally established to be equal to 1.000028 cubic decimetre. For scientific and technological purposes the cubic metre, its multiples and submultiples constitute the sole references for volume measurements in the International System of Units. Use of the litre and its submultiples, such as the centilitre and the millilitre, will henceforth tend to fall into disuse except for ordinary transactions in trade.

LITTLE BROTHER. A secondary tropical cyclone sometimes following a more severe disturbance. (17)

LITTORAL. Of or pertaining to a shore, especially of the sea. A coastal region. (11)

LITTORAL DEPOSITS. Deposits of LITTORAL DRIFT. (11)

LITTORAL DRIFT. The material that moves in the LITTORAL ZONE under the influence of waves and currents. (27)

LITTORAL TRANSPORT. The movement of material along the shore in the LITTORAL ZONE by waves and currents. (11)

LITTORAL ZONE. Areas of the ocean bottom reached by sufficient light to support the growth of plant life. (27)

LOAD ADMITTANCE. Load admittance may be defined as the reciprocal of the load impedance. (4)

LOAD CURRENT. The load current of an energy load is the rms current through the terminals of that load when connected to a specified source. (4)

LOAD IMPEDANCE. The load impedance of an energy load is the impedance which would be measured at the terminals of that load if they were not connected to a source. (4)

LOAD POWER. The load power of an energy load is the average rate of flow of energy through the terminals of that load when connected to a specified source. (4)

LOAD TRANSITION LOSS. The load transition loss at the junction between the energy load and a transducer connecting that load to an energy source is the transmission loss measured by the ratio of the output power of the transducer to the load power of the load. (4)

LOAD VOLTAGE. The load voltage of an energy load is the rms voltage between the terminals of that load when connected to a specified source. (4)

LOBES. If a three-dimensional representation of a transducer directivity is made by rotating the two-dimensional directivity pattern these sectors generate zones, or regions, on the constant distance surface. These regions are known as lobes. The term is also used with reference to the corresponding portions of the directivity pattern. The region, or sector, which includes the reference axis is known as the primary lobe; the remaining regions, or sectors, are known as the secondary lobes. When the primary lobe is the only lobe showing maximum response it is often called the major lobe. In that case the secondary lobes are called minor lobes. (4)

LOCH. 1. A lake.
2. An arm of the sea, especially when nearly landlocked (Scotland). (17)

LOCO. Long Core Drilling Program.

LOESS. A buff-colored, unstratified deposit ranging in grain size from clay to fine-grain sand and distributed and deposited by wind action. (27)

LOGARITHMIC DECREMENT. The logarithmic decrement is the natural logarithm of the ratio of any two successive amplitudes of like sign, in the decay of a single-frequency oscillation. (2)

LOG LINE. A graduated line used to measure the speed of a vessel through the water or to measure the velocity of the current from a vessel at anchor. (24)

LONG CRESTED WAVES. Waves having crests which are long compared to the wavelength.

LONGITUDE. Angular distance in a great circle of reference reckoned from an accepted origin to the projection of any point on that circle. Longitude on the earth's surface is measured in the equator east and west of the meridian of Greenwich and may be expressed either in degrees or in hours, the hour being taken as the equivalent of 15° of longitude. Celestial longitude is measured in the ecliptic eastward from the vernal equinox. The mean longitude of a celestial body moving in an orbit is the longitude that would be attained by a point moving uniformly in the circle of reference at the same average angular velocity as that of the body and with the initial position of the point so taken that its longitude would be the same as that of the body at a certain specified position in its orbit. With a common initial point, the mean longitude of a body will be the same in whatever circle it may be reckoned. (14)

LONGITUDINAL WAVE. A longitudinal wave is a wave in which the direction of displacement of each particle in the medium is perpendicular to the wave itself. Sound waves in air or water are longitudinal waves. (9)

LONGSHORE BAR. A BAR which extends generally parallel with the shoreline and is submerged at least by high tides. (27)

LONGSHORE CURRENT (LITTORAL CURRENT). The resultant current produced by waves being deflected at an angle by the shore. In this case the current runs roughly parallel to the shoreline.
The longshore current is capable of carrying a certain amount of material as long as its velocity remains fairly constant; however, any obstruction, such as a submarine rock ridge or a land point cutting across the path of the current will cause loss of velocity and consequent loss of carrying power. (24)

LONG WAVE. Waves under conditions where the relative depth is less than 0.05, and where the phase velocity is dependent upon water depth, but independent of wave length.

LOOMING. A common form of mirage. The appearance in the sky or on the horizon of objects that are normally hidden below the horizon is a common occurrence in the Far North. Images, sometimes upside down, may appear well up in the sky, resting on a pedestal or floating just above the horizon. The opposite, known as sinking, causes nearby objects which should be in clear view to disappear.
Looming may interfere with the identification of landmarks by distortion, may make estimation of vertical distances more difficult, may cause ICE-

BERGS to resemble ships, and may suddenly reveal one's own craft to a distant observer. (25)

LOOPS. 1. In standing-wave patterns, points at which the acoustic pressure, or other measure of acoustic energy, exhibit maximum values are known as loops. (4)
2. That part of a STANDING WAVE or CLAPOTIS where the vertical motion is greatest and the horizontal velocities are least. Loops (sometimes called antinodes) are associated with clapotis, and with SEICHE action resulting from resonant wave reflections in a harbor or bay. (11)

LOPHOPHORE. A ridge about the mouth region bearing tentacles in some invertebrates. (19)

LORAC. Lorac is a continuous wave, phase comparison, hyperbolic positioning system that uses three shore stations and permits an unlimited number of users. It uses frequencies in the vicinity of two megacycles. The useful range is about 200 nautical miles, and accuracies range from about 15 feet on the base line to about 400 feet at the outer limits of the usable area. The shore equipment consists of four transmitters and two receivers and establishes the hyperbolic lattice by using two pairs of frequencies with an audio "beat" frequency of 315 cycles between the two frequencies of the red pair and 135 cycles between the frequencies of the green pair. The red, center, and green stations should be established at about 60 to 120 miles apart, with the angle between the two base lines less than 135. and preferably with the triad concave toward the area of interest. A position is read from the phase meters of the shipboard receiver in the red and green "lanes". A lane is a half-wave length which is roughly 230 feet wide (depending upon the frequency being used) on the base line. (29)

LORAN (LONG RANGE NAVIGATION). An electronic navigational system developed by the United States during World War II. Hyperbolic lines of position are determined by measuring the difference in the time of reception of synchronized pulse signals from two fixed transmitters. See also LORAN A. (29)

LORAN-A. A radio navigation system in which the transmitting stations operate in pairs to provide the navigator a line of position. The operation of a loran system can be summarized as follows: A master ground station transmits signals consisting of short pulses of radio frequency energy on a channel in the 1,800 to 2,000 kc. band. A slave station receives these pulses and uses them to synchronize its transmitter, which in turn transmits similar short pulses of radio frequency energy. The two signals are received aboard a ship or aircraft on a specially designed radio receiver. The difference in time of arrival between the master and slave signals, measured in microseconds, is shown on the receiver. This time difference determines a unique hyperbolic line of position on the earth's surface. The same procedure with another pair of signals provides an additional line of position which is crossed with the first line to obtain a Loran fix. (34)

LORAN-B. Loran B is similar to standard LORAN (LORAN A) in that it is a pulse and hyperbolic system. The envelopes are matched as in standard Loran to determine proper lane identification.
For greater accuracy, the cycles of radio frequency energy inside the envelopes (or pulses) are compared in phase, the same as any phase comparison system. The only difference being that the information presented on the dials is given in nanoseconds instead of fractional parts of a lane. (29)

LORAN-C. Loran C is similar to standard LORAN (LORAN A) in that it is a pulse and hyperbolic positioning system. In Loran C, the envelopes (or the shape of the pulse) are used to determine the proper lane identification. This is accomplished by matching the pulses as is now done in standard Loran.
Loran C has the advantage of being a very long range hi-precision system capable of giving a position with a high degree of accuracy, without the problem of lane count identification. It has frequencies in the vicinity of 100 kilocycles. It has a further advantage over other phase comparison systems in that there is no sky wave contamination. Regular phase systems radiate continuously, and the sky waves can cause phase cancellation or distortion of the received signal. Since LORAN C is a pulse system, the sky waves arrive too late to cause interference with the ground wave. Only the beginning or the front of the pulse is used, and any signals which arrive earlier or later are automatically rejected by the receiver. (29)

LOST TIME. The period in an FM sonar, just after FLYBACK, during which the sound field must be reestablished. Its duration equals travel time of the signal to and from the target. (5)

LOWER HIGH WATER (LHW). The lower of the two high waters of any tidal day. (11)

LOWER LOW WATER (LLW). The lower of the two low waters of any tidal day. The single low water occurring daily during periods when the tide is diurnal is considered to be a lower low water. (11)

LOW-PASS FILTER. A low-pass filter is a wave filter having a single transmission band extending from zero up to some critical or cutoff frequency which is not infinite. (9)

LOW WATER (LW). The minimum height reached by a falling tide. The height may be due solely to the periodic tidal forces or it may have superimposed upon it the effects of meteorological conditions. (14)

LOW WATER DATUM. An approximation to the plane of mean low water that has been adopted as a standard reference plane for a limited area and is retained for an indefinite period regardless of the fact that it may differ slightly from a better determination of MEAN LOW WATER from a subsequent series of observations. (14)

LOW WATER EQUINOCTIAL SPRINGS. Low water springs near the times of the equinoxes. Expressed in the terms of the harmonic constants, it is a plane depressed below MEAN SEA LEVEL by an amount equal to the sum of the amplitudes of the constants M_2, S_2, and K_2. (14)

LOW WATER INEQUALITY. See DIURNAL INEQUALITY.

LOW WATER INTERVAL. See LUNITIDAL INTERVAL.

LOW WATER LINE. The intersection of any standard low tide datum plane with the shore. (11)

LOW WATER OF ORDINARY SPRING TIDES (LWOST). A tidal datum appearing in some British publications, based on low water of ordinary spring tides. (11)

LOW WATER SPRINGS. See MEAN LOW WATER SPRINGS.

LPD. U. S. Navy ship designation for an Amphibious Transport, Dock.

LPH. U. S. Navy designation for an Amphibious Assault Ship.

LS. Light-Ship.

LSD. U. S. Navy designation for a Dock Landing Ship.

LSM. U. S. Navy designation for a Medium Landing Ship.

LSMR. U. S. Navy designation for a Medium Landing Ship (Rocket).

LST. U. S. Navy designation for a Tank Landing Ship.

LSV. U. S. Navy designation for a Vehicle Landing Ship.

LUBBER'S LINE. A reference line on any direction-indicating instrument, marking the reading which coincides with the heading. (17)

LUNAR DAY. The time of the rotation of the earth with respect to the moon, or the interval between two successive upper transits of the moon over the meridian of a place. The mean lunar day is approximately 24.84 solar hours in length, or 1.035 times as great as the mean solar day. (14)

LUNAR MONTH. Same as SYNODICAL MONTH.

LUNAR TIDE. That part of the tide on the earth due solely to the moon as distinguished from that part due to the sun. (14)

LUNISOLAR TIDES. Harmonic tidal constituents K_1 and K_2, which are derived partly from the development of the LUNAR TIDE and partly from the SOLAR TIDE, the constituent speeds being the same in both cases. Also the lunisolar synodic fortnightly constituent MSf. (14)

LUTITE. Material of grain size less than 4 microns. This term may be used instead of clay, to avoid mineralogical implications. (27)

LW. LOW WATER.

M

MA. Maritime Administration.

MAB. The Materials Advisory Board of the National Academy of Sciences - National Research Council.

MACKEREL SKY. An area of sky with a formation of rounded and isolated cirrocumulus or altocumulus resembling the pattern of scales on the back of a mackerel. (17)

MACROPLANKTON. See MARINE LIFE.

MAD. 1. Magnetic Airborne Detection.
2. Magnetic Anamoly Detection.

MADREPORE. A stony coral which often forms an important building material for reefs. (17)

MAELSTROM. Famous whirlpool off the Coast of Norway in the Lofoten Islands between Moskenesoy and Mosken. (14)

MAESTRO. A northwesterly wind with fine weather which blows, especially in summer, in the Adriatic; it is most frequent on the western shore, and is equivalent to the ETESIANS of the eastern Mediterranean. It is also found on the coasts of Corsica and Sardina. (12)

MAGMA. A naturally occurring liquid molten mass, the molten material from which igneous rocks are formed by solidification. (27)

MAGNETIC ANOMALY. Variation of the measured magnetic pattern from a theoretical or empirically smoothed magnetic field on the earth's surface. (27)

MAGNETIC EFFECT. Phenomenon exhibited by certain metals, particularly nickel and its alloys, which change in length when magnetized, or, (Villari effect) when magnetized and then mechanically distorted, undergo a corresponding change in magnetization. (6)

MAGNETIC ELEMENTS. Consist of the declination (D), the horizontal intensity (H), the vertical intensity (Z), the total intensity (F), the inclination or dip (I), the strength of the force toward geographic north (X), and the strength of the force toward geographic east (Y). (27)

MAGNETIC EQUATOR. An imaginary line passing through the points on the earth's surface where the earth's magnetic field is parallel to the earth's surface (i.e., the inclination is zero). (27)

MAGNETIC MERIDIAN (GEOMAGNETIC MERIDIAN). The horizontal line which is oriented, at any specified point on the earth's surface, along the direction of the horizontal component of the earth's magnetic field at that point; not to be confused with ISOGONIC LINE. (24)

MAGNETIC NORTH. At any point on the earth's surface, the horizontal direction of the earth's magnetic lines of force (direction of a MAGNETIC MERIDIAN) toward the north magnetic pole, i.e., a direction indicated by the needle of a magnetic compass. Because of the wide use of the magnetic compass, magnetic north, rather than TRUE NORTH, is the common 0° (or 360°) reference in much of navigational practice, including the designation of airport runway alignment.. A heading or course toward magnetic north would be written: 0° mag. See also ACLINIC LINE. (24)

MAGNETIC PICKUP ROTOR. See SAVONIUS ROTOR.

MAGNETIC POLE (DIP POLE). 1. In geomagnetism, either of the two points on the earth's surface at which the MAGNETIC MERIDIANS converge, i.e., where the magnetic field is vertical.
The exact locations of these two magnetic poles shift in complex fashion. The north magnetic pole is now about 200 miles north of the Boothia Peninsula in Canada, while the south magnetic pole is in South Victoria Land on the Antarctic continent. The two poles do not lie at extremes of a diameter of the earth, for the line joining them misses the exact center of the earth by about 750 miles.
2. In magnetic theory, a fictitious entity analogous to a unit electric charge of electrostatic theory. In nature only dipoles, not isolated magnetic poles, exist. (24)

MAGNETOMETER. An instrument for measuring:
1. Any magnetic element.
2. The variations in the earth's magnetic field. See also NUCLEAR RESONANCE MAGNETOMETER.

MAGNETOSTRICTION. Magnetostriction is the phenomenon wherein ferromagnetic materials experience an elastic strain when subjected to an external magnetic field. Also, magnetostriction is the converse phenomenon in which mechanical stresses cause a change in the magnetic induction of a ferromagnetic material. (1)

MAGNETOSTRICTION TRANSDUCER. A magnetostriction transducer is a transducer that depends for its operation on the interaction between the magnetization of the deformation of a material having magnetostrictive properties. (1)

MAJOR LOBES. (See LOBES)

MALKUS BATHYPITOTMETER. A pitot-type current meter, devised by Willem Malkus, having the shape of a large BATHYTHERMOGRAPH, which responds to currents in the range 50 to 250 cm/sec. It is necessary to move the ship ahead slowly if the current speeds do not fall in this range and then allow the instrument to come to equilibrium at each of a succession of depths to obtain readings. Readings on two headings must be made and compared to evaluate the resultant velocity at each level if this is not known at the start or if the current turns with depth. (32)

MAMOS. Marine Automatic Meteorological Oceanographic Station.

MANOMETER. An instrument for measuring pressure of gases and vapors both above and below atmospheric pressure.

MAP. An inshore navigation system employing a good quality Radar as a part of the system. This radar is modified to give a high precision range accuracy and a selective azimuth control so that only the desired shore targets are indicated. These shore targets are mutually perpendicular screens mounted on the top of a tower. Two or more targets may be located ashore (or on the water) to cover the survey area.

An automatic plotter fastened over the boat-sheet automatically follows the course of the vessel over the sheet. The ship's position can be pricked into the boat-sheet or observed through cross hairs. The ship's distance from both targets is also printed on a tape at any time of command. (29)

MARAD. Maritime Administration.

MARES' TAILS. Long slender streaks of cirrus thickening into cirrostratus, and then gradually lowering into watery altostratus. (17)

MARIGRAM. A graphic representation of the rise and fall of the tide in which time is represented by the abscissas and the height of the tide by ordinates, particularly the record traced by a marigraph; a tide curve. (17)

MARINE CLIMATE. The type of climate characteristic of coastal areas, islands, and the oceans, the distinctive features of which are small annual and daily temperature range and high relative humidity, in contrast with continental climate, which is characteristic of the interior of a large land mass, and the distinctive features of which are large annual and daily temperature range and dry air with few clouds. (17)

MARINE LIFE. Classified upon the basis of common habits of locomotion and mode of life, and upon common ecological distribution the population of the sea may be divided into three large groups. These are: (1) Benthos, which includes the sessile, creeping, and burrowing organisms found on the bottom of the sea, with representatives of the group extending from the high-tide level down into the abyssal depths. The benthos comprises (a) sessile animals, such as the sponges, barnacles, mussels, oysters, crinoids, corals, hydroids, bryozoa, some

of the worms, all of the seaweeds and eel grass, and many of the diatoms, (b) creeping forms, such as crabs, lobsters, certain copepods, amphipods, and many other crustacea, many protozoa, snails, and some bivalves and fishes, and (c) burrowing forms, including most of the clams and worms, some crustacea, and echinoderms. (2) Nekton, which is composed of swimming animals found in the pelagic division. In this group are included most of the adult squids, fishes, and whales---namely, all of the marine animals that are able to migrate freely over considerable distances. Obviously, there are no plants in this general group. (3) Plankton, which includes all of the floating or drifting life of the pelagic division. The organisms, both plant and animal, of this division are usually microscopic or relatively small; they float more or less passively with the currents and are therefore at the mercy of prevailing water movements. Many of the animals are able to make some progress in swimming, although their organs of locomotion are relatively weak and ineffective.

The plankton is divided into two main divisions: (A) Phytoplankton, which comprises all of the floating plants, such as diatoms, dinoflagellates, coccolithophores, and sargassum weeds. (B) Zooplankton, which includes (a) myriads of animals that live permanently in a floating state, and (b) countless numbers of helpless larvae and eggs of the animal benthos and nekton. On the basis of size the plankton may be further subdivided as follows: (C) Macroplankton, includes those organisms of about 1 mm in length which can be caught with a net of No. 00 or 000 bolting cloth. (D) Mesoplankton, includes those organisms between 1 mm and 1 cm, but is infrequently used because of possible confusion with the use of the same term to indicate those plankton living at mid-depth. (E) Megaloplankton, occasionally used to indicate the largest plankton forms. (F) Microplankton, also in part called Net Plankton, is that which is composed of individuals below about 1 mm in size, but yet large enough to be retained by a net of No. 20 bolting cloth with a mesh aperture of about 0.076 mm. (G) Nannoplankton, comprises many of the very small forms (about 5 to 60) which must be collected by centrifuging the water. (H) Ultraplankton, includes those organisms smaller than the nannoplankton.

The planktonic eggs and larvae of the benthos and nekton make up what is known collectively as the Temporary Plankton, or Meroplankton. That part of the plankton which is made up of animals living their complete life cycle in the floating state is called the Permanent Plankton, or Holoplankton. The term Hypoplankton is sometimes used to indicate those forms whose swimming power puts them somewhere in between the plankton and nekton, such as some mysids, amphipods, cumacids, etc. which live both on or near the bottom. (13)

MARINE METEOROLOGY. That part of meteorology which deals mainly with the study of oceanic areas, including island and coastal regions. In particular it serves the practical needs of surface and air navigation over the oceans.

Since there is a close interaction between ocean and atmosphere, and oceanic influences upon weather and climate can be traced far inland over the continents, modern meteorology uses this name mainly for making regional or administrative distinctions. (12)

MARINE RAINBOW. A rainbow seen in ocean spray, sometimes called sea rainbow. (17)

MARINE SEDIMENTS. Marine sediments are subdivided into two major groups, termed PELAGIC and TERRUGENOUS. The pelagic deposits are those found in deep water far from shore and may be predominantly either organic or inorganic in origin. They are light-colored, reddish or brown, fine-grained and, generally, they contain some skeletal remains of plankton organisms. The inorganic deposits are referred to as RED CLAY and the organic deposits as OOZES. Pelagic deposits are classified in the following way:

I. Inorganic deposits. Those which contain less than 30 per cent of organic remains are known as red clay.

II. Organic deposits. Those which contain more than 30 per cent of material of organic origin are known as oozes. This class is further subdivided into:

    1. Calcareous oozes. These contain more than 30 per cent calcium carbonate, which represents the skeletal material of various plankton animals and plants. The calcareous oozes may be further divided into three types, depending upon a characteristic type of organism present in the sediment, namely:

        a. Globigerina ooze, in which the calcium carbonate is in the tests of pelagic foraminifera.

        b. Pteropod ooze, containing conspicuous shells of pelagic molluscs.

        c. Coccolith ooze, containing large numbers of coccoliths and rhabdoliths that form the protective structures of the minute Coccolithophoridae.

    2. Siliceous oozes. These are pelagic deposits which contain a large percentage of siliceous skeletal material produced by planktonic plants and animals. The siliceous oozes are subdivided into two types on the basis of the predominance of the forms represented, namely:

        a. Diatom ooze, containing large amounts of diatom frustules, hence, produced by plankton plants.

        b. Radiolarian ooze, containing large proportions of radiolarian skeletons formed by these plankton animals.

The terrigenous deposits are found near shore and generally contain at least some coarse material of terrigenous origin. They cover a wide range in depth and a great variation in color, texture, and composition. The color may range from white to black with the addition of blue, yellow, or red, or mixtures of these. Several systems of classification have been used without wide application due to the dependance of terrigenous deposits on local conditions. On the basis of texture they may be classified as follows:

    1. Sand. More than 80 per cent of the material coarser than 62 microns in diameter.

    2. Silty sand. Between 50 per cent and 80 per cent coarser than 62 microns.

    3. Sandy silt. More than 50 per cent coarser than 5 microns and more than 20 per cent coarser than 62 microns.

    4. Silty mud. More than 50 per cent coarser than 5 microns and less than 20 per cent coarser than 62 microns.

    5. Clayey mud. Less than 50 per cent coarser than 5 microns. (13)

MARINE SEXTANT. A sextant designed primarily for marine navigation. On a clamp screw sextant the position of the tangent screw is controlled by a clamp screw; on an endless tangent screw sextant the position of the index arm and the vernier or micrometer drum is controlled by an endless tangent screw. A vernier sextant provides a precise reading by means of a vernier used directly with the arc, and may have either a clamp screw or an endless tangent screw for controlling the position of the tangent screw or the index arm. A micrometer drum sextant provides a precise reading by means of a micrometer drum attached to the index arm, and has an endless tangent screw for controlling the position of the index arm. A marine sextant is generally used with the visible horizon as the horizontal reference. (17)

MARINE SNOW. Suspended living and dead organic material and inorganic debris of the sea which is present in concentrated amounts at density boundaries such as the thermocline. (35)

MARINE SURVEY. See OCEANOGRAPHIC SURVEY

MARINE WEATHER OBSERVATION. The weather as observed from a ship at sea, usually taken in accordance with procedures specified by the World Meteorological Organization. The following elements usually are included: total cloud amount; wind direction and speed; visibility; weather; pressure; temperature; selected cloud-layer data, that is amount, type, and height; pressure tendency; seawater temperature; dew-point temperature; state of the sea (waves); and sea ice. Also included are the date and time, and the name, position, course, and speed of the ship. (24)

MARINOSTAT. A controlled - environment facility (Hopkins Marine Station, Pacific Grove, California.)

MARK IX SHORE WAVE RECORDER. The Mark IX was designed as a general purpose wave measuring instrument for permanent installation. The principal component is a differential pressure potentiometer, used as the transducer. The movement of a pressure sensitive brass bellows is magnified by a potentiometer contact lever which, in the normal position of zero differential pressure, divides the resistance of the potentiometer windings equally. Variations of differential pressure cause the potentiometer contact arm to move across the windings. The position variation of the potentiometer arm is converted to a proportional current by the bridge circuit and recorded. (35)

MARKER BUOY. 1. A temporary buoy used in surveying to mark a location of particular interest, such as a shoal or reef.
    2. Station buoy. (17)

MARL. A general term for calcareous clay or calcareous loam. A calcareous clay or intimate mixture of clay and particles of calcite or dolomite, usually fragments of shells. In America the term Marl is chiefly applied to incoherent sands but abroad, compact impure limestones are also called marls. (27)

MARS (MOBILE ATLANTIC RANGE STATION). An acoustic navigation system. See also STAR for principle of operation description. (35)

MARS Transponder

Command frequency (transmitted from ship-board equipment)	16 kc
Reply frequency	10, 11 or 12 kc
Transmitter power	<100 watts
Angle of coverage in vertical plane	$\pm 50°$ from vertical
Angle of coverage in horizontal plane	360°
Life	2 x 10 interrogations or >1 year
Depth	20,000 ft
Power supply	lead-acid batteries
Range	5 to 10 miles depending on patterns of ship-board transducer used.
Range accuracy	0.1% of range + 20 ft
Readout	Depth sounder recorders, digital counters.

MARSH. A tract of soft, wet or periodically inundated land, generally treeless and usually characterized by grasses and other low growth. (11)

MARSH, SALT. A MARSH periodically flooded by salt water. (11)

MASCARET. See BORE.

MASS TRANSPORT. The net transfer of water by wave action in the direction of wave travel. (11)

MAXIMAL BREATHING CAPACITY. The greatest respiratory minute volume which a person can produce during a short period of extremely forceful breathing. In healthy young men, it may average as much as 170 liters per minute. (37)

MAXIMUM FLOOD. See FLOOD CURRENT.

MAXIMUM SOUND PRESSURE. The maximum sound pressure for any given cycle of a periodic wave is the maximum absolute value of the instantaneous sound pressure occurring during that cycle. (2)

MBA. Marine Biological Association.

MBL. Marine Biological Laboratory (Woods Hole, Massachusetts).

MCS. U. S. Navy designation for a Mine Warfare Command & Support Ship.

MEAN DEPTH. The average depth of the water area between the still water level and the SHOREFACE profile from the water-line to any chosen distance seaward. (27)

MEAN DIAMETER, GEOMETRIC. The diameter equivalent of the arithmetic mean of the logarithmic frequency distribution. In the analysis of beach sands it is taken as that grain diameter determined graphically by the intersection of a straight line through selected boundary sizes (generally points

on the distribution curve where 16 and 84 percent of the sample by weight is coarser) and a vertical line through the median diameter of the sample. (11)

MEAN DIURNAL HIGH WATER INEQUALITY. See DIURNAL INEQUALITY.

MEAN HIGHER HIGH WATER (MHHW). The average height of the higher high waters over a 19-year period. For shorter periods of observations, corrections are applied to eliminate known variations and reduce the result to the equivalent of a mean 19-year value. (14)

MEAN HIGH WATER (MHW). The average height of the high waters over a 19-year period. For shorter periods of observations, corrections are applied to eliminate known variations and reduce the result to the equivalent of a mean 19-year value.
All high water heights are included in the average where the type of tide is either semidiurnal or mixed. Only the higher high water heights are included in the average where the type of tide is diurnal. So determined, mean high water in the latter case is the same as MEAN HIGHER HIGH WATER. (14)

MEAN HIGH WATER SPRINGS. The average height of the high waters occurring at the time of spring tide. Frequently abbreviated to High Water Springs. (11)

MEAN LOWER LOW WATER (MLLW). Frequently abbreviated lower low water. The average height of the lower low waters over a 19-year period. For shorter periods of observations, corrections are applied to eliminate known variations and reduce the result to the equivalent of a mean 19-year value. (14)

MEAN LOW WATER (MLW). The average height of the low waters over a 19-year period. For shorter periods of observations, corrections are applied to eliminate known variations and reduce the result to the equivalent of a mean 19-year value.
All low water heights are included in the average where the type of tide is either semidiurnal or mixed. Only the lower low water heights are included in the average where the type of tide is diurnal. So determined, mean low water in the latter case is the same as mean lower low water. (11)

MEAN LOW WATER SPRINGS (MLWS). Frequently abbreviated low water springs. The average height of low waters occurring at the time of the spring tides. It is usually derived by taking a plane depressed below the half-tide level by an amount equal to one-half the spring range of tide, necessary corrections being applied to reduce the result to a mean value. This plane is used to considerable extent for hydrographic work outside of the United States and is the plane of reference for the Pacific approaches to the Panama Canal. (14)

MEAN RANGE OF TIDE (Mn). The difference in height between mean high water and mean low water. (14)

MEAN RISE INTERVAL (MRI). The average interval between the transit of the moon and the middle of the period of the rise of the tide. It may be computed by adding the half of the duration of rise to the mean low water interval, rejecting the semidiurnal tide period of 12.42 hours when greater than this amount. The mean rise interval may be either local or Greenwich according to whether it is referred to the local or Greenwich transit. (14)

MEAN RISE OF TIDE. The height of mean high water above the plane of reference or datum of chart. (14)

MEAN RIVER LEVEL. The average height of the surface of a river at any point for all stages of the tide over a 19-year period, usually determined from

hourly height readings. In rivers subject to oc-
casional freshets, the river level may undergo wide
variations and for practical purposes certain
months of the year may be excluded in the determination of tidal datum planes. For charting purposes, tidal datum planes for rivers are usually
based on observations during selected periods when
the river is at or near low water stage. (14)

MEAN SEA LEVEL. (Abbreviated MSL; popularly called
sea level.) The average height of the sea surface,
based upon hourly observation of tide height on the
open coast or in adjacent waters which have free
access to the sea. These observations are to have
been made over a "considerable" period of time. In
the United States, mean sea level is defined as
the average height of the surface of the sea for
all stages of the tide over a nineteen-year period.
    Selected values of mean sea level serve as the
sea level datum for all elevation surveys in the
United States. In meteorology, mean sea level is
used as the reference surface for all altitudes in
upper-atmospheric work; and in aviation it is the
level above which altitude is measured by a pressure altimeter.
    Along with MEAN HIGH WATER, MEAN LOW WATER,
and MEAN LOWER LOW WATER, mean sea level is a
type of tidal datum. (24)

MEAN SPHERE DEPTH. The uniform depth to which the
water would cover the earth if the solid surface
were smoothed off and were parallel to the surface
of the geoid. The accepted figure for this depth
is 2440 meters. The MEAN DEPTH of the sea is 3800
meters. (27)

MEAN STEEPNESS. The ratio of the MEAN DEPTH to
the horizontal distance over which the mean depth
was determined. (27)

MEAN TIDE LEVEL (MTL). Same as HALF-TIDE LEVEL.

MEAN WATER LEVEL. The mean surface level as determined by averaging the height of the water at equal
intervals of time, usually at hourly intervals.
(14)

MECHANICAL ANALYSIS OF SEDIMENTS. The operation
of determining the distribution of grains of a
granular material in accordance with size. The
separations of the relatively large grains are
made by the use of sieves with varying sized mesh,
the material passing through mesh of one size and
being retained on the sieve of the next smaller
size being considered as coming within one size
range or bracket. Generally expressed in percentage of weight of materials within specific limits
of size. Other methods are used for silt and clay
separation. (27)

MECHANICAL IMPEDANCE. The mechanical impedance of
a given surface area of an acoustic medium perpendicular, at every point, to the direction of propagation of sinusoidal acoustic waves of given frequency and having equal acoustic pressures and equal
volume velocities per unit area at every point of
the surface at any instant, is the quotient obtained
by dividing (1) the phasor corresponding to the
force, due to the acoustic pressure on the given
area, by (2) the phasor corresponding to the volume
velocity per unit area. (4)

MECHANICAL OHMS. Mechanical impedance is measured
in mechanical ohms. One mechanical ohm is equal to
one gm/sec, or to one dyne sec/cm. (4)

MEDIAN DIAMETER. The diameter which marks the
division of a given sample into two equal parts by
weight, one part containing all grains larger than
that diameter and the other part containing all
grains smaller. (27)

MEDIASTRINAL EMPHYSEMA. See EMPHYSEMA.

MEDIUM FLOE. See FLOE.

MEDUSA. An umbrella-shaped coelenterate with tentacles around the periphery and having no hard
parts which represents the sexual generation of a
hydrozoan or scyphozoan. Commonly known as a jellyfish, and ranges in size from about 12mm to over
2m in diameter, with the largest having tentacles
up to 10m long. (19)

MEG. A prefix indicating one million.

MEGALOPLANKTON. See MARINE LIFE.

MESOGLEA. The gelatinous filling between the outer
and inner cell layers of a two-layered animal such
as a jellyfish.

MESON. Sub-atomic particles, varying in weight
but heavier than electrons and lighter than protons,
highly unstable, very short-lived and having either
a positive or negative charge, which are supposed
to form the binding energy in atomic nuclei or at
least are very closely related to nuclear forces.
Their complete nature is highly disputed. (39)

MESOPLANKTON. See MARINE LIFE.

MESSENGER. A brass weight, usually hinged and with
a latch so that it can be fastened around a wire,
used to actuate NANSEN BOTTLES and other oceanographic instruments after they have been lowered
to the desired depth. (12)

METABOLISM. The utilization of oxygen by all cells
of the body for the production of energy and heat.
In this process carbon dioxide is produced. (37)

METACENTER. Metacenter is the point of intersection of a vertical line through the center of
buoyancy of a floating body and a vertical line
through the new center of buoyancy. (33)

METAGENESIS. See ALTERNATION OF GENERATIONS.

METAL ION CONCENTRATION CELL. A cell established
on a metallic surface caused by different concentrations of its ions in the electrolyte where it is
in contact with the metallic surface.

METAMORPHIC ROCK. Rock formed by the alteration of
pre-existing rocks which have developed new physical and chemical characteristics as the result of
pressure, heat, or other geologic agents within the
earth's crust. (27)

METER (OR HALF-METER) PLANKTON SAMPLER. This sampler consists essentially of three parts: a metal
ring, one or one-half meter in diameter, provided
with rope bridles for attaching to a tow line; a
conical bag or net made of silk bolting which acts
as a sieve; and a metal collecting bucket at the
cod end of the net.
    This sampler is easy for one man to rig and
operate and will capture a greater number of macroplankton than nets of smaller aperture. For qualitative work of a reconnaissance type, this net is
rapid and effective and a typical net is a half-
meter (diameter) conical net with a No. 0 mesh. A
special bottle or bucket fits the small end of the
cone. The bottle is secured to the net by several
turns of strong thread or twine. The bucket is
secured by fastening to a metal ring on the net.
Three lines, each about 18 inches long, are attached at equidistant points to the brass ring at
the large end of the net and are joined at 1 point
to the towline, forming a bridle. The towline
should be approximately 150 feet long.
    The mesh size of a plankton net varies. The
selection of mesh size depends on the size of the
plankton organisms sought. An identification number
is on every net; the larger the number, the finer

the mesh. Deep tows and simultaneous collections are not considered practical with this sampler. (35)

METEOROLOGICAL EQUATOR. See EQUATORIAL TROUGH.

METEOROLOGICAL TIDES. Tidal constituents having their origin in the daily or seasonal variations in weather conditions which may occur with some degree of periodicity. The principal meteorological constituents recognized in the tides are Sa, Ssa, and S_1. (14)

METEOROLOGY. The study dealing with the phenomena of the ATMOSPHERE. This includes not only the physics, chemistry, and dynamics of the atmosphere, but is extended to include many of the direct effects of the atmosphere upon the earth's surface, the oceans, and life in general. The goals often ascribed to meteorology are the complete understanding, accurate prediction, and artificial control of atmospheric phenomena.

A distinction can be drawn between meteorology and climatology, the latter being primarily concerned with average, not actual, weather conditions. Meteorology may be subdivided, according to the methods of approach and the applications to human activities, into a large number of specialized sciences. The following are the most generally recognized: aerology, aeronomy, aeronautical meteorology, agricultural meteorology, applied meteorology, dynamic meteorology, hydrometeorology, physical meteorology, radio meteorology, synoptic meteorology, macrometeorology, mesometeorology, micrometeorology. (12)

METONIC CYCLE. A period of 19 years or 235 lunations. Devised by Meton, an Athenian astronomer who lived in the fifth century before Christ, for the purpose of obtaining a period in which new and full moon would recur on the same day of year. Taking the Julian year of 365.25 days and the synodic month as 29.530588 days, we have the 19-year period of 6939.75 days as compared with the 235 lunations of 6939.69 days, a difference of only 0.06 day. (14)

MEYER-OVERTON THEORY. A physiological concept that relates the narcotic action of certain gases directly to their comparative solubility in fat and water. (37)

MHA. U. S. Navy ship designation for a Mine Hunter, Auxiliary.

MHC. U. S. Navy ship designation for a Mine Hunter, Coastal.

MHD. Magnetohydrodynamics.

MHO. The unit of conductance. It is equal to the reciprocal of resistance. (36)

MICROAEROPHILES. Those bacteria which require a reduction of free oxygen, but not to the point of anaerobic conditions. (13)

MICROBAR. A microbar is a unit of pressure commonly used in acoustics. One microbar is equal to 1 $dyne/cm^2$. (1)

MICRODIST. See ELECTROTAPE.

MICROPHONE. A microphone is an electroacoustic transducer that responds to sound waves and delivers essentially equivalent electric waves. (1)

MICROPLANKTON. See MARINE LIFE.

MICROSPORE. A spore which germinates to form the male gametophyte. (18)

MICROWAVE POSITION-FIXING. A navigation system, developed by the National Research Council of Canada, capable of measuring bearing in $0.02°$ increments to three shore based unattended transmitters. On the ship is a rotary radar type antenna that scans the signals from the three shore stations. Equipment design aboard the ship permits a three point fix type of plot. (29)

MID-CHANNEL BUOY. A buoy marking the middle of a channel. (17)

MIDDLE GROUND BUOY. A buoy marking a shoal with channels on both sides. (17)

MID-EXTREME TIDE. A plane midway between the extreme high water and the extreme low water occurring in any locality. (14)

MIDWATER TRAWL. The Isaacs-Kidd Midwater Trawl was developed at the University of California, Scripps Institution of Oceanography. It is capable of collecting some of the larger and more active animal forms found in the ocean. As implied by its name, the trawl was primarily designed for use in midwater, that is, ocean water below the surface layers. An ordinary net will surface behind the towing vessel unless hauled at extremely slow speeds. To counteract this tendency, the midwater trawl has an inclined plane surface rigged in a manner opposite to the elevating action of a kite surface.

The Midwater Trawl has been manufactured with both a 10- and 15-foot mouth, and in 31- and 72-foot lengths, respectively. (35)

MILLI. A prefix indicating one-thousandth.

MILLIGAL. A measure of gravity equal to 1 thousandth part of a GAL.

MINIATURE CURRENT METER. The passage of current past a probe on each blade of a propeller type, or each cup of a PRICE type meter can be detected by the change of electrical resistance between that probe and a distant electrode. A voltage pulse is produced as each blade passes the electrode the pulse rate which depends on the velocity of the current is indicated on a milliammeter.

An oscillator supplies, via a cathode follower, a wheatstone bridge network of which the probe impedance forms one arm. Any out-of-balance signal from the bridge is filtered, amplified and rectified. After removal of the carrier frequency the signal is again amplified and drives an electronic frequency meter which in turn drives the indicating meter and recorder. The indicating meter may be connected to the second amplifier for the initial balancing of the bridge. (30)

MINIMUM FLOOD. See FLOOD CURRENT.

MINLANT. Mine Warfare Forces, Atlantic (USN).

MINOR LOBES. (See LOBES).

MINPAC. Mine Warfare Forces, Pacific (USN).

MISTRAL. A cold, dry wind blowing from the north over the northwest coast of the Mediterranean Sea, particularly over the Gulf of Lion. Also called cierzo. (17)

MIXED CURRENT. Type of tidal current characterized by a conspicuous velocity difference between the two floods or two ebbs usually occurring each tidal day. See MIXED TIDE. (14)

MIXED LAYER. In oceanography, the surface layer of virtually isothermal water, which frequently exists above the THERMOCLINE. (12)

MIXED TIDE. Type of tide in which the presence of

a diurnal wave is conspicuous by a large inequality in either the high or low water heights with two high waters and two low waters usually occurring each tidal day. In strictness all tides are mixed but the name is usually applied without definite limits to the tides intermediate to those predominantly semidiurnal and those predominantly diurnal. (14)

MIXING LENGTH. A mean length of travel, characteristic of a particular motion, over which an eddy maintains its identity; analogous to the mean free path of a molecule. Physically, the idea implies that mixing occurs by discontinuous steps, that fluctuations which arise as eddies with different characteristics wander about, and that the mixing is done almost entirely by the small eddies. Mathematically, the theory assumes that the fluctuations can be adequately represented by the first term in the Taylor expansion of the mean quantity in question. Considering the velocity, for example, the eddy velocity is represented by

$$u' \cong L \frac{d\overline{u}}{dz},$$

where L is the mixing length and z the height. The Reynolds stresses then have the form

$$\overline{\tau} = - \overline{\rho u'w'} = \rho L^2 \frac{d\overline{u}}{dz} \frac{d\overline{w}}{dz}$$

and the coefficient of eddy viscosity is

$$K_M = L^2 \frac{d\overline{u}}{dz}. \qquad (24)$$

MLR. Marine Life Resources (Program).

MMA. U. S. Navy ship designation for a Minelayer, Auxiliary.

MMF. U. S. Navy ship designation for a Minelayer, Fleet.

MOAT. An annular depression that may not be continuous, located at the base of many seamounts or islands. (27)

MODE OF VIBRATION. In a system undergoing vibration, a mode of vibration is a characteristic pattern assumed by the system, in which the motion of every particle is simple harmonic with the same frequency. Two or more modes may exist concurrently in a multiple-degree-of-freedom system. (2)

MODERATE GALE. See GALE.

MODIFIED VAN DORN WATER SAMPLER. A large water capacity, non toxic (usually non metallic) sampler used especially by phytoplankton biologists to obtain water samples for subsequent chlorophyll determinations.

The sampler contains 2 plumber's-helper valves (pure gum-rubber) and the tension between the valves is applied by gum-rubber tubing. The valves are kept in an open position by two connected chains.

A number of these bottles may be attached to the wire and tripped by messengers. Routinely, 4 to 5 samples are filtered at a time in the shipboard laboratory. After the samples are filtered they may be: (1) used for pigment analysis, (2) measured to determine their dry weight or some other biochemical parameter, (3) examined by special microtechniques, or (4) identified and individually counted on the filter. (35)

MODULATION. Modulation is the variation in the value of some parameter characterizing a periodic oscillation. The most well-known of these are amplitude modulation and frequency modulation. AM and FM radio receivers are common devices for detecting such modulations. (9)

MODULUS OF ELASTICITY. A measure of stiffness of a material. Not to be confused with Modulus of

rubber. A term applied to two different relationships between stress and strain below the Elastic Limit. Tangent Modulus of Elasticity is the slope of a Stress-Strain Diagram at a specified stress. Secant Modulus of Elasticity is the ratio of stress to strain at a specified stress or strain. It is also called the Stress-Strain Ratio. For a material exhibiting a true Proportional Limit of any significant magnitude, both moduli are equal to the slope of the straight-line portion of the Stress-Strain Diagram and are therefore equal to each

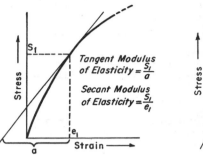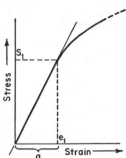

other. For a material without a definite Proportional Limit, the two moduli may differ significantly. For many materials, the Proportional Limit is nominal in that the stress-strain curve is only approximately the straight line predicted by Hooke's Law. For such materials the two moduli are different but usually the difference is of no practical significance. Depending on the type of loading represented by the Stress-Strain Diagram, Modulus of Elasticity may be known as Compressive Modulus of Elasticity (or Modulus of Elasticity in Compression). Flexural Modulus of Elasticity (or Modulus of Elasticity in Flexure), Shear Modulus of Elasticity (or Modulus of Elasticity in Shear), Tensile Modulus of Elasticity (or Modulus of Elasticity in Tension), or Torsional Modulus of Elasticity (or Modulus of Elasticity in Torsion). Shear Modulus of Elasticity is almost invariably equivalent to Torsional Modulus of Elasticity and they are more commonly known as Modulus of Rigidity. The term Modulus of Elasticity alone generally refers to Tensile Modulus of Elasticity. Moduli of Elasticity in Tension, Compression or Flexure are usually approximately equal for a given material and may be calculated from Modulus of Rigidity as follows:

E = 2G (1 + r)
where E = Modulus of Elasticity, psi
      G = Modulus of Rigidity, psi
      r = Poisson's Ratio
Below the Elastic Limit, Modulus of Elasticity may be used to predict the stress corresponding to a specified strain or vice versa. A higher Modulus of Elasticity indicates greater stiffness.

MODULUS OF RESILIENCE. The Resilience of a material subjected to a stress corresponding to its Proportional Limit.

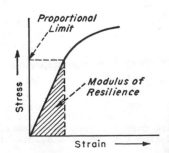

MODULUS OF RIGIDITY. Also called Shear Modulus of Elasticity, Modulus of Elasticity in Shear, Torsional Modulus of Elasticity and Modulus of Elasticity in Torsion. A measure of stiffness of a material subjected to shear loading. Usually the tangent or secant Modulus of Elasticity of a material in the Torsion Test. The relationship between Torsional Stress and Torsional Strain. The tangent modulus may also be obtained from the Torque-Twist Diagram by dividing slope of the straight-line portion by the polar moment of inertia (in.^{4}) of the specimen. For cast iron, where the specimen has been standardized, Modulus of Rigidity is calculated by multiplying slope of the Torque-Twist Diagram by 32.2. In the Gehman Torsional Test, Modulus of Rigidity is calculated as follows:

$$G = \frac{0.795 \, K \, (180 - \theta)}{bh^3 \, \mu \theta}$$

where G = Modulus of Rigidity, psi
θ = total angular deflection, deg
K = torsional constant of wire, g-cm/deg twist
b = specimen width, in.
h = specimen thickness, in.
μ = factor based on b/h
Modulus of Rigidity may also be calculated from Modulus of Elasticity in Tension, Compression or Flexure:

$$G = \frac{E}{2 \, (1 + r)}$$

where E = Modulus of Elasticity, psi
r = Poisson's Ratio
An Apparent Modulus of Rigidity is sometimes determined for plastics.

MOHO. A short, popular form of MOHOROVICIC DISCONTINUITY. (27)

MOHOLE. A word coined for use in referring to a project which comprises an attempt to drill, at sea, through the crust of the earth to the MOHOROVICIC DISCONTINUITY. (27)

MOHOROVICIC DISCONTINUITY. The level at which primary seismic waves suddenly increase to a speed of about 8.1 km./sec. This boundary is usually taken to indicate the upper limit of the mantle, separating it from the crust above, although it has also been suggested that it may only indicate a change of state and not of material. (27)

MOISTURE FILM COHESION. See APPARENT COHESION.

MOLE. In coastal terminology, a massive solid-fill structure of earth, (generally revetted), masonry, or large stone. It may serve as a breakwater or pier. (11)

MOLECULE. The smallest division of a chemical compound which retains all of its chemical properties. Molecules are composed of chemically united atoms; the simplest compounds are composed of only two atoms, other complex compounds are composed of thousands of atoms of many different kinds. (39)

MOLLUSCS (MOLLUSKS). Marine animals (usually with shells) significant as fouling forms, including mussels, jingle shells, oysters, and boring forms, such as shipworms and boring clams. (15)

MONACO OCEANOGRAPHIC INSTITUTION. The Oceanographic Institute at 195 Rue St. Jacques, Paris 5, was founded by Prince Albert I of Monaco. The Institute conducts studies on oxygen content of Mediterranean water and on the physiology of fish migration. The Institute is supported by funds obtained from the Monaco Museum, and by the Centre Nationale de la Recherche Scientifique.

MONACO OCEANOGRAPHIC MUSEUM. Founded in 1899 by Prince Albert I of Monaco, "The Prince of Oceanographers", this museum is one of the world's most elaborate and finest structures devoted to oceanography.

MONAXON. See SPICULE.

MONSOON. A name for seasonal winds (derived from Arabic mausim, a season). It was first applied to the winds over the Arabian Sea, which blow for six months from northeast and for six months from southwest, but it has been extended to similar winds in other parts of the world. Even in Europe the prevailing west to northwest winds of summer have been called the "European monsoon". The primary cause is the much greater annual variation of temperature over large land areas compared with neighboring ocean surfaces, causing an excess of pressure over the continents in winter and a deficit in summer, but other factors such as the relief features of the land have a considerable effect.

The monsoons are strongest on the southern and eastern sides of Asia, the largest land mass, but monsoons also occur on the coasts of tropical regions wherever the planetary circulation is not strong enough to inhibit them. They have been described in Spain, northern Australia, Africa except the Mediterranean, Texas and the western coasts of the United States and Chile.

In India the term is popularly applied chiefly to the southwest monsoon and, by extension, to the rains which it brings. (24)

MONSOON CURRENT. A seasonal Indian Ocean current flowing eastward and southeastward across the Arabian Sea and the Bay of Bengal. During the northern hemisphere summer this current forms the northern and northeastern part of the general clockwise oceanic circulation of the northern part of the Indian Ocean. During the northern hemisphere winter the monsoon current is replaced by a westward setting NORTH EQUATORIAL CURRENT. (17)

MONSOON FOG. An advection type of fog occurring along a coast where monsoon winds are blowing, when the air has a high specific humidity and there is a large difference in the temperature of adjacent land and sea. (17)

MOORE AND NEILL SAMPLER. This sediment coring device is essentially a protected glass tube through which water flows freely during descent and which is forced by impact into the sediment. On hauling, a simple valve mechanism closes the top of the tube and the sample may be brought to the surface. The body of the sampler is a brass cylinder into which fits a thinner metal tube holding the glass sampling tube. When the glass tube is in position it is closed by a rubber bung which comes hard against the upper surface of the main body of the sampler in the center of which is a hole. Through this hole passes a short piece of small-bore glass tube which in turn passes through the rubber bung closing the glass sampling tube. The upper end of this short glass tube is joined by a rubber to a second similar tube which fits against a simple valve. The latter consists of a flat ground rim on which lies a ground glass plate confined in a cage. As the sampler descends, water streams through the whole device and escapes through the valve, since the glass closing-disc is lifted up in its cage by the upward pressure of the water. The weight of the sampler drives the tube into the bottom and a core of material is forced into the glass sampling tube. The glass plate then drops on to the ground surface (being no longer forced up by the water) and when the device is raised gives a watertight joint. At the upper end of the device is a pillar on which is mounted a propeller which revolves freely and thereby helps to maintain a vertical descent. (35)

MOORE FREE CORER. This sediment sampler is designed to drop free from a ship to the sea floor, obtain a core and return to the surface leaving its expendable weight and casing embedded in the bottom. The free corer consists of two basic assemblies: (1) a recoverable core barrel, check valve, buoyant chamber assembly filled with gasoline, and (2) an expendable weight and casing assembly. When these two assemblies are combined, the core barrel fits loosely inside the casing. The device is dropped over the side of the ship and allowed to fall free to the bottom. A simple release-delay timer made of magnesium releases the core barrel and its buoyant float rises from the weight and casing assembly. (35)

MOORING BUOY. A buoy secured to the bottom by permanent moorings and provided with means for mooring a vessel by use of its anchor chain or mooring lines. In its usual form a mooring buoy is equipped with a ring. If it has an opening through which a mooring pendant is passed, it is called a trunk buoy. (17)

MOORING SYSTEM. A mooring system is that arrangement of components intended to locate the moored object in a body of water such that its location remains within pre-established boundaries for a specified time.

Mooring systems may be classified according to:
1. The nature of the moored object
   a. instrument skiffs
   b. instrument lines or pendants
   c. full sized vessels
   d. structures
   e. buoys
2. the location of the moored object
   a. on the surface
   b. submerged
3. the depth of water in which the mooring system is located
   a. deep ocean
      (1) very deep
      (2) intermediate depths
      (3) deep sea mounts
   b. shallow water
      (1) bays, harbors
      (2) continental shelf
      (3) shallow sea mounts
4. the type of moor
   a. taut-line
   b. slack line
5. the configuration of the moor
   a. single leg, single catenary
   b. multi-leg, single catenary per leg
   c. multi-multi-leg, single catenary per leg
   d. those above but with compound (multi-catenary) legs
   e. those above but with buoyant mooring lines.
(35)

MOTION, EQUATIONS OF. A set of hydrodynamical equations representing the applications of Newton's second law of motion to a fluid system. The total acceleration on an individual fluid particle is equated to the sum of the forces acting on the particle within the fluid.

Written for a unit mass of fluid in motion in a coordinate system fixed at a point on the earth's surface, the vector equation of motion for the atmosphere is $\frac{dv}{dt} = -2\Omega \times v - gk - \frac{1}{\rho}\nabla p + F$,

where V is the three-dimensional velocity vector, Ω the angular velocity of the earth, k a unit vector directed upward, perpendicular to the earth's surface at the point in question, ρ the density, p the pressure, g the acceleration of gravity, and F the frictional force per unit mass. When applied to the atmosphere's horizontal motion, the coriolis acceleration terms $2\Omega \times v$ are usually approximated by the two horizontal components $i2\Omega \sin \phi v$, and $-j2\Omega \sin \phi u$, where i and j are the unit vectors along the horizontal x and y axes, respectively, while u and v are the velocity components along these same axes. Here Ω is the magnitude of Ω, and ϕ is the geographical latitude. In the equation of vertical motion, the vertical component of the coriolis force is frequently neglected and it is often assumed, in addition, that $\frac{dw}{dt} = 0$, where

w is the vertical velocity. With these simplifications, the equation of vertical motion is recognized as the hydrostatic equation.

The usual form for the scalar equations of motion in Cartesian coordinates (x, y, z), x taken positive eastward, y northward, and z locally upward, is as follows:

$$\frac{\partial u}{\partial t} + u\frac{\partial u}{\partial x} + v\frac{\partial u}{\partial y} + w\frac{\partial u}{\partial z} = fv - 2\Omega\cos\phi w - \frac{1}{\rho}\frac{\partial p}{\partial x} + Fx;$$

$$\frac{\partial v}{\partial t} + u\frac{\partial v}{\partial x} + v\frac{\partial v}{\partial y} + w\frac{\partial v}{\partial z} = -fu - \frac{1}{\rho}\frac{\partial p}{\partial y} + Fy;$$

$$\frac{\partial w}{\partial t} + u\frac{\partial w}{\partial x} + v\frac{\partial w}{\partial y} + w\frac{\partial w}{\partial z} = 2\Omega\cos u - \frac{1}{\rho}\frac{\partial p}{\partial z} - g + Fz.$$

(14)

MOVING-COIL TRANSDUCER. A moving-coil transducer is a moving-conductor transducer in which the movable conductor is in the form of a coil. (1)

MRI. Meteorological Research Institute.

MSA. U. S. Navy ship designation for a Minesweeper, Auxiliary.

MSB. Maritime Safety Board.

MSC. U. S. Navy ship designation for a Minesweeper, Coastal (Nonmagnetic).

MSC(O). U. S. Navy ship designation for a Minesweeper, Coastal (Old).

MSF. U. S. Navy ship designation for a Minesweeper, Fleet (Steel Hulled).

MSI. U. S. Navy ship designation for a Minesweeper, Inshore.

MSL. Mean Sea Level.

MSO. U. S. Navy ship designation for a Minesweeper, Ocean (Nonmagnetic).

MSS. U. S. Navy ship designation for a Minesweeper, Special.

MSTS. Military Sea Transport Service.

MT. MEGATONS. The yield of a nuclear detonation equivalent to 1,000,000 tons of TNT.

MTL. Mean Tide Level.

MTS. Marine Technology Society. A professional membership, non profit society of the marine technological community. The society was founded and incorporated in 1963 and has its headquarters in Washington, D. C.

MUD. Pelagic or terrigeneous detrital material consisting of particles smaller than sand, that is, an undifferentiated sediment made up of particles mostly within the silt-clay range smaller than 0.0025 inch (0.0625 millimeter). (16)

"MUD PENETRATOR". A continuous seismic profiling system using electronically generated acoustic pulses to determine the sub-bottom structure of the sea floor in shallow water areas.

MUD SNAPPER. The Mud Snapper is a small clamshell type snapper which is about 11 inches long and weighs 3 pounds. It is attached to the bottom of a sounding lead by means of a hole drilled in the lead. The jaws are cast bronze and are actuated by a spring. The jaws are held open by engaging two trigger pins within the jaws. The Mud Snapper and sounding lead may be operated in shallow water by hand lowering or by lowering from a BATHYTHERMOGRAPH or OCEANOGRAPHIC WINCH. (35)

MULTIPLE SHOT UNDERWATER CAMERA. See UNDERWATER CAMERAS.

MULTIPLE TIDE STAFF. A succession of tide staffs on a sloping shore so placed that the vertical graduations on the several staffs will form a continuous scale referred to the same datum. (14)

MULTISPOT ARRAY. The factors which determine the directive properties of any transducer may be considered most logically by first examining the behavior of a number of discrete receiving points uniformly spaced along a straight line. Such an arrangement is known as a linear multispot array.(4)

MUSSELS. Marine, brackish, or fresh-water molluscs sometimes called clams. (15)

MUTUAL ADMITTANCE. The mutual admittance of a transducer may be defined as the quotient obtained by dividing the phasor representing the short-circuited current at one pair of terminals by the phasor representing the voltage across the second pair of terminals when the first pair is short-circuited. (4)

MUTUAL IMPEDANCE. The mutual impedance of a transducer is the quotient obtained by dividing the phasor representing the open-circuit voltage between one pair of its terminals by the phasor representing the current through the other pair. (4)

NADC. Naval Air Development Center, Johnsville, Pennsylvania.

NANNOPLANKTON. Those plankton that will pass through an ordinary net, but can be removed from the water by centrifuging or passage through filter paper. (See MARINE LIFE)

NANSEN BOTTLE. The Nansen bottle is a metal reversing water sampler with a 1.25-liter capacity. Its purpose is to bring an uncontaminated water sample from a desired depth to the surface. It is fitted with a tapered plug valve at either end and is lowered on the oceanographic wire in the open position, thus flushing itself during the lowering. When the bottle reaches any predetermined depth, a

brass messenger is dropped from the deck. The messenger serves to disconnect the top of the bottle from the wire; the bottle then reverses, making a 180° arc with the wire. The plug valves close when reversal occurs, entrapping a water sample from the desired depth, and a second messenger is released which in turn effects the reversal of a lower bottle, and so on.

To keep contamination of water samples to a minimum, Nansen bottles are constructed of brass. To provide resistance to action of salt water the exterior parts are chromium plated and the interior is silver or tin plated. The exterior is painted yellow to increase visibility in the water. Should a Nansen bottle be inadvertently lowered with the plug valves closed, the pressures encountered will crush it.

Each Nansen bottle is fitted with a frame to hold deep-sea reversing thermometers. Most frames hold 2 thermometers, although frames for 3 thermometers are sometimes used. Brass tubes in the frame, into which the thermometers are inserted, are slotted to permit easy reading of the scale. One end of each tube is perforated to permit water circulation so that the thermometers may come to temperature more rapidly. The ends of the tubes contain coil springs and rubber pads to hold the thermometers securely yet provide a certain amount of protection against shock. The thermometers are always inserted into the tubes in such a manner that the large mercury reservoir is in the end of the tube having the small perforations. (35)

NANSEN CAST. A series of NANSEN-BOTTLE water samples and associated temperature observations resulting from the release of a MESSENGER. (12)

NARTU. Naval Air Reserve Training Unit.

NAS. National Academy of Sciences.

NASA. National Aeronautics and Space Administration.

NASCAS. Committee on Atmospheric Sciences of the National Academy of Sciences - National Research Council.

NASCO. National Academy of Sciences Committee on Oceanography.

NAS/NRC. National Academy of Sciences-National Research Council.

NATO. North Atlantic Treaty Organization.

NATURAL FREQUENCY. The natural frequency of a system is the frequency of free oscillation of the system. If a system has many degrees of freedom, there will be as many natural frequencies as there are degrees of freedom. (9)

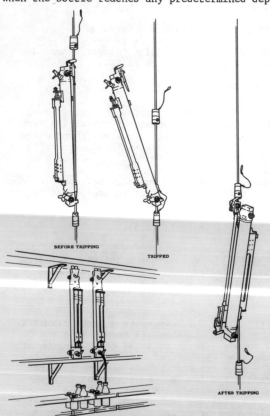

BEFORE TRIPPING

TRIPPED

AFTER TRIPPING

NANSEN BOTTLES IN RACKS

NATURAL SLOPE. See ANGLE OF REPOSE.

NAUTICAL. Of or pertaining to ships, navigation (chiefly marine), or seamen. In contrast, navigational refers to navigation only, marine refers to the sea, maritime indicates relationship or proximity to the sea, and naval refers to the Navy. (17)

NAUTICAL MILE. The distance unit in the nautical system, defined as the length of one minute of arc along any great circle on the earth's surface. Since this actual distance varies slightly with latitude, a nautical mile by international agreement is defined as 1852 meters (6076.103 feet or 1.1508 statute miles). (24)

NAVAL ENGINEERING. According to the American Society of Naval Engineers, Naval Engineering is the art and science applied in the design, construction, operation and maintenance of naval ships and their installed equipment.

NAVAIRLANT. Naval Air Forces, Atlantic.

NAVAIRPAC. Naval Air Forces, Pacific.

NAVFORJAP. Naval Forces, Japan.

NAVFORKOR. Naval Forces, Korea.

NAVIER-STOKES EQUATIONS. The equations of motion for a viscous fluid which may be written

$$\frac{dv}{dt} = -\frac{1}{\rho}\,\nabla p + F + v\nabla^2 V + \frac{1}{3}v\nabla(\nabla \cdot V),$$

where p is the pressure, ρ the density, F the total external force, V the fluid velocity, and v the kinematic viscosity. For an incompressible fluid, the term in $\nabla \cdot V$ (divergence) vanishes and the effects of viscosity then play a role analogous to that of temperature in thermal conduction and to that of density in simple diffusion.

Solutions of the Navier-Stokes equations have been obtained only in a limited number of special cases; in atmospheric motion, the effects of molecular viscosity are usually overshadowed by the action of turbulent processes and the Navier-Stokes equations have been of little direct application. The use of the concept of eddy viscosity has overcome this limitation in certain problems.

The equations are derived on the basis of certain simplifying assumptions concerning the stress tensor of the fluid; in one dimension they represent the assumption referred to as the Newtonian friction law. (24)

NAVMAR. Naval Forces, Marianas.

NAVOCEANO. U. S. Naval Oceanographic Office.

NAVOCS. Naval Officer Candidate School (USN).

NAVPHIL. Naval Forces, Philippines.

NAVSAT. Navigational Satellite.

NAVSUPORANT. Naval Support Forces, Antarctica.

NAVUWSEC. U. S. Naval Underwater Weapons Systems Engineering Center, Newport, Rhode Island.

NBS. National Bureau of Standards.

NCEL. Naval Civil Engineering Laboratory, U. S. Navy (BuDocks) Port Hueneme, California.

NCOR. National Committee on Oceanographic Research.

NEAP RANGE. See NEAP TIDES.

NEAP RISE. The height of neap high water above the plane of reference or datum of chart. (14)

NEAP TIDES OR TIDAL CURRENTS. 1. Tides of decreased range or tidal currents of decreased velocity occurring semi-monthly as the result of the moon being in quadrature. The neap range of tide is the average semidiurnal range occurring at the time of neap tides and is most conveniently computed from the harmonic constants. It is smaller than the mean range where the type of tide is either semidiurnal or mixed and is of no practical significance where the type of tide is diurnal. The average height of the high waters of the neap tide is called neap high water or high water neaps and the average height of the corresponding low waters is called neap low water or low water neaps. (14)

2. The tides occurring near the times of first and last quarter of the moon, when the range of tide tends to decrease. Tides occurring near the times of full and new moon when the range tends to increase are called SPRING TIDES. (17)

NEARSHORE CIRCULATION. The ocean circulation pattern composed of the NEARSHORE CURRENTS and COASTAL CURRENTS. (11)

NEARSHORE (ZONE). In beach terminology an indefinite zone extending seaward from the shore line somewhat beyond the breaker zone. It defines the area of NEARSHORE CURRENTS. The SHOREFACE. (11)

NECK. The narrow band of water flowing seaward through the surf. (11)

NEENAH PAPER EXPANSIMETER. A device used to evaluate the dimensional stability of paper material for the construction of maps.

NEES. Naval Engineering Experimental Station, Annapolis, Maryland.

NEGATIVE GRADIENT. Describes conditions in a layer where the temperature decreases with increasing depth. (3)

NEKTON. A division made up of all the swimming animals found in the pelagic division. (See MARINE LIFE)

NEL. Navy Electronics Laboratory, U. S. Navy, San Diego, California.

NEL DREDGE. Designed by the U. S. Navy Electronics Laboratory, this dredge is constructed of a 1/4 inch steel plate, and is 1 foot deep, 2 feet wide, and 3 feet long. The forward end is open, but the aft end has a heavy grill of 3/4 inch round steel bars. This grill is designed to retain large rock samples. When it is desired to obtain finer sized material, a screen of heavy hardware cloth is placed over the grill. A bridle consisting of 7-foot lengths of galvanized steel chain on 1/2 inch wire is attached to shackling tabs on the sides of the dredge. The bridle is attached to a swivel which is made fast to a 1/2 inch diameter lowering wire. During dredging operations, the ship is hove to as the dredge is lowered. A boom or boat crane, 1/2 inch wire, and dynamometer to indicate bottom contact are used. Towing the dredge along the bottom should be done only by ships that can operate at very slow speeds; i.e., at 2 or 3 knots. (35)

NEPHELOMETER. An instrument which measures the scattering of light by determining the amount of light emitted at right angles to the original beam direction.

Such devices are useful in studies of particles (size and amount) suspended in water. (35)

NERITIC. Shallow water marine environment. (27)

NET BUOYANCY. The weight of fluid displaced by a floating or submerged body, minus the weight of the body. Thus, an object floating has positive buoyancy; an object sunk has negative buoyancy; and an object in the hovering state has zero (or neutral) buoyancy. (27)

NET PLANKTON. Those plankton which can be removed from the water by filtration through a fine net. (See MARINE LIFE)

NEURISTOR. A microelectronic device used in a synthetic structure device used to duplicate the command transmission phenomena of the nerve cells of living animals.

    Neuristors are active one-dimensional fiber-like devices with properties such that a network of them used in information processing can perform arbitrarily complex logical functions without any additional connections or elements.

NÉVÉ. More or less loose, granular ice in transition from snow to GLACIER ICE. Névé, in being buried about 100 feet, becomes compacted and gradually changes to glacier ice. The upper layers of glaciers and SHELF ICE are usually composed on névé. (25)

NICHE. See BIOTOPE.

NIMBOSTRATUS. A dark, low, shapeless cloud layer (mean upper level below 6,500 feet) usually nearly uniform; the typical rain cloud. When precipitation falls from nimbostratus, it is in the form of continuous or intermittent rain or snow, as contrasted with the showery precipitation of cumulonimbus. (17)

NIMBUS. A characteristic rain cloud. The term is not used in the international cloud classification except as a combining term, as cumulonimbus. (17)

NIO. National Institute of Oceanography (England).

NIP. The cut made by waves in a shore line of emergence. (11)

NIRS. National Institute of Radiological Sciences.

NITROGENATION. See SATURATION.

NITROGEN NARCOSIS. Like most inert gases, nitrogen in air or N_2 - O_2 mixtures breathed at high ambient pressure can decrease mental clarity, impair judgment and produce poor muscle coordination in a manner similar to that found in alcohol intoxication. The narcotic effect is related to the PARTIAL PRESSURE of inspired nitrogen; it is therefore a function of depth of diving and the percentage of nitrogen in the respired gas. Nitrogen narcosis is not in itself harmful, but when air (80% nitrogen) is breathed (as in OPEN CIRCUIT SCUBA equipment) at depths below about 60 - 80 feet the resulting impaired judgment and incoordination begins to interfere with the diver's performance and predispose him to accidents. The narcotic effects increase progressively with depth until at about 280 - 300 feet even routine tasks become extremely difficult. As in the drinking of alcohol, personality, motivation, and training in a specific task account for the different reactions among different men.

    In orthodox deep sea diving narcosis can be reduced by substitution of helium for nitrogen. Unfortunately, on deep dives of short duration typical of underwater swimming, the use of helium in place of nitrogen increases the decompression time required to avoid BENDS. (37)

NMDL. Navy Mine Defense Laboratory, Panama City, Florida.

NOBLE METAL. An inert metal which is usually found as uncombined metal in nature. It always exhibits a relatively large electro-positive potential which is not dependent upon the existence of chemical films on its surface. Platinum, gold and silver are noble metals. (35)

NOCTILUCENT CLOUD. A luminous cirrus-like cloud occasionally seen a great distance (about 50 miles) above the surface of the earth. It is faintly visible when the sun is a short distance below the horizon, when it is illuminated by the sun. Its nature and origin are obscure. (17)

NODAL LINE. A line in an oscillating area along which there is little or no rise and fall of the tide. (14)

NODAL POINT. The no-tide point in an AMPHIDROMIC REGION. (14)

NODAL ZONE. An area at which the predominant direction of the LITTORAL TRANSPORT changes. (11)

NODC. National Oceanographic Data Center, Washington, D. C.

NODE CYCLE. Period of approximately 18.61 Julian years required for the regression of the moon's nodes to complete a circuit of 360° of longitude. It is accompanied by a corresponding cycle of changing inclination of the moon's orbit relative to the plane of the earth's equator with resulting inequalities in the rise and fall of the tide and velocity of the tidal current. (14)

NODES. In standing-wave patterns, points at which the acoustic pressure, or other measure of acoustic energy, exhibit minimum values, or are zero, are known as nodes. (4)

NOISE. Noise is any undesired sound. By extension, noise is any unwanted disturbance within a useful frequency band, such as undesired electric waves in a transmission channel or device. (1)

NOISE LEVEL. The transmission level of interference computed from its equivalent plane wave intensity is usually spoken of as the noise level. (4)

NOISE RADIALS. The brightening of all range points on a specific PPI bearing, caused by the reception of noise from the direction indicated. (7)

NOL. Naval Ordnance Laboratory, U. S. Navy, White Oak, Maryland.

NOL CORONA. Naval Ordnance Laboratory, Corona, California.

NOMAD (NAVY OCEANOGRAPHIC AND METEOROLOGICAL AUTOMATIC DEVICE). NOMAD measures and transmits weather data. This unit has been given periodic sea trials since 1957 while anchored in 2,000 fathoms in the Gulf of Mexico. It has successfully operated under extreme weather conditions and has remained on station for periods up to 6 months. The buoy is 20-feet long, 10-feet wide, and 8-feet deep. It weighs 12 tons when loaded and has 18 tons of buoyancy. The unit is moored with a polypropylene and dacron line. Wind velocity, air temperature, surface water temperature, and barometric pressure are telemetered at 5540 kc in Morse code. Each dot and dash consists of a series of high energy spikes rather than a continuous tone. This method of transmission, called pulse-recurrent FM, allows greater range (800 miles) with less overall power expenditure (200 watts average). The unit is powered with 12-volt, wet cell batteries and 5-watt wind chargers. (35)

NOMINAL BANDWIDTH. The nominal bandwidth of a filter is the difference between the nominal upper and lower cutoff frequencies. This difference may be expressed: in cycles per second, as a percentage of the pass-band center frequency, or as the difference between the upper and lower cutoffs in octaves. (9)

NOMINAL PASS-BAND CENTER FREQUENCY. The nominal pass-band center frequency is the geometric mean of the nominal cutoff frequencies. If the lower and upper cutoff frequencies of a filter are 200 and 800 cycles per second respectively, the center frequency will be 400 cycles per second. (9)

NOMSS. National Operational Meteorological Satellite System operated by the U. S. Weather Bureau. Its mission is to continuously observe worldwide weather conditions and to process, analyse and catalog the data obtained for use in weather services and research.

NONLINEAR DAMPING. Nonlinear damping is damping due to a damping force that is not proportional to velocity. (2)

NONTIDAL CURRENT. A current that is due to causes other than the tide-producing force. Classed as nontidal are the permanent ocean currents such as the GULF STREAM and the EQUATORIAL CURRENTS, which are a part of the general ocean circulation, the fresh-water discharge of a river, and temporary currents caused by the wind. These currents lack the periodicity which characterizes the tidal currents. (14)

NORC. National Oceanographic Research Center.

NORMAL ICE LIMIT. See AVERAGE LIMIT OF ICE.

NORMALIZED AMPLITUDE. The response along the axis of the major lobe plotted with a value of unity (or 0 db). (7)

NORMALLY DISPERSIVE. Waves which travel faster as their wavelengths increase. A characteristic of gravity waves.

NORMAL MODE OF VIBRATION. A normal mode of vibration is a mode of free vibration of an undamped system. In general, any composite motion of the system is analyzable into a summation of its normal modes. (2)

NORMAL WATER (COPENHAGEN WATER, STANDARD SEA WATER, EAU DE MER NORMALE). A standard sea-water preparation, the chlorinity of which lies between 19.30 and 19.50 per mille (0/00) and has been determined to within ± 0.001 per mille.
Normal water is used as a convenient comparison standard for chlorinity measurements of sea water samples by titration. It is prepared by the Hydrographical Laboratories, Copenhagen, Denmark. (24)

NORMAL WINTER. Refers to normal ice season, that is, the average ice conditions based on a number of recorded winters in a given area.

NORTH ATLANTIC CURRENT. A continuation of the GULF STREAM, originating at about 40°N latitude and 50°W longitude, comprising all the easterly and northerly currents of the North Atlantic originating in the region east of the Grand Banks. The branches of the North Atlantic current are often masked by shallow and variable wind-driven surface movements so that they are sometimes called the North Atlantic drift.
Along the mid-Atlantic ridge the North Atlantic current is divided into two major branches; the northern branch flows between latitudes 50°N and 52°N separated from the Labrador current by the cold wall. The other branch flows approximately in latitude 45°N and carries undiluted Gulf Stream water. Of these branches the northern continues mainly toward the east-northeast and divides, part flowing into the Norwegian Sea and part turning toward the north and northwest eventually giving rise to the IRMINGER CURRENT. (24)

NORTH CAPE CURRENT. An Arctic Ocean current flowing northeastward and eastward around northern Norway, and curving into the Barents Sea. The North Cape current is the continuation of the northeastern branch of the NORWEGIAN CURRENT. (17)

NORTHEAST DRIFT CURRENT. A North Atlantic Ocean current flowing northeastward toward the Norwegian Sea, gradually widening and, south of Iceland, branching and continuing as the IRMINGER CURRENT and the NORWEGIAN CURRENT. The northeast drift current is the northern branch of the NORTH ATLANTIC CURRENT. (17)

NORTH EQUATORIAL CURRENT. In the Atlantic the north Equatorial current originates to the northward of the Cape Verde Islands and flows almost due west at an average speed of about 0.7 knots. In the western part of the Atlantic Ocean the north Equatorial current joins the branch of the SOUTH EQUATORIAL CURRENT which has crossed the Equator and turns northward. It terminates in the current through the Yucatan Channel and the ANTILLES CURRENT. The continuation of these currents represents the beginning of the GULF STREAM system which dominates the circulation of a great part of the North Atlantic Ocean. In the Pacific the beginning of the north Equatorial current is found where the waters of the EQUATORIAL COUNTER-CURRENT turns to the north off Central America. The volume transport is periodically increased along its path by water added from the north by such currents as the CALIFORNIA CURRENT. At about 160 degrees West longitude the volume transport above a depth of 1000 m is about 45 million m^3/sec, and this value is approximately equal to the maximum transport of the corresponding current in the Atlantic Ocean. (12, 13)

NORTH PACIFIC CURRENT. A Pacific Ocean current flowing eastward and southeastward from a point between the Aleutian and Hawaiian Islands toward the west coast of North America, gradually widening and the greater part curving southward, a small part nearest the California coast merging with the southern branch of the ALEUTIAN CURRENT to continue southeastward as the CALIFORNIA CURRENT. The North Pacific current is the continuation of the KUROSHIO, and forms the northern and northeastern part of the general clockwise oceanic circulation of the North Pacific Ocean. (17)

NORWEGIAN CURRENT. Part of the northern branch of the NORTH ATLANTIC CURRENT, which flows northward along the coast of Norway. The water of the Norwegian current eventually enters the Arctic Ocean, from which the main discharge is via the EAST GREEN-LAND CURRENT. (24)

NORWESTLANT. Northwest Atlantic (Project).

NOTOCHORD. The elastic cellular axial support formed ventral to the nerve cord in the early embryo of all chordates; either surrounded or supplanted by the vertebrae in most vertebrates. (19)

NOTS. Naval Ordnance Test Station, U. S. Navy, China Lake, California.

NP. Neap Range. The mean semidiurnal range of tide when NEAP TIDES are occurring; the mean difference in height between neap high water and neap low water. Sometimes called MEAN NEAP RANGE. (17)

NPFSC. North Pacific Fur Seal Commission.

NRC. National Research Council.

NRL. Naval Research Laboratory.

NSF. National Science Foundation.

NSIA. National Security Industrial Association.

NUCLEAR RESONANCE MAGNETOMETER. With this instrument the measurement of the earth's magnetic field depends on the magnetic moment of the atom. Hydrogen atoms are generally used, and these can be in a compound such as water. Each hydrogen atom can be looked upon as a tiny electromagnet whose strength and direction are determined by the revolution of the electron of the atom about its nucleus. In a magnetic field, atoms of hydrogen have a tendency to align themselves in opposition to the field. If the direction of the field is suddenly changed, there will be a moment pulling the atoms toward the new direction. But each atom is a midget gyroscope, and instead of shifting directly to the new field direction, it will precess about this direction. The frequency of this precession will be a function only of the strength of the magnetic field. To measure the strength of the earth's magnetic field, a bottle of water is subjected to a strong magnetic field at right angles to the earth's field. The voltage induced in a coil of wire wrapped around the bottle is observed when the auxiliary field is suddenly removed. This voltage will have a frequency of alternation of the order of 2,000 cycles per sec, its exact value depending on the strength of the earth's field. The time of 2,000 cycles of this voltage can be measured using a 100-kc oscillator and a high-speed counter, giving an accuracy of measurement of 1 part in 10^5, or of the order of $\pm$ 1/2 gamma. (35)

NUMERICAL FORECASTING (MATHEMATICAL FORECASTING, DYNAMIC FORECASTING, PHYSICAL FORECASTING, NUMERICAL WEATHER PREDICTION.) The forecasting of the behavior of atmospheric disturbances by the numerical solution of the governing fundamental equations of hydrodynamics, subject to observed initial conditions. When applied to the cyclonic-scale atmospheric disturbances in the form of a dynamical model, these solutions form a method of forecasting the behavior of the migratory pressure systems of middle latitude. Numerical forecasting is usually performed with the aid of high-speed computing devices. (24)

NUMERICAL WEATHER PREDICTION. (Abbreviated NWP.) Same as NUMERICAL FORECASTING. (24)

NUNATAK. An island of exposed rock standing above a surrounding ice sheet. (17)

NUN BUOY. A buoy the above water part of which is in the shape of a cone or a truncated cone. (17)

NUOS. Naval Underwater Ordnance Station.

(US)NUSL. Navy Underwater Sound Laboratory.

NWL. Naval Weapons Laboratory, Naval Facility, Dahlgren, Virginia.

NWPFC. Northwest Pacific Fisheries Commission.

NWRC. National Weather Records Center.

O

OAS. Organization of American States.

OBLIGATE AEROBES. Bacteria which use free oxygen in respiration. (13)

OBLIGATE ANAEROBES. Bacteria which function in the total absence of free oxygen. (13)

OCAS. Organization of Central American States.

OCEAN CURRENT. 1. A movement of ocean water characterized by regularity, either of a cyclic nature, or more commonly as a continuous stream flowing along a definable path.
   Three general classes, by cause, may be distinguished: (a) currents related to sea water density gradients, comprising the various types of gradient current; (b) wind-driven currents, which are those directly produced by the stress exerted by the wind upon the ocean surface; (c) currents produced by long-wave motions. The latter are principally tidal currents, but may include currents associated with INTERNAL WAVES, TSUNAMIS, and SEICHES. The major ocean currents are of continuous, stream-flow character, and are of first-order importance in the maintenance of the earth's thermodynamic balance. (24)
   2. A current constituting part of the general oceanic circulation. A periodic current is one having a velocity which changes cyclically at somewhat regular intervals, as a tidal current. A seasonal current is one which has large changes in velocity due to seasonal winds. A permanent current is one which continues with relatively little periodic or seasonal change. A DRIFT CURRENT is any broad, shallow, slow-moving ocean current. A STREAM CURRENT is a relatively narrow, deep, fast-moving ocean current. (17)

OCEAN FLOOR. See FLOOR.

"OCEANEERING". A term which has been used in the technical literature to identify OCEAN ENGINEERING.

OCEAN ENGINEERING. Ocean Engineering is the engineering concerned with the development of new equipment concepts and the methodical improvement of techniques which enable man to successfully operate beneath the surface of the ocean in order to develop and exploit its many resources.

OCEANIC. Of or pertaining to the ocean. (17)

OCEANIC ANTICYCLONE. See SUBTROPICAL HIGH.

OCEANIC HIGH. See SUBTROPICAL HIGH.

OCEANICITY (OCEANITY). The degree to which a point on the earth's surface is in all respects subject to the influence of the sea; the opposite of continentality. Oceanicity usually refers to climate and its effects. One measure for this characteristic is the ratio of the frequencies of maritime to continental types of air mass. (24)

OCEANITY. See OCEANICITY.

OCEANOGRAPHIC. Of or pertaining to oceanography, or knowledge of the oceans. (17)

OCEANOGRAPHIC DREDGES. Apparatus used aboard ships to bring up quantity samples of the ocean bottom deposits and sediments. See also NEL DREDGE. (35)

OCEANOGRAPHIC SURVEY. A study or examination of conditions in the ocean or any part of it, with reference to animal or plant life, chemical elements present, temperature gradients, etc. Also called marine survey. (17)

OCEANOGRAPHY. The application of the sciences to the phenomena of the oceans. It includes a study of their forms; physical, chemical, and biological features; and phenomena. Thus, it embraces the widely separated fields of geography, geology, chemistry, physics, and biology. Many subdivisions of these sciences, such as sedimentation, ecology (biological relationship between organisms and their environment), bacteriology, biochemistry, hydrodynamics, acoustics, and optics, have been extensively studied in the oceans. (12)

OCEAN (SEA). 1. The intercommunicating body of salt water occupying the depressions of the earth's surface.

　　　　2. One of the major primary subdivisions of the above, bounded by continents, the equator, and other imaginary lines. (24)

OCEAN STATION. As defined by the International Civil Aviation Organization. a specifically located area of ocean surface, roughly square and 200 nautical miles on a side. An ocean station vessel on patrol is said to be "on station" when it is within the perimeter of the area. (24)

OCEAN STATION VESSEL. (OCEAN WEATHER SHIP, WEATHER PATROL SHIP, WEATHER SHIP.) An ocean-going vessel assigned to patrol an OCEAN STATION.

These ships are specially equipped to take comprehensive meteorological observations of conditions both at the surface and aloft. The United States vessels are provided by the U. S. Coast Guard, and the meteorological personnel and equipment are provided by the U. S. Weather Bureau. (24)

OCEAN WATER. Water having the physical-chemical characteristics of the open sea and where continental influences are at a minimum. (15)

OCEAN WEATHER SHIP. See OCEAN STATION VESSEL.

OCEAN WEATHER STATION. As defined by the World Meteorological Organization, a specific maritime location occupied by a ship equipped and staffed to observe weather and sea conditions and report the observations by international exchange. (24)

OCELLUS. A small simple eye as on many invertebrates. (19)

OCTAVE. A band ratio having the value $f_b/f_z = 2$ is the ratio long known to musicians as the octave. Physicists and acoustical engineers have now adopted this term. (4)

OECD. Organization for Economic Co-operation and Development.

OEEC. Organization for European Economic Co-operation.

OFFSHORE. 1. In beach terminology, the comparatively flat zone of variable width, extending from the breaker zone to the seaward edge of the CONTINENTAL SHELF.

　　　　2. A direction seaward from the SHORE. (11)

OFFSHORE BARRIER. See BARRIER BEACH.

OFFSHORE CURRENT. 1. Any current in the OFFSHORE zone.

　　　　　　2. Any current flowing away from SHORE. (11)

OFFSHORE WIND. A wind blowing seaward from the land in the coastal area. (11)

OHM'S LAW. A fundamental law of electricity. It expresses the definite relationship existing between the voltage E, the current I, and the resistance R; E = IR. (36)

OIC. Oceanographic Instrumentation Center.

OMEGA. A long range (hyperbolic) navigation system.
Originally Omega was developed for the use of submerged submarines, giving world wide coverage with 6 - 10 ground stations.
The Omega and RADUX systems are identical in principle and both are quite similar to DELRAC. Both Omega and Radux use pulsed signals on the 10 kc band. These and Delrac appear to be the most practical of all long range navigational systems. Omega can provide navigational control of submarines, surface ships and aircraft simultaneously. (29)

OMM. Organization Meteorologique Mondiale.

OMNIDIRECTIONAL HYDROPHONE. An omnidirectional hydrophone is a hydrophone whose response is essentially independent of angle of arrival of the incident sound wave. (1)

ONE-PING PROBABILITY. The probability of detection by using a single ping. (8)

ONI. Office of Naval Intelligence.

ONR. Office of Naval Research.

O/O. Office of Oceanography (UNESCO).

OOP. Oceanographic Observations of the Pacific.

OOZE. An unconsolidated deposit composed largely of the shells and undissolved remains of FORAMINIFERA, DIATOMS and other marine life; for example, diatom ooze, foraminiferal ooze, etc. (27)

OPEN CIRCUIT SCUBA. Open circuit equipment is in general the simplest type of SCUBA. Air or a preset mixture of oxygen and nitrogen is stored under high pressure (about 2000 psi) in cylinders. This high pressure gas is reduced to an intermediate pressure (about 55 to 85 psi) by a first stage reduction valve. The gas is obtained by the swimmer on inspiration through a second demand-type reduction valve which is actuated by respiratory action. The pressure of gas delivered to the swimmer is about equal to the ambient hydrostatic pressure. In some equipments (Aqualung and Northill) the two stages of pressure reduction are accomplished within the same valve casing. Other units (Scott, Emerson, Swedish) have the two valves in different locations. All exhaled gas is discharged as an intermittent stream of bubbles into the water and the utilization of gas is therefore equal to the mass exhaled. (37)

OPEN COAST. A coast that is not sheltered from the sea. (17)

OPEN SEA. 1. That part of the ocean not enclosed by headlands, within narrow straits, etc.
　　　　2. That part of the ocean outside the territorial jurisdiction of any country. The opposite is closed sea. (17)

OPERATING RANGE. As applied to reversible transducer, the operating range is the frequency range over which the transducer is operable; that is, the range over which it will produce a useable acoustic signal in the water as a transmitter, or a useable electrical signal as a listening device. Instruments are generally operable over a range that is considerably wider than the range in which they may be calibrated or may be reciprocal. They are not necessarily stable over the entire operating range. In addition, directivity patterns may be poor and frequency response rough beyond the reciprocity range. (1)

OPERCULUM. The plate covering the gills of a bony fish; also, the plate serving to cover the opening of some snail shells. (19)

OPPOSING WIND. In wave forecasting, a wind blowing in the opposite direction to that in which the waves are travelling. (11)

OPTICAL PROCESSING. Light, including visible and infrared, has a relatively high frequency, which means that larger bandwidths and higher rates are potentially available for handling data processing information. Performing logical functions with electronic devices requires the moving of electrons, and here one must deal with, and is limited by, the inductance and capacitance of transmission lines and devices. By using light and treating it as a wave (interference effects) or as a particle quantum interaction) new classes of circuits appear possible which are not charge limited. Considerably higher "fan outs" in the order of 100 to 1000 have been achieved in optical systems at millisecond speeds.

ORANGE PEEL BUCKET SAMPLER. This sampler is used primarily to obtain bottom samples in shallow water and several sizes are available. The size considered here weighs 45 pounds and holds about 300 cubic inches of sediment. A small hook,attached to the end of the lowering wire,supports the sampler as it is lowered and also holds the jaws (four curved triangular blades which form a hemisphere when closed) in the open position. When contact with the bottom is made the sampler jaws sink into the sediment and the wire tension is released, allowing the hook to swing free of the sampler. Upon hoisting, the wire takes a strain on the closing line which is also attached to a handle which activates a ratchet chain and sheave that close the jaws. The closing line supports the sampler as it is being hoisted. To prevent washing out of the sample from the top, a canvas cover is frequently used. (35)

ORBIT. In water waves, the path of a water particle affected by the wave motion. In deep water waves the orbit is nearly circular and in shallow water waves the orbit is nearly elliptical. In general, the orbits are slightly open in the direction of wave motion giving rise to MASS TRANSPORT. (11)

ORBITAL CURRENT. The flow of water accompanying the orbital movement of the water particles in a wave. Not to be confused with wave-generated LITTORAL CURRENTS. (11)

ORBITAL MOTION. In hydrodynamics, the motion of a fluid particle induced by the passage of a progressive GRAVITY WAVE. When the wave height is small and the fluid depth is great, the orbit is a circle whose radius decreases exponentially with depth. In shallow fluid the orbit is an ellipse, which degenerates into a horizontal line at the bottom boundary of the fluid. (12)

ORDA. Oceanographic Research for Defense Application.

ORDER OF MAGNITUDE (A FACTOR OF 10). Two quantities of the same kind which differ by less than a factor of 10 are said to be of the same order of magnitude. 'Order of magnitude' is used loosely

by many writers to mean a pronounced difference in quantity but with the difference much less or much more than a factor of 10. (31)

ORDINARY TIDES. 1. This expression is not used in a technical sense by the Coast and Geodetic Survey, but the word "ordinary" when applied to tides, may be taken as the equivalent of the word "mean". Thus, "ordinary high water line" may be assumed to be the same as "mean high water line."

2. Waves having periods of 12 hours to 24 hours. (14)

OROGENY. An EPOCH of mountain building, usually associated with the formation of a fold mountain range; for example, the Caledonian orogeny which built mountains in north-west Britain and Scandinavia from a geosynclinal environment, during the Palaeozoic era. (27)

OROGRAPHY. A branch of physical geography which treats with mountains.

ORSA. Operations Research Society of America.

ORSTOM. Office de la Recherche Scientifique et Technique d'outre Mer.

ORTHOGONAL. On a refraction diagram, a line drawn perpendicular to the wave crests. (11)

OS. OCEAN STATION.

OSCILLATION. Oscillation is the variation, usually with time, of the magnitude of a quantity with respect to a specified reference when the magnitude is alternately greater and smaller than the reference. (2)

OSCILLATORY WAVE. A wave in which each individual particle oscillates about a point with little or no permanent change in position. The term is commonly applied to progressive oscillatory waves in which only the form advances, the individual particles moving in closed orbits. Distinguished from a WAVE OF TRANSLATION. (11)

OSCILLOSCOPE. An instrument for showing visually graphical representations of the waveforms encountered in electrical circuits. (36)

OST. Office of Science and Technology.

OSV. Ocean Station Vessel.

OSW. Office of Saline Water (Department of Interior).

OTITIS EXTERNA. An infection of the external ear canal. A frequent physical disorder incurred in SCUBA diving. (37)

OUTFALL. 1. The vent of a river, drain, etc.
2. A structure extending into a body of water for the purpose of discharging sewage, storm runoff, or cooling water. (11)

OUTPUT CURRENT. The output current of a transducer connected to a given source is the rms current which would be measured at its load terminals if they were short-circuited. (4)

OUTPUT IMPEDANCE. The output impedance of a transducer connected to a given source is the impedance which would be measured at its load terminals if they were not connected to a load and if the source voltage of the source were zero. (4)

OUTPUT POWER. The output power of a transducer connected to a given source is the available power at its load terminals. (4)

OUTPUT VOLTAGE. The output voltage of a transducer

connected to a given source is the rms voltage which would be measured at its load terminals if they were open-circuited. (4)

OVERFALLS. Breaking waves caused by a conflict of currents or by the wind moving against the current. (14)

OVERLOAD LEVEL. The overload level of a component or system is that level at which operation ceases to be satisfactory as a result of signal distortion, overheating, etc. In an acoustical system, sound pressure level is to be understood, unless otherwise specified. (2)

OVERTIDE. A harmonic tidal constituent with a speed that is an exact multiple of the speed of one of the fundamental constituents derived from the development of the tide-producing force. The presence of overtides is usually attributed to shallow-water conditions. The overtides usually considered in tidal work are the harmonics of the principal lunar and solar semidiurnal constituents M_2 and S_2 and are designated by the symbols M_4, M_6, M_8, S_4, S_6, etc. The magnitudes of these harmonics relative to those of the fundamental constituents are usually greater in the tidal current than in the tide. (14)

OVERTURN (CONVECTIVE OVERTURN). The renewal of bottom water that occurs annually in lakes and ponds in regions wherever winter temperatures are cold enough. As the surface waters are cooled in the autumn and early winter, they become denser and therefore sink, until the whole body of water is at $4^{\circ}C$, the temperature of maximum density. Further cooling is restricted to the surface layers, since both ice and water colder than $4^{\circ}C$ are less dense than the underlying waters at $4^{\circ}C$.
This phenomenon does not take place over most areas in the ocean because of the salinity stratification, and usually the resulting brine is dense enough to sink to the bottom only in the extreme polar regions, where extensive freezing occurs. (12)

OVERWASH. That portion of the uprush that carries over the crest of a BERM or of a structure. (11)

OVIPAROUS. In reproduction, animals are either oviparous or viviparous. The oviparous forms deposit eggs that develop outside the mother's body, while in the VIVIPAROUS forms the young are nourished by the mother and are born alive in a post-embryonic state. An intermediate condition exists in the OVOVIVIPAROUS forms, where the eggs are incubated and hatched within the body, as in certain sharks, perch, and blennies. The term larviparous is sometimes used to indicate that larval stages are born. An embryo derives its nourishment from the yolk of the egg or directly from the mother, whereas typically a larva is morphologically adapted with mouth and digestive tract for the purpose of seeking its own nourishment. (13)

OVOVIVIPAROUS. See OVIPAROUS.

OWN-SHIP'S NOISE. In many cases the limiting noise registered by a sonar receiver is that set up by the vessel itself or as a result of its motion. This has come to be known as own-ship's noise. (4) (Also known as self noise.)

OXYGEN CONCENTRATION CELL. A cell established on a metal surface caused by a difference in oxygen concentration in the solution at one point as compared to another. (35)

OXYGEN DEFICIENCY. See ANOXIA.

OXYGEN TOXICITY. Pure oxygen cannot be breathed indefinitely at pressures greater than atmospheric. Following a safe period which becomes shorter as diving depth increases, symptoms of oxygen toxicity occur. These include involuntary fine twitches around the eyes and mouth that later extend to include larger muscle groups including the diaphragm, causing abruptness of inspiration. Anxiety, and apprehension may occur and some times loss of lateral visual fields and ringing in ears. These preliminary symptoms are followed by general convulsions and unconsciousness. These can be avoided by not exceeding the safe depth-time relationships for pure oxygen breathing. The onset of oxygen poisoning can usually be arrested by inhaling a few breaths of a gas mixture with a high proportion of nitrogen or other inert gas. Permanent after effects from oxygen poisoning do not appear to occur, even after repeated exposures. This of course does not alter the risk for the underwater swimmer at depths great enough to produce toxicity.
The basic physiological mechanism of oxygen poisoning and the effects of oxygen at depths from 15 to 60 feet, and greater, are subjects that require much more study, since oxygen poisoning is the major factor limiting diving depth and duration with mixed gas as well as pure oxygen apparatus. (37)

OYASHIO CURRENT. A North Pacific Ocean current flowing southwestward from the Bering Sea, along the southeast coast of Siberia and the Kuril Islands, and then curving southward and eastward, the greater part then joining the NORTH PACIFIC CURRENT, and the remaining northern part continuing eastward to feed the ALEUTIAN CURRENT. The Oyashio is formed by the merging of those parts of the Aleutian and ALASKA CURRENTS that enter the Bering Sea from the south and flow northward and northwestward to join with water flowing southward through Bering Strait. (17)

P

PACK ICE. Any large area of floating ice which has been driven closely together. (15)

PAIGH. Pan American Institute of Geography and History.
Headquarters: Mexico City.
Established in 1928 in Havana by a resolution adopted at the 5th Conference of American States. In 1903 recommendations were made for the creation of a Pan-American organization dealing with Geography and Cartography and the establishment of an Inter-American Institute of Oceanography. The present organization is an outgrowth of this recommendation.
Activities: Principal scientific programs of the Institute are conducted by three commissions on cartography, geography and history. PAIGH has established special committees on Oceanography, the International Geophysical Year, Volcanology, etc.

PALEOCRYSTIC ICE. PRESSURE ICE, usually more than ten years old, well weathered, and irregularly heaped and tumbled. The type locality is the Lincoln Sea. (25)

PAN. See PANCAKE ICE.

PANCAKE ICE (PLATE ICE). Circular pieces of newly-formed ice from about 1 foot to 6 feet in diameter, with raised rims. The shape is the result of almost constant collision among the various pieces. An individual piece of pancake ice is called a pan. Sometimes called LILLYPAD ICE when the individual pieces are not more than about 18 inches in diameter. Pancakes frozen together are called compound pancake ice. (17)

PARALLEL. A circle on the surface of the earth, parallel to the plane of the equator and connecting all points of equal latitude, or a circle parallel to the primary great circle of a sphere or spheroid; also a closed curve approximating such a circle. An astronomical parallel is a line connecting points having the same astronomical latitude. A geodetic parallel is a line connecting points of equal geodetic latitude. Geodetic and sometimes astronomical parallels are also called geographic parallels. Geodetic parallels are shown on charts. A standard parallel is one along which the scale of a chart is as stated. A fictitious, grid, transverse or inverse, or oblique equator, respectively. A magnetic parallel is a line connecting points of equal magnetic dip. Also called parallel of latitude, circle of longitude. (17)

PARALLEL OF LATITUDE. 1. A circle (or approximation of a circle) on the surface of the earth, parallel to the equator, and connecting points of equal latitude. Also called parallel.

2. A circle of the celestial sphere, parallel to the ecliptic, and connecting points of equal celestial latitude. Also called circle of longitude. (17)

PARALOC. This patented (Bissett-Berman) system is a precise telemetry subcarrier phase-shift oscillator, whose frequency is modulated by the change in a sensed variable. This frequency is controlled by the ratio of the output voltage to the input voltage of a 4-terminal network sensor "bridge". Its high sensitivity makes possible the amplification and telemetering of signals from low-output devices such as strain gages, resistance thermometers, displacement transducers, conductivity sensors, etc. The frequency output can be made to deviate $\pm$ 30% for a $\pm1/2$% change in the "error" signal with very stable operation. The sum (E_r) of the quadrature voltage (E_q) and the sensor voltage (E_o) are applied to the input amplifier (A_1), thus forming a complete loop, which will oscillate

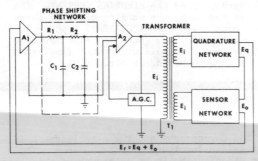

at a frequency where the sum of phase shift between (E_1) and the resultant (E_r) of the quadrature network and the sensor network and the phase shift between the input and the outputs of the phase-shifting network totals 180°. Linearity is in the order ±0.01%; frequency stability is ±0.02% for temperature changes of $\pm30°$ and supply voltage changes of ±20%; sensitivity adjustments are made in the quadrature network and zero adjustments in the sensor network with complete interdependency.
The Paraloc oscillator is used in sea water salinity sensors, temperature sensors, and pressure sensors installed on the ASWEPS "fish" and the Office of Naval Research long range telemetering buoy. (35)

PARAMETRONS. Oscillatory devices whose phase can be used to store and manipulate information.

PARAPET. A low wall built along the edge of a structure as on a SEAWALL or QUAY. (11)

PARASITIC. Growing on or in living tissues of plants or animals, obtaining nourishment at the expense of the host. (18)

PARTIAL NODE. A partial node is the point, line or surface in a standing wave system where some characteristic of the wave field has a minimum amplitude differing from zero. (2)

PARTIAL PRESSURE. See DALTON'S LAW.

PARTICLE ACCELERATOR. Modern machines which accelerate subatomic particles to such great velocities that as these particles strike atoms, the nucleus of the atom may be altered or "split". Among these now in use are the cyclotron, the linear accelerator, the Van de Graaff generator, Proton Synchrotron, and the Bevatron. (39)

PARTICLE VELOCITY. In ocean wave studies, the instantaneous velocity of a water particle undergoes ORBITAL MOTION. It has the scalar value

$$\frac{\pi}{T} He^{-2\pi z/L}$$

where T is the wave period, H the wave height, z the depth below still-water level, and L the wave length.
At the crest, its direction is the same as the direction of progress of the wave, and at the trough it is in the opposite direction. (12)

PASS. In hydrographic usage a navigable channel, through a BAR, REEF, or SHOAL, or between closely adjacent islands. (11)

PASSIVE SONAR. Passive sonar is the method or equipment by which information concerning a distant object is obtained by evaluation of sound generated by the object. (1)

PASSIVE STATE (Corrosion). State of a metal active in the EMF series, or an alloy composed of such metals, when it exhibits an appreciably greater resistance to corrosion and behaves similarly to those having a noble potential in a galvanic series. Chromium and stainless steel are passive in certain environments. (35)

PASSIVE TRANSDUCER. A transducer connecting a given source and a given load, and developing a load power which is independent of sources of energy controlled by the given source, is known as a passive transducer. (4)

PATENT LOG. See TAFFRAIL LOG.

PC. U. S. Navy ship designation for a Sub Chaser.

PCCECMRP. Permanent Commission of the Convention on the Exploitation and Conservation of the Maritime Resources of the Pacific.

PCE. U. S. Navy ship designation for an Escort Sub Chaser.

PCER. U. S. Navy ship designation for a Rescue Escort.

PCH. U. S. Navy ship designation for a Sub Chaser, Hydrofoil.

PCIFC. Permanent Commission of the International Fisheries Convention.

PCS. U. S. Navy ship designation for a Sub Chaser.

PD. Pulse Doppler.

PDM. Pulse Duration Modulation.

PDR. Precision Depth Recorder.

PEAK. A SEAMOUNT rising more than 500 fathoms from the sea floor and having a pointed or round top. (26)

PEAK LEVEL. The peak level is the maximum instantaneous level that occurs during a specified time interval. In acoustics, peak sound pressure level is to be understood, unless some other kind of level is specified. (2)

PEAK SOUND PRESSURE. The peak sound pressure for any specified time interval is the maximum absolute value of the instantaneous sound pressure in that interval. (2)

PEAK-TO-PEAK VALUE. The peak-to-peak value of an oscillating quantity is the algebraic difference between the extremes of the quantity. (2)

PEBBLES. Small, usually rounded rock fragments ranging in size from 0.16 to 2.59 (4 to 64 millimeters) in diameter. Pebbles are classed as gravel on bottom sediment charts.

PELAGIC. Pertaining to the open sea, when used in connection with sediment type; it also refers to fish which do not spend their whole life on the bottom, although they may remain fairly near the shore, such as herrings or sardines. (27)

PELAGIC DIVISION. A primary division of the sea which includes the whole mass of water. The division is made up of the NERITIC PROVINCE which includes that water shallower than 200 meters, and the OCEANIC PROVINCE which includes that water deeper than 200 meters.

PELAGIC ORGANISMS. Pertaining to all organisms inhabiting the open sea, except bottom dwellers. (15)

PELORUS. An instrument used on a boat in connection with a log line to obtain the direction of current. In its simplest form, it is a disk about 8 inches in diameter and graduated clockwise for every 5° or 10°. It is mounted rigidly on the boat, usually with the 0° mark forward and the diameter through this mark parallel with the keel of the boat. (14)

PENINSULA. An elongated portion of land nearly surrounded by water, and connected to a larger body of land. (11)

PERIGEAN TIDES OR TIDAL CURRENTS. Tides of increased range or tidal currents of increased velocity occurring monthly as the result of the moon being in perigee or nearest the earth. The perigean range of tide is the average semidiurnal range occurring at the time of perigean tides and is most conveniently computed from the harmonic constants. It is larger than the mean range where the type of tide is either semidiurnal or mixed, and is of no practical significance where the type of tide is diurnal. (14)

PERIOD. Interval required for the completion of a recurring event, such as the revolution of a celestial body, or the time between two consecutive like phases of the tide or current. A period may be expressed in angular measure and is then taken as 360°. The word is also used to express any specified duration of time. (14)

PERIOD. See PRIMITIVE PERIOD.

PERIODIC CURRENT. An oscillating current the values of which recur at somewhat regular intervals. (17)

PERIODIC CURRENT. See OCEAN CURRENT.

PERMANENT CURRENT. A current that runs continuously independent of the tides and temporary cause. Permanent currents include the fresh water discharge of a river and the currents that form the general circulatory systems of the oceans. (14)

PERMANENT CURRENT. See OCEAN CURRENT.

PERMANENT ICE FOOT. An ICE FOOT that does not melt completely during the summer months. (25)

PERMANENT PLANKTON. See MARINE LIFE.

PERMANENT THERMOCLINE. Frequently used in acoustics to describe the decrease in temperature which always occurs at great depths. (3)

PERMEABILITY. The property of a material which permits appreciable movement of water through it when saturated and actuated by hydrostatic pressure. (27)

PERTROGRAPHY. The description and systematic classification of rocks. (11)

PERU CURRENT (HUMBOLDT CURRENT). The cold ocean current flowing north along the coasts of Chile and Peru. It is one of the swiftest of ocean currents. The Peru current originates where part of the water that flows toward the east across the subantarctic Pacific Ocean is deflected toward the north as it approaches South America. The northern limit of the current can be placed a little south of the equator, where the flow turns toward the west, joining the SOUTH EQUATORIAL CURRENT.
The southern portion of the Peru current is sometimes called the CHILE CURRENT. (24)

PETERSEN GRAB. In the Petersen (or van Veen) type of grab two semicircular buckets of varying sizes are hinged along a central axis. The buckets are held apart for lowering to the bottom by some form of catch. On striking the bottom this is released so that on hoisting the buckets move round on their axis, take a bite out of the sediment, and come together to form a closed container. With this configuration the rate at which the grab hits the bottom affects the bite and when the ship is drifting a poor sample may be obtained if the grab does not hit the bottom vertically. (35)

PETERSEN (GRAB)

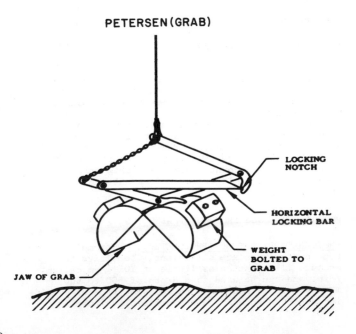

LOCKING NOTCH

HORIZONTAL LOCKING BAR

WEIGHT BOLTED TO GRAB

JAW OF GRAB

PETTERSSON CURRENT METER. A meter designed by Prof. O. Pettersson and Dr. Hans Pettersson to give a photographic record of both velocity and direction of the current. A detailed description by Dr. Hans Pettersson is contained in the Quarterly Journal of the Royal Meteorological Society (London) vol. XLI, No. 173, January 1915. There is also a description of the meter in Coast and Geodetic Survey Special Publication No. 124, Instructions for Tidal Current Surveys. (14)

PF. U. S. Navy ship designation for a Patrol Escort.

PGM. U. S. Navy designation for a Motor Gunboat.

PGR. Precision Graphic Recorder.

pH. The acidity of a solution is determined by the concentration of hydrogen ions in it. The pH of a solution is a term used to express the effective hydrogen ion concentration. It ranges from pH = 1 to pH = 14. pH = 7 indicates a neutral solution. Values lower than 7 indicate an acid condition. The stronger the acidity the lower the pH. Conversely, values of pH above 7 indicate an alkaline condition, the higher the pH the more alkaline the solution. Fresh waters usually exhibit a pH of about 6 to 7. Sea water ranges from pH = 7.8 to 8.4 with an average of about 8.2. (35)

PHANTOM BOTTOM. A false bottom indicated by an echo sounder, some distance above the actual bottom. Such an indication, quite common in the deeper parts of the ocean, is due to large quantities of small organisms. (17)

PHASE SPEED (WAVE SPEED, PHASE VELOCITY, WAVE VELOCITY, WAVE CELERITY). The speed of propagation of a point of constant phase (or phase angle) of a simple harmonic wave component. Thus, the component $\sin (2\pi/\lambda)(x - ct)$ represents a wave of length λ traveling in the positive x-direction with phase speed c. This concept is to be distinguished from signal velocity, GROUP VELOCITY, and the velocity of fluid parcels.

In oceanography, the terms wave velocity or wave celerity are used more commonly than "phase speed". (12)

PHASE VELOCITY. See PHASE SPEED.

PHIBLANT. Amphibious Forces, Atlantic (USN).

PHIBPAC. Amphibious Forces, Pacific (USN).

PHLEGER CORER. Designed to obtain cores up to about 4 feet in length, the Phleger corer is utilized where only the upper layers of the sea bottom are to be analyzed. Coring tubes 12 and 36 inches in length, a main body weight, an upper tube, check valve, and tailfin assembly account for the overall length of 3 to 5 feet. The upper tube, main body weight, check valve, and tailfin assembly comprise the mainweight. A check valve, located at the tailfin, prevents the flow of water into the upper section and a consequent washing out of the core sample while hoisting the corer. Plastic liners are used to collect and store the cores. A short free fall is provided by a counterweight and triggering mechanism. The Phleger corer does not employ a piston. (35)

PHOTOMETER. See PHOTOMULTIPLIER TUBE.

PHOTOMULTIPLIER TUBE (PHOTOMETER). Photomultiplier-type photometers are sufficiently sensitive to measure illumination as little as 10^{-12} gm cal/cm^2 /min. and can be used to a depth of 500 to 600 meters. It is necessary to use some type of shielding device when using a photomultiplier tube in illumination greater than 5×10^{-5} gm cal/cm^2/min., and a neutral filter of density 4 is necessary if the instrument is to be used at the surface.

A photomultiplier tube is more sensitive to short wave lengths than is a BARRIER LAYER CELL. Its peak sensitivity is around 4,500 Å. In deep water it should be necessary to use only a blue-green filter; however, an automatic filter changing device has been developed. (35)

PHOTOSYNTHESIS. The manufacture of carbohydrate from carbon dioxide and water in the presence of chlorophyll, using light energy and releasing oxygen. (18)

PHOTOTUBE CURRENT METER. In this instrument, a light of constant intensity is emitted from a light source, and is reflected by a cylindrical mirror into a phototube producing photoelectric current. A disc (with a hole) which rotates in accordance with the current by means of a propeller, is placed in the path of the light between the light source and the mirror. Therefore, an intermittent flash of light is produced by a rotating disc, the frequency of flashes being proportional to the speed of the current. Thus, the latter can be measured from the frequency of the flashes. The phototube output is amplified and activates a recorder. (30)

PHS. Public Health Service.

PHYCHROPHILE. See STENOHALINE.

PHYCOCYANIN. A blue, water-soluble accessory pigment found in such plants as blue-green algae. (13)

PHYCOERYTHRIN. Any of the red protein pigments in the cells of red algae. (20)

PHYCOXANTHIN. See DIATOMIN.

PHYTOPLANKTON. See MARINE LIFE.

PIEDMONT ICE. An ice sheet formed by the joining of two or more glaciers on a comparatively level plain at the base of the mountains down which the glaciers descended. It may be partly afloat. (17)

PIER. A long, narrow structure extending into the water to afford a berthing place for vessels, to serve as a promenade, etc. Such a structure usually of solid construction, intended as a berthing place for vessels is also called a JETTY in British terminology. See also MOLE, WHARF. (17)

PIERHEAD. 1. The outer end of a pier.
2. A breakwater. This meaning is general in the Great Lakes area but is only occasionally used elsewhere. (17)

PIEZOELECTRIC EFFECT. Phenomenon, exhibited by certain crystals, in which mechanical compression produces a potential difference between opposite crystal faces, or, an applied electric field produces corresponding changes in dimensions. (6)

PIEZOELECTRICITY. Piezoelectricity is the property exhibited by some asymmetrical crystalline materials which when subjected to strain in suitable directions develop electric polarization proportional to the strain. Inverse piezoelectricity is the effect in which mechanical strain is produced in certain asymmetrical crystalline materials when subjected to an external electric field; the strain is proportional to the electric field. (1)

PIEZOMETRIC. Of or related to pressure or the PIEZOMETER. (20)

PILE. A long, slender piece of wood, concrete, or metal to be driven or jetted into the earth or sea bed to serve as a support or protection. (11)

PILING. A group of PILES. (11)

PILLAR BUOY. A buoy composed of a tall central structure mounted on a broad flat base. Pillar buoys are not used in United States waters. Also called beacon buoy. (17)

PING. Acoustic pulse signal projected by an echo-ranging transducer. (6)

PINNACLE. Any characteristic rocky column which is dangerous to surface navigation. Any high tower or spire-shaped pillar or rock, alone or cresting a summit. (27)

PINNACLED ICEBERG (PYRAMIDAL ICEBERG, IRREGULAR ICEBERG). An iceberg weathered in such manner as to produce spires or pinnacles. (17)

PINRO. Polar Institute for Fishing and Oceanography (USSR).

PIOSA. Pan-Indian Ocean Science Association.

PIP. An echo trace on an indicator screen. (7)

PIPICO. Panel on International Programs of the ICO.

PISCIVOROUS. Fish-eating. For instance, the food habit of bathypelagic fishes must be mainly piscivorous due to the lack of plankton at great depths. (13)

PITCH. The oscillation of a ship about the lateral axis, i.e., alternate rising and falling of bow and stern. (12)

PITTING. A type of corrosion that develops cavities or pits in highly localized areas on a metal surface that is not particularly affected elsewhere. These pits may vary from deep cavities of small diameter to relatively shallow depressions.

PLAIN. A flat, gently sloping or nearly level region of the sea floor. (26)

PLANE POLARIZED SOUND WAVE (LINEARLY POLARIZED SOUND WAVE). A plane polarized sound wave is a transverse wave; hence, every particle in the medium is moving at right angles to the direction of propagation of the wave. There is added, however, the additional requirement that the motion at each point shall be along a straight line. (9)

PLANE WAVE. A plane wave is a wave in which the wave fronts are everywhere parallel planes normal to the direction of propagation. (9)

PLANFORM. The outline or shape of a body of water as determined by the still water line. (11)

PLANKTON. All the floating or drifting life found in the pelagic division of the sea. Plankton are further divided into PHYTOPLANKTON which includes all the floating and drifting plants, and ZOOPLANKTON which includes (1) myriads of animals that live permanently in a floating or drifting state and countless numbers of helpless larvae and eggs of the animal benthos and nekton. See MARINE LIFE. (2)

PLATEAU. A comparatively flat-topped elevation of the sea floor greater than 60 nautical miles across the summit and normally rising more than 100 fathoms on all sides. (26)

PLATE ICE. See PANCAKE ICE.

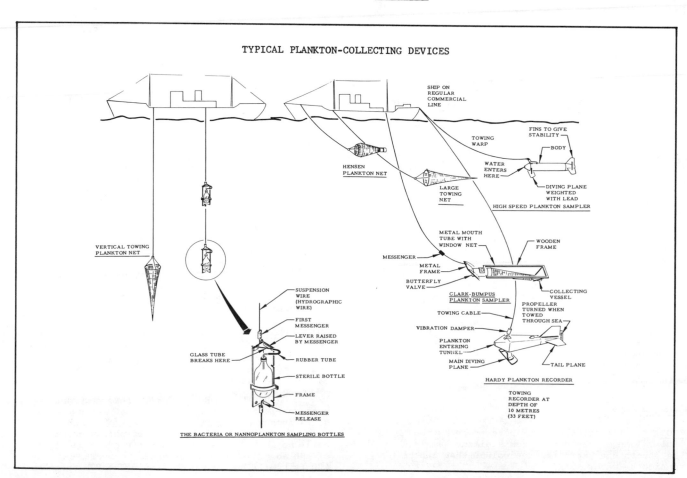

TYPICAL PLANKTON-COLLECTING DEVICES

PLUNGE POINT. 1. For a plunging wave, the point at which the wave curls over and falls.
2. The final breaking point of the waves just before they rush up on the beach. (11)

PLUTONIC ROCK. Igneous rocks which have cooled some distance below the surface and usually possess phaneritic (coarse-grained) structures. (27)

PMR. Pacific Missile Range (BuWeps).

PNEUMOTHORAX. If the surface of the lung is accidentally ruptured by a sudden excessive pressure inside the lungs, or if the chest wall is perforated by some external means, air will be pulled in between the membranes when the chest expands. An actual air pocket will then exist between the lung and the chest wall. This condition is known as pneumothorax (pneumo-air/thorax-chest) and may occur as an accident in diving or submarine escape. (37)

PNL. Pacific Naval Laboratory.

POFI. Pacific Oceanographic Fisheries Investigation.

POG. Pacific Oceanographic Group (British Columbia).

POIKILOTHERMOUS. Cold-blooded animals whose body temperatures are essentially at those of the environment ih which they live. (19)

POINT. The extreme end of a cape; or the outer end of any land area protruding into the water, usually less prominent than a CAPE. (11)

POISSON'S RATIO. The ratio of lateral strain to corresponding axial strain for a material subjected to axial loading. Poissons ratio for an isotropic material at a stress below the PROPORTIONAL LIMIT may be calculated:
$$r = \frac{E}{2G} \; 1$$
where:
  r = Poissons Ratio
  E = Modulus of Elasticity in Tension or Compression
  G = Modulus of Elasticity in Shear, psi.

POLAR ICE. Polar ice is the thickest and heaviest form of SEA ICE more than one year old. Undisturbed polar ice is about 12 feet thick on the average. (25)

POLDER. Land reclaimed from the sea or other body of water by the construction of an embankment to restrain the water. (17)

POLYAXON. See SPICULE.

POLYMORPHISM. The existence of individuals of more than one form in a species. (19)

POLYNYA (ICE CLEARING). A frequently used Russian term for a water area, other than a lead, lane or crack, which is surrounded by sea ice. The term window is sometimes used for a similar open area in river ice. (24)

POLYZOA. Broyozoa, a colonial animal that secretes a calcareous, horny, or membraneous covering in a multitudinous variety of forms and structures. Bryozoa may form insignificant colonies on shells, or they may be an important constituent of a reef. (16)

POROROCA. See BORE.

POROSITY. The percentage of pore space in the total volume of the dry bottom sediment sample. This percentage expresses the volume that can be occupied by water. (27)

PORT. 1. A place provided with terminal and transfer facilities for loading and discharging cargo or passengers, usually located in a harbor.
2. The left side of a craft, facing forward. The opposite is STARBOARD. (17)

PORTABLE PNEUMATIC CORE SAMPLER. This device, which weighs 700 pounds, was developed by the U. S. Navy Ordnance Laboratory for sampling coral and sand bottoms. It consists of a 4-legged pyramidal frame about 8 feet high, a pneumatic hammer with air supply and exhaust hosing, 400 pounds of lead weight, an anvil, and a 4-foot long aluminum barrel with a driving head for cutting through coral. (35)

PORTABLE TIDE STAFF. See TIDE STAFF.

PORTUGUESE MAN OF WAR. This familiar stinging jelly fish is strictly speaking not a true jelly fish but a hydroid found floating on the surface of the sea. The Portuguese Man of War (Physolia) has a world wide distribution in temperate and tropical waters. Venom cells and stinging apparatus are contained in its long trailing tenacles which are suspended from a balloon-like float. Its sting causes a urticarial lesion on the skin of its human victim.

POSITION BUOY. An object towed astern to assist a following vessel in maintaining the desired or prescribed distance, particularly in conditions of low visibility. Also called fog buoy, towing spar. (17)

POSITIVE GRADIENT. Describes conditions in layers where the temperature increases with increasing depth. (3)

POTENTIAL ENERGY (OF WAVES). In a progressive oscillatory wave, the energy resulting from the elevation or depression of the water surface from the undisturbed level. This energy advances with the wave form. (11)

POTENTIOMETER. A variable voltage divider. (36)

POTENTIOSTAT. A device used for the direct study of corroding metals where both anodic and cathodic reactions are taking place simultaneously.

POWER GAIN. Power gain in decibels is the amount by which the output power level in decibels exceeds the input power level in decibels. Thus, if the output power of a device is ten times that of the input, the power gain is ten decibels. On the other hand, if the output is one hundred times that of the input, the gain is twenty decibels. (9)

POWER LEVEL. Power level, in decibels, is ten times the logarithm to the base ten of the ratio of a given power to a reference power. The reference power must be indicated. (2)

POWER PER UNIT BAND. The limit approached by the quotient obtained by dividing (1) the power of the energy being transmitted by a given system, at a given time and in a given frequency band, by (2) the width of this band as the width of this band approached zero. (4)

POWER SPECTRUM. See SPECTRUM DENSITY.

PPI. Plan Position Indicator. A scope (i.e., radarscope) on which reflections are so depicted to indicate the range and bearing of objects.

PRECISION DEPTH RECORDER (PDR). This recorder uses an electro-sensitive paper, has a paper speed of 24 inches per hour, and displays 400 fathoms over a width of 18.85 inches. It phases automatically so that depths to the full range capability of the sonar set can be recorded in increments of 400 fathoms with high precision. The PDR triggers the sonar set and performs the time measuring function. (35)

PRECISION GRAPHIC RECORDER (PGR). This instrument is similar to the Precision Depth Recorder, but it is considered to be more versatile in that it has many scale and depth combinations readily available. However, the PGR is also rather more complex than the PDR and it uses a helix instead of the stylus of the PDR for recording.

PRESSURE COMPONENT. Any change in velocity with depth not accounted for by a change in temperature or in salinity may best be described as the pressure component of the velocity gradient. (4)

PRESSURE GAGE. A tide gage that is operated by the change in pressure at the bottom of a body of water due to the rise and fall of the tide. It has sometimes been used for tide observations on shoals at some distance from land. (14)

PRESSURE-GRADIENT HYDROPHONES. A pressure-gradient hydrophone is a hydrophone in which the electric output substantially corresponds to a component of the gradient (space derivative) of the sound pressure. (1)

PRESSURE-GRADIENT TRANSDUCER. Transducer, such as a moving-ribbon hydrophone, in which the moving element responds to pressure difference rather than to pressure. (6)

PRESSURE HYDROPHONE. A pressure hydrophone in which the electric output substantially corresponds to the instantaneous sound pressure of the impressed sound wave. (1)

PRESSURE ICE. Ice having any readily observed roughness of the surface. FLAT ICE is the result of undisturbed ice growth and development. Such disturbed development is the result of wind, current, tide, and/or temperature change. Types of pressure ice are: RAFTED, RIDGED, HUMMOCKED, TENTED, ROPAK, and WEATHERED. (25)

PRESSURE IN THE OCEAN (General). In oceanographic work pressure is measured in atmospheres or in units of the centimeter-gram-second system. An atmosphere is defined as the pressure exerted per square centimeter by a column of mercury 760 mm high at a temperature of 0 degrees C, where the acceleration of gravity is 980. 665 cm/sec^2. In chemical oceanography a related unit, the Torr, is used which equals the pressure exerted per square centimeter by a column of mercury 1 mm high at a temperature of 0 degrees C and at the above-mentioned acceleration of gravity. The c.g.s. unit of pressure is dyne/cm^2, and 1 atmosphere is equal to 1.0133 X 10^6 dynes/cm^2. One million dynes/cm^2 was designated as 1 bar by V. Bjerknes. The corresponding practical unit used in physical oceanography is 1 decibar, which equals 0.1 bar. The pressure exerted per square centimeter by 1 m of sea water very nearly equals 1 decibar; that is, the hydrostatic pressure in the sea increases by 1 decibar for approximately every meter of depth. Therefore, the depth in meters and the pressure in decibars are expressed by <u>nearly</u> the same numerical value. The distribution of temperature and salinity in the ocean, and the slight compressibility of water are among the factors responsible for the small difference in these values.

In dealing with the pressure in the oceans, the atmospheric pressure is always neglected and the pressure at the sea surface is entered as zero. Since the pressure is essentially a function of depth and the numerical value in decibars nearly equals the depth in meters, the range in pressure will be from zero at the sea surface to over 10,000 decibars in the deepest part of the ocean. (12,13)

PRESSURE-OPERATED PLANKTON NET. This device has a pressure mechanism for opening and closing a plankton sampler using a spring-loaded damper actuated by the pressure element from a conventional 900-foot bathythermograph. The sampler fishes between depth intervals preselected by inserting pins of different lengths into the arresting gear. The first pin governs the point at which the sampler will open as the BT element is compressed

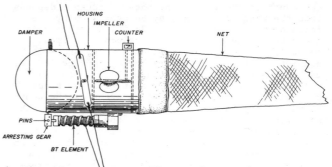

by the water pressure. The sampler remains open until further pressure releases the second and longer pin. Larger plankton nets are not as easily opened and shut, one of the means that we have considered is to use so-called strangle lines which are successive attachments to the net for pursing it off. Pressure pistons can be used to sever the strangle attachments.

PRESSURE RIDGE. PRESSURE ICE in the form of a ridge. Pressure ridges may be several miles long and up to 100 feet high. (25)

PRICE CURRENT METER. The Price current meter was originally designed by Assistant Engineer W. G. Price, Corps of Engineers, U. S. Army. It is designed to measure current speeds from 0.1 to 11 feet per second (0.06 to 6.6 knots). It does not measure current direction. Current direction must be determined by other means when using this instrument.

The meter consists of a number of cone-shaped cups mounted on a vertical rotating shaft called the cup shaft. For every 1, 5, or 10 revolutions of the cup shaft, depending on the model being used, an electrical circuit in a contact chamber is closed and transmits a signal to the observer through a 2-conductor electrical cable and a set of earphones. In place of earphones, an automatic recorder with a time-marking system may be connected to the circuit. Power for the circuit can be supplied by dry-cell batteries. The number of revolutions of the cup shaft, when applied to the calibration or rating table, indicates the speed of the current. (35)

PRIMARY LOBES. See LOBES.

PRIMARY PRESSURE INSTRUMENTS. Primary pressure instruments are manometers and gauges which can be calibrated without reference to another pressure measuring instrument. The mercury barometer and dead weight scale are examples of such primary pressure instruments. (35)

PRIMING OF TIDE. The periodic acceleration in the time of occurrence of high and low waters due to changes in the relative positions of the moon and the sun. (14)

PRIMITIVE PERIOD. The primitive period of a periodic quantity is the smallest increment of the independent variable for which the function repeats itself. (2)

PRINCIPAL AXIS. The principal axis of a transducer used for sound emission or reception is a reference direction for angular coordinates used in describing the directional characteristics of the transducer. It is usually an axis of structural symmetry, or the direction of maximum response; but if these do not coincide the reference direction must be described explicitly. (1)

PROGRESSION (OF A BEACH). See ADVANCE.

PROGRESSIVE WAVE. A wave whose crest advances horizontally. For a wave with a length less than the depth of the water, the rate of advance depends upon the wave length and may be expressed by the formula: $r = (gL/2\pi)^{\frac{1}{2}} = 2.26\sqrt{L}$, in which r is the rate of advance in feet per second, g is equal to 32.17, L the length of wave in feet, and π is equal to 3.1416. The corresponding wave period (P) may be expressed by the formula: P (in seconds) $= (2\pi L/g)^{\frac{1}{2}} \ 0.442\sqrt{L}$. For a progressive tidal wave with a length many times as great as the depth of water, the rate of advance is independent of the wave length but is determined by the depth of the water and may be expressed by the formula: $r = \sqrt{gd} = 5.67\sqrt{d}$, in which d is the depth of water in feet, the other symbols being the same as previously given. The corresponding period may be expressed by the formula: $P = L/\sqrt{gd} = 0.176L/\sqrt{d}$. (14)

PROJECT NEPTUNE. An Office of Naval Research (ONR) program designed to demonstrate the feasibility of using EXPENDABLE (Marine) INSTRUMENTATION on ships of the Merchant fleet.

PROJECTOR. An underwater acoustic transmitter. See UNDERWATER SOUND PROJECTOR, SPLIT PROJECTOR. (6)

PROJECTOR LOSS. The projector loss of a sonar transducer, used for the transmission of acoustic energy, at a specified frequency, may be defined as the transmission loss measured by the ratio of (1) the input power of the electric energy delivered to the transducer to (2) the resulting load power of the acoustic energy delivered by the transducer to a water surface having an area of one square centimeter and lying perpendicular to the maximum response reference axis of the transducer at its index point. (4)

PROLATE CYCLOID. See TROCHOID.

PROMONTORY. A high point of land projecting into a body of water; a HEADLAND. (11)

PROPAGATION ANOMALY. The difference between the actual propagation loss for a given length of water path and the nominal value of propagation loss identified with the distance covered by that path is known as the propagation anomaly. (4)

PROPAGATION LOSS. Propagation loss may be defined as the transmission loss association with any given length of ray path in the water. (4)

PROPAGATION VELOCITY. (See WAVE VELOCITY).

PROPORTIONAL BAND LEVEL CHARACTERISTIC. A proportional band level characteristic is one in which the band levels of a series of proportional bands are plotted against their geometric mean frequencies, or against their upper or lower boundary frequencies. (4)

PROPORTIONAL BANDS. Whenever the members of a series of frequency bands have equal band ratios the bands are said to be proportional bands. (4)

PROPORTIONAL LIMIT. The proportional limit represents an aspect of elastic behavior similar to the elastic limit, the principal difference lying in the method of determination. The straight-line proportionality between stress and strain in the elastic range has already been discussed. It is the upper limit of the range of proportionality

that defines the proportional limit. In other words, the proportional limit is the greatest stress which a material is capable of developing without a deviation from the law of proportionality (Hooke's Law).

In practice, the proportional limit is determined from a plot of stress against strain, being taken as the stress at the first visible departure

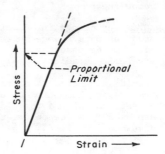

from the straight line drawn through the points in the elastic range. Since the departure from linearity is in general quite gradual, the determined value will depend on the accuracy and sensitivity of the strain-measuring device employed in the test. The experimentally determined value for a given material will be found to decrease as the sensitivity of extensometer used is increased, that is, as the ability to detect smaller and smaller strain increments is increased. Because of these uncertainties, proportional limit is very seldom employed in specifications.

PROTON. The positive particles of an atom. The smallest quantity of positive electricity which can exist in a free state; associated with electrons and neutrons, it makes up the atom. (36)

PROTOPLASM. Living substance; the complex colloidal physico-chemical system that constitutes living matter and is the viscid, semifluid material of animal and plant cells. (19)

PROTOTYPE. In laboratory usage, the original structure, concept, or phenomenon used as a basis for constructing a scale model or copy. (11)

PROTOZOANS. Minute one-celled animals, most of which are invisible to the naked eye and occur universally in the surface layers of the sea. Several genera are capable of producing bioluminescence, usually of the sheet type. (15)

PROVINCE. A region composed of a group of similar bathymetric features whose characteristics are markedly in contrast with surrounding areas. (26)

PSA. Pacific Science Association.
Founded 1920 in Honolulu.
Activities: PSA is a private international association of scientists interested in problems of the Pacific Ocean. The Association sponsors a Pacific Science Congress every three years. The main objectives are the promotion of scientific study of problems of the Pacific region, exchange of information, and the publication of reports of congresses and a Pacific Science Bulletin.

PSAC. President's Scientific Advisory Committee.

PSEUDOCHITIN. See TECTIN.

PSEUDOPODIUM. A flowing extension of protoplasm used in locomotion or feeding by a cell or protozoan. (19)

PSMFC. Pacific States Marine Fisheries Commission.

PSMSL. Permanent Service for Mean Sea Level.

PSYCHROMETER. An instrument used for measuring the water vapor content of the atmosphere; a type of hygrometer. It consists of two thermometers, one of which (dry bulb) is an ordinary glass thermometer, while the other (wet bulb) has its bulb covered with a jacket of clean muslin which is saturated with distilled water prior to an observation. When the bulbs are suitably ventilated, they indicate the thermodynamic WET- and DRY-BULB TEMPERATURE of the atmosphere. (14)

PT. U. S. Navy designation for a Motor Torpedo Boat.

PTC. U. S. Navy ship designation for Motor Sub Chaser. Also Pacific Tuna Conference.

PTEROPODS. Pelagic, swimming-type gastropods in which the foot is modified into a pair of winglike lobes or fins. Pteropod ooze contains conspicuous shells of these pelagic mollusks and is an important constituent of the deep ocean deposits. Pteropod ooze usually is classed as mud on bottom sediment charts. (16)

PTF. U. S. Navy designation for a Fast Patrol Boat.

PULSE RISE TIME. The pulse rise time is the interval of time required for the leading edge of a pulse to rise from some specified small fraction to some specified larger fraction of the maximum value. (2)

PUMICE. An excessively cellular, glassy lava. It is very light and floats on water until it becomes water logged and sinks. Pumice is classed as gravel on bottom sediment charts. (16)

PW. Pulse Width.

PY. U. S. Navy ship designation for a Yacht.

PYRAMIDAL ICEBERG. See PINNACLED ICEBERG.

PYROCLASTIC. Solid material ejected from a volcano, ranging from large volcanic bombs to fine volcanic ash and dust. (27)

PYRHELIOMETER. General term for the class of actinometers which measure the intensity of direct solar radiation.
   The instrument consists of a radiation sensing element enclosed in a casing which is closed except for a small aperture, through which the direct solar rays enter, and a recorder unit. Pyrheliometers can be classified on the basis of the sensing elements employed. In one form the sensing element is a blackened water calorimeter. The rise in the temperature of the water gives a measure of the amount of radiant energy absorbed during the exposure of the instrument. Another type of sensing element consists of a blackened plate of high heat capacity. When radiation is allowed to fall on the plate for a period short compared to the thermal time constant, the temperature rise of the plate is proportional to the intensity of the incoming radiation. A third type of sensing element consists of a pair of plates, one blackened and one reflecting, which are continuously exposed to the incoming radiation. The temperature differential between the plates is proportional to the intensity of the incoming radiation. (24)

Q

Q (QUALITY FACTOR). The quantity Q is a measure of the sharpness of resonance or frequency selectivity of a resonant vibratory system having a single degree of freedom, either mechanical or electrical. A high value for Q means that the resonance is sharp; i. e., and small change in the frequency of the excitation causes a large drop in the response of the system. (9)

QUARANTINE BUOY. A buoy marking the location of a quarantine anchorage. In U. S. waters a quarantine buoy is yellow. (17)

QUARTERING SEA. Waves moving in a direction approximating 45° from a vessel's heading, striking the vessel on the quarter. Those moving in the general direction of the heading are called following sea, those moving in a direction approximately opposite to the heading are called head sea, and those moving in a direction approximately 90° from the heading are called beam sea. (17)

QUARTZ PROJECTORS. X-cut quartz crystals are laid flat on a steel plate, arranged in a mosaic so that the plate is adequately covered. An identical plate is then laid on top of the crystals, forming a sandwich. Insulating washers make it possible to connect the plates to the terminals of the ac

source. When the potential of the upper face of the crystal is positive, the thickness increases. Simultaneously, the other two dimensions shrink. Since the plate will be compressed during one half of the cycle of an ac field, and extended the same amount during the other half, it will vibrate with the same period as that of the field. If this is the natural period of the crystal, the amplitude of the vibrations will be a maximum. (30)

QUAY. A WHARF approximately parallel to the shore line and accommodating ships on one side only, the other side being attached to the shore. It is usually of solid construction, as contrasted with the open pile construction usually used for PIERS. (17)

QUENCHED WATER. There are many occasions when the apparent propagation loss of some water path, of only moderate length, will be such as to indicate an attenuation much greater than would be predicted. Such abnormally high attenuations are attributed to what has come to be called quenched water. This is a condition often encountered in shallow water, or near shores where there are strong currents accompanied by considerable turbulence. It is believed that the excessive reductions in acoustic intensity are the result of occluded air. (4)

QUICKSAND. Sand which has lost its grain-to-grain contact by the buoyancy effect of water flowing upward through the voids. Such material, having some of the characteristics of a fluid, possesses no load-bearing value. It is a condition and not a type of material. (27)

R

RACE. A rapid current or a constricted channel in which such a current flows. The term is usually used only in connection with a tidal current, when it may be called a tide race. (17)

RADAR. The name radar is derived from the words, Radio Detection and Ranging.

Radar is a system of determining the distance of an object by measuring the interval of time between transmission of a radio signal and reception of a signal returned as an echo, or by a transmitter triggered by the outgoing signal. The bearing of the object may be determined by noting the orientation of the directional antenna. (17)

RADIATION. The transmission of heat by invisible waves not unlike radio waves. Every warm object puts out such waves; and if an object is hot enough, it will also produce similar waves which we recognize as light. Although a diver will also lose some heat by radiation, the amount is very small compared to the loss by conduction. (37)

RADIOACTIVITY METER FOR LIQUIDS. A device developed by the U. S. Naval Applied Science Laboratory monitors the gross beta activity of drinking water, boiler water, and other liquids aboard nuclear powered ships. Called "Evaporation and Concentration Unit for Dilute Radioactive and Non-Radioactive Solutions", it evaporates a given mass of sample liquid and the solid remnants are evenly arranged on a small disk surface allowing accurate geiger-muller radiation measurement. (30)

RADIOBEACON BUOY. A buoy equipped with a marker radiobeacon. Such a buoy is usually used to mark an important entrance to a channel. The beacon is of low power, providing a signal for a short range. (17)

RADIO CURRENT METER. An instrument for observing currents developed by the Coast and Geodetic Survey. It operates from an anchored buoy from which signals indicating the velocity and direction of the current are automatically transmitted by radio to a conveniently located recording station. The Roberts Radio Current Meter Operating Manual, issued by the Coast and Geodetic Survey, contains a detailed description of the meter and auxiliary equipment. (14)

RADIOISOTOPE. See ISOTOPE.

RADIOLARIA. Minute marine protozoans which have a siliceous skeleton of spicules and radiating threadlike pseudopodia. Radiolarian ooze contains large proportions of radiolarian skeletons and is an important constituent of the deep ocean deposits. Radiolarian ooze is classed as mud on bottom sediment charts. (16)

RADIOMETER. This instrument is essentially a heat flow meter used to measure long wave radiation as well as solar radiation. It can be used both for daytime and nighttime measurements and to measure the net heat transfer through a surface.

See also GEIR AND DUNKLE RADIOMETER.

RADIOSONDE. A balloon-borne instrument for the simultaneous measurement and transmission of meteorological data. (31)

RAFOS. Rafos is a long range navigation system. Rafos, the reverse spelling of SOFAR, uses this acronym since the system is the direct reverse of the sofar system. In rafos, explosive charges are released at fixed shore stations and the time of release is known. For example, the charges could be exploded once an hour, exactly on the hour. The ship would time the arrival of each of the explosive sound waves and thus would have the transit time for each such wave. This information and the average velocity would enable the ship to compute its distance from the shore stations. (29)

RAFTED ICE. A type of PRESSURE ICE formed by one CAKE overriding another, or RAFTING. Rafted ICE has well defined contours and when observed may be regarded as a relatively recent occurrence. (25)

RAFTING. 1. The overriding of one ice cake on another as a result of pressure. See BENDING, TENTING.

2. The transporting of sediment, rocks, silt, and other matter of land origin out to sea by ice, logs, etc., with subsequent deposition of the rafted matter when the carrying agent disintegrates. (17)

RAM. The sloping, underwater ledge of an ICEBERG or of a GLACIER terminus bathed in water. More rapid melting at the water line than above and below causes a notch to be formed at the water line below which is the ram. As a result of underwater CALVING, the ram may become detached and is then buoyed up to the surface. This process can be a serious hazard for boats, even of large size, in the immediate vicinity. (25)

RAMP. Solid material forming an incline between two levels, such as an accumulation of snow forming an inclined plane between land or land ice and sea ice or shelf ice. Also called drift ice foot. (17)

RANA. Rana is a medium range surveying phase comparision system developed by the French for their hydrographic surveys in North Africa. It is quite similar to LORAC. Through the use of 4 radio frequencies with certain relationship, the difference in frequency results in lane widths at the base line of 200 meters, 4 kilometers, and 80 kilometers. The 4 radio frequencies are so chosen that a difference frequency is selected from a combination of two of the frequencies. For the fine lane of 200 meters, the fundamental frequency of 1600 kilocycles is used for phase comparison. Then a difference frequency of 80 kilocycles produces lanes of 4 kilometers while a difference in frequency of 4 kilocycles produces lanes 80 kilometers wide at the base line. (29)

RANDOM NOISE. Random is a word which is used to denote the idea of unpredictability. Thus we may know the magnitude of a sound or oscillation at a given moment, but this in no sense allows us to predict what it will be even a short time ahead, except perhaps in a statistical sense. (9)

RANGE COMPREHENSION. The difference between the minimum and maximum ranges of an FM sonar system. (5)

RANGE OF TIDE. The difference in height between consecutive high and low waters. The mean range is the difference in height between mean high water and mean low water. The great diurnal range or diurnal range is the difference in height between mean higher high water and mean lower low water. Where the type of tide is diurnal the mean range is the same as the diurnal range. For other ranges see SPRING, NEAP, PERIGEAN, APOGEAN, and TROPIC TIDES. (14)

RANGE RESOLUTION. The minimum range separation of two targets, on the same bearing, for which the two are individually detectable. (5)

RAPHE. The median line or slit of a valve of a DIATOM. (20)

"RAPTURES OF THE DEEP". Inert gas narcosis. See NITROGEN NARCOSIS.

RASTER. The rectangular pattern developed on a CRO screen by the combined effects of the horizontal and vertical sawtooth sweeps. (5)

RATE OF DECAY. The rate of decay is the time rate at which the sound pressure level, or any other stated characteristic, decreases at a given point in a given time. A commonly used unit to express the rate of decay is the decibel per second. (9)

RATE RANGE. Rate of change of range between own ship and target. (5)

RAWIN. Radar wind sounding or the determination of winds by the radar observation of a balloon.

RAWINSONDE. RADIOSONDE and RAWIN methods combined. Rawinsonde is an electronic means of observing temperature, humidity, pressure and winds.

RAYDIST (TYPES E, R, ER, AND N). Raydist is a radio system for medium range precision surveying in which the phases of two continuous-wave signals are compared. It is based on the heterodyne principle and uses low or medium frequencies. It requires a minimum number of frequencies and these frequencies usually need bear no fixed relationship with each other.

    A number of designs of the Raydist system enable position lines of various configurations, such as circular, hyperbolic, and elliptic. The mobile portion of the apparatus can be made very light and the ground equipment both highly transportable and free from complex or bulky antenna structures. It operates automatically and requires no specially trained personnel. Its range, due to the waves used, is not limited to line-of sight operation. The range varies for each type, depending upon the power of the transmitters. (29)

RAYLEIGH WAVE. A Rayleigh wave is a surface wave associated with the free boundary of a solid. The wave is of maximum intensity at the surface and diminishes quite rapidly as one proceeds into the solid. Hence, it has a tendency to hug the surface of the solid. Such waves have been used quite effectively in detecting surface cracks and flaws in castings. (9)

RAY PATH. The energy associated with a point on a wave front moves along an imaginary line known as a ray path. The ray paths encountered in acoustics, which are commonly called sound rays, are analogous to the light rays of optics. Ray paths and wave fronts are mutually perpendicular. (4)

RDX. A type of high explosive.

REAR RESPONSE. The maximum pressure with $\pm 60^\circ$ from the rear of the transducer in db relative to the pressure on the acoustic axis. (6)

RECEIVING BAND RESPONSE. The receiving band response of a hydrophone, for a given bearing and for a given frequency band, may be defined as the response measured by the quotient obtained by dividing (1) the available power of the electric energy generated by the hydrophone in the given frequency band when receiving over the given bearing plane acoustic waves occupying the same frequency band by (2) the free-field intensity of these received acoustic waves. (4)

RECEIVING DIRECTIVITY FACTOR. The receiving directivity factor of a sonar transducer, for a specified frequency, is the ratio of (1) the available power per unit band of the electric energy generated at the specified frequency by the transducer when receiving over all bearings and at the specified frequency acoustic energy having a given free-field intensity per unit band which is the same for all bearings to (2) the available power per unit band of the electric energy which would be generated at the same frequency and when receiving the same acoustic energy over the same bearings, if the receiving response of the transducer for that frequency were the same for any bearing as for the maximum response reference bearing. (4)

RECEIVING RESPONSE. The receiving response of a hydrophone, for a given bearing and for a given frequency, may be defined as the response measured by the quotient obtained by dividing (1) the available power of the sinusoidal electric waves of the given frequency generated in the hydrophone when receiving over the given bearing plane sinusoidal acoustic waves of the same frequency by (2) the free-field intensity of these received acoustic waves. (4)

RECESSION (OF A BEACH) (RETROGRESSION).
1. A continuing landward movement of the shore line.

RECIPROCAL TRANSDUCER. A reciprocal transducer is a transducer that satisfies the principle of reciprocity. (1)

RECIPROCITY CALIBRATIONS. By means of the reciprocity relation it is possible to measure the projector loss and the hydrophone loss of a reversible transducer by comparisons with the known transmission losses of an electric network without knowing the actual value of either the electric power or the acoustic power. Measurements made in this manner are known as reciprocity calibrations. (4)

RECIPROCITY RANGE. The reciprocity range is the frequency range over which a reversible transducer obeys the reciprocity principle; i. e., the frequency range over which it may be used as the reversible transducer in reciprocity calibration measurements. (1)

RECIPROCITY THEOREM. The reciprocity theorem states that if, in any electric network composed of linear elements, a given electromotive force applied between two given terminals produces a current at a point in some branch of the network then the same voltage acting at this second point in the network will produce the same current between the two original terminals if they are short-circuited. (4)

RECOGNITION DIFFERENTIAL. The recognition differential for a specified listening system is that amount by which the signal level exceeds the noise level presented to the ear when there is a fifty per cent probability of detection of the signal. This quantity is most valuable in evaluating the effectiveness of military communication channels, since it is most important that no order be misunderstood. (9)

RECORDING PYRHELIOMETER. An instrument used to provide information on the heat budget between atmosphere and ocean.

    The pyrheliometer is a thermopile enclosed in a glass bulb and measures radiation incident on a horizontal surface. The receiving surface consists of two flat concentric disks, a black disk forming an absorbing surface and a white disk forming a reflecting surface. The resulting temperature dif-

ference between the two disks acts on the thermopile and produces an electromotive force (EMF) which is proportional to the intensity of the incident radiation. This EMF is transmitted to a recording potentiometer.
See also PYRHELIOMETER. (35)

RED CLAY. A fine-grained deposit that is predominantly clay, of low carbonate and silica content, that covers most of the deeper portions of the ocean basins. Also called BROWN CLAY. (27)

RED MUD. A reddish-brown terrigenous deep-sea mud which accumulates on the sea floor in the neighborhood of deserts and off the mouths of great rivers; contains calcium carbonate up to 25 per cent. (27)

RED TIDE. A growth of DINOFLAGELLATES (single-celled plant-like animals) in surface waters in such quantities as to color the sea red and kill fish. (24)

REEF. An offshore consolidated rock hazard to navigation with a least depth of ten fathoms or less. (27)

REEF BARRIER (BARRIER REEF). A reef which roughly parallels land but is some distance offshore, with deeper water intervening. (27)

REFERENCE PLANE (DAILY WATER). The plane to which sounding and tidal data are referred. The following reference planes are used by various countries:
MEAN LOW WATER - United States (Atlantic Coast), Argentina, Sweden and Norway.
MEAN LOWER LOW WATER - United States (Pacific Coast), including Alaska and Island Possessions.
MEAN LOW WATER SPRINGS - Great Britain, Germany Italy, Brazil and Chile.
LOWEST LOW WATER SPRINGS - Portugal.
INDIAN SPRING LOW WATER - India and Japan.
LOWEST LOW WATER - France, Spain and Greece.
MEAN LAKE LEVEL - Great Lakes of U. S. and Canada.
MEAN SEA LEVEL - Used in Denmark.
See also DATUM PLANE. (27)

REFERENCE STATION. A station for which tidal constants have previously been determined and which is used as a standard for the comparison of simultaneous observations at a second station; also a station for which independent daily predictions are given in the tide or current tables from which corresponding predictions are obtained for other stations by means of differences or factors. (11)

REFLECTED WAVE. The wave that is returned seaward when a wave impinges upon a very steep beach, barrier, or other reflecting surfaces. (11)

REFLECTION LOSS. The reflection loss at the junction between an energy source and an energy load is the transmission loss measured by the ratio of (1) the load power which would be measured if source and load were connected by a hypothetical transducer having an input impedance equal to the load impedance of the load, and developing the same volt-amperes at its load terminals as are developed at its source terminals, to (2) the actual load power when source and load are connected directly to each other. (4)

REFRACTION COEFFICIENT. The square root of the ratio of the spacing between adjacent orthogonals in deep water and in shallow water at a selected point. When multiplied by the SHOALING FACTOR, this becomes the WAVE HEIGHT COEFFICIENT or the ratio of the refracted wave height at any point to the deep water wave height. Also the square root of the ENERGY COEFFICIENT. (11)

REFRACTION DIAGRAM. A drawing showing positions of wave crests and/or orthogonals in a given area for a specific deep water wave period and direction. (11)

REFRACTION LOSS. Refraction loss is that part of the transmission loss which is due to refraction in the medium. These losses arise from nonuniformities in the medium. (9)

REFRACTION OF WATER WAVES. (1) The process by which the direction of a wave moving in shallow water at an angle to the contours is changed. The part of the wave advancing in shallower water moves more slowly than that part still advancing in deeper water, causing the wave crest to bend toward alignment with the underwater contours. (2) The bending of wave crests by currents. (11)

REGULAR LAY. See WIRE ROPE.

RELATIVE DEPTH. Ratio of the wavelength to the water depth.

RELATIVE PRESSURE FIELD. The pressure field that would be present if the pressure distribution depended only upon the distribution of mass in the sea.

RELATIVE PRESSURE RESPONSE. It is possible to measure the relative response of a projector in terms of acoustic pressure, as well as in terms of acoustic intensity. When so measured the relative response of a projector is known as its relative pressure response. (4)

RELATIVE RECEIVING RESPONSE. The relative receiving response of a hydrophone, for any bearing and for any frequency, may be defined as the ratio of the receiving response for that bearing and that frequency to the receiving response for a specified bearing and a specified frequency. (4)

RELATIVE RESPONSE. The relative response of a transducer, in decibels, is the amount by which the response under some particular condition exceeds the response under a reference condition that should be stated explicitly. (1)

RELATIVE TRANSMITTING RESPONSE. The relative transmitting response of a sonar projector, for any bearing and for any frequency may be defined as the ratio of the transmitting response for that bearing and that frequency to the transmitting response for a specified bearing and a specified frequency. (4)

REPRODUCTIVE EURYHALINE. See STENOHALINE.

REPRODUCTIVE STENOHALINE. See STENOHALINE.

RESA. Scientific Research Society of America.

RESEARCH. A process of scientific investigation prior to and during development. It has for its aim the discovery of new scientific facts, techniques, and natural laws; an extension of the "state-of-the-art." (42)

RESEARCH, APPLIED. Research aimed at specific application of scientific laws, principles, and phenomena. In contrast to basic research, the prospect of practical application of the results is a primary motive for applied research. Frequently even the methods to be used are clear before work is begun. (42)

RESEARCH, BASIC. The theoretical or experimental study directed toward the increase of knowledge. It may result in the discovery of new scientific phenomena, principles, techniques, or significant data which add to the store of scientific knowledge. Immediate practical application is not necessarily a direct objective. (42)

RESIDUAL VOLUME. In physiology - the amount of air that remains in the lungs even after the most forceful expiration. It normally amounts to between 1 and 1-1/2 liters. Note that the sum of the vital capacity plus the residual volume equals the total lung capacity. (37)

RESISTANCE WIRE WAVE STAFF. This fixed wave gage type instrument consists of an oscillator, a vacuum tube voltmeter, a recording milliammeter, and a continuous length of Chromel wire which is strung through a telescopic stainless steel tube. The resistance of the Chromel wire changes linearly as the sea water moves up and down its length. A full scale deflection equivalent to 15 feet of wave height is possible on the recorder.

Since the diameter of the wire is small, the sea water tends to drain off rapidly as the trough of a wave passes the gauge. Thus, the "wetting" problem which has troubled the operation of other fixed wave gauges in the past is overcome. (35)

RESISTIVITY PROBE-ELECTRODELESS. This device is used to determine resistivity of large bodies of water or other conducting liquid in a large vessel. The probe has an input and output coil, both mounted on toroidal cores of identical dimensions and properties. Number of output turns is a multiple of the number of input turns. The two coils are mounted on a glass tube. The whole assembly being potted in epoxy resin. When the probe is immersed in a conducting fluid and a.c. voltage is applied to the input coil, current loops are established which go through the cylindrical opening and around the outside of the block. The voltage appearing at the output coil is then a function of the resistance of the fluid. The probe, because it is a dipole, is not influenced by discontinuities in the medium, unless they are very close to the ends of the probe. (30)

RESONANCE. Resonance of a system in forced oscillation exists when any change, however small, in the frequency of excitation causes a decrease in the response of the system. (2)

RESPIRATION. The process of drawing air, or another breathing medium, into the lungs to supply oxygen and purify the blood. (37)

RESPIRATORY CYCLE. One complete "breath" - an inspiration followed by an expiration, including any pause that may occur between the movements. (37)

RESPIRATORY DEAD SPACE. That part of the respiratory system which has no alveoli and in which little or no exchange of gas between air and blood takes place. It normally amounts to less than 0.2 liter but becomes larger as the depth of breathing increases. Air which occupies the dead space during each breath does not take part in the active process of breathing. Certain parts of a diver's breathing apparatus can add to the volume of the dead space and thus reduce the proportion of the tidal volume which serves the purpose of respiration. To compensate, the diver must increase his tidal volume. (37)

RESPIRATORY EXHAUSTION. Resistance to underwater breathing has four components: 1) airway resistance caused by valves, length and diameter of tubing, and possibly inertial factors due to the density of the inspired gas at increased depth; 2) hydrostatic resistance caused by the difference in pressure between the level of the swimmer's center of breathing (most commonly believed to be at the bottom of his throat) and the level of the inlet or demand valve; 3) inertial resistance introduced by the inertia of water which must be displaced during respiratory movements of the chest; and 4) miscellaneous factors such as the resistance of breathing bag fabric to inflation and deflation. (37)

RESPIRATORY MINUTE VOLUME (RMV). The total amount of air moved in and out of the lungs in a minute. Multiplying the tidal volume times the rate gives the respiratory minute volume. Minute volume varies greatly with the body's activity. It is about 6 liters at complete rest and may be over 100 liters during very heavy work. (37)

RESPIRATORY QUOTIENT. The ratio between the amount of carbon dioxide produced and the amount of oxygen consumed in breathing. The average value for a working diver is 0.9. This means that 9/10's of every liter of CO_2 is produced for every liter of oxygen consumed. (37)

RESPIRATORY RATE (FREQUENCY). Indicates the number of complete respiratory cycles that take place in 1 minute. At rest, a normal adult will have a respiratory rate somewhere between 10 and 20 "breaths" per minute. The rate normally increases during work. (37)

RESPONSE. The response of a device or system is the motion or other output resulting from an excitation or stimulus under special conditions. (9)

RESTING SPORE. A SPORE that remains dormant for a period before germination and is usually invested with a thickened cell wall to withstand adverse conditions (as of desiccation, heat, or cold). (20)

RETROGRESSION. See RECESSION (OF A BEACH).

REVERBERATION. (1) Reverberation is the persistence of sound in an enclosed space as a result of multiple reflections after the sound source has stopped. (2) Reverberation is the sound that persists in an enclosed space, as a result of repeated reflection or scattering, after the source of the sound has stopped. (1)

REVERBERATION FACTOR. The reverberation factor for a reversible sonar transducer, for a specified frequency, may be defined as the ratio of (1) the available power per unit band of the electric energy generated at the specified frequency by the transducer when receiving over all bearings acoustic energy which has previously been radiated over these bearings by the transducer in response to electric energy having a given power per unit band at the specified frequency, and which has then been returned to the transducer by propagation paths of equal length and equal transmission loss, to (2) the available power per unit band of the electric energy which would be generated at the same frequency and when receiving over the same bearings the acoustic energy which would have been radiated over those bearings in response to the same previously received electric energy and returned by the same propagation paths, if the transmitting and receiving responses of the transducer for that frequency were the same for any bearing as for the maximum response reference bearing. (4)

REVERBERATION INDEX. Measure of the ability of an echo-ranging transducer to distinguish the desired echo from the reverberation. Computed from the directivity patterns as ratio in decibels of the bottom, surface, or volume reverberation response of a specific transducer to the corresponding response of a non-directional transducer. (5)

REVERBERATION STRENGTH. Reverberation strength may be defined as the difference between the level of a plane wave producing in a non-directional transducer a response equal to that produced by the reverberation corresponding to a range of one yard from the effective center of the transducer and the index level of the pulse transmitted, on any bearing, by the same non-directional transducer. (4)

REVERBERATION-SUPPRESSION FILTERS. The circuits by which selective discrimination may be provided against interference restricted to a known narrow frequency band are described as reverberation-suppression filters. (4)

REVERSE BLOCKED ADMITTANCE. The reverse blocked admittance of a transducer is the reciprocal of the reverse free impedance. (4)

REVERSE BLOCKED IMPEDANCE. The reverse blocked impedance of a transducer is its output impedance when its source terminals are open-circuited. (4)

REVERSE FREE ADMITTANCE. The reverse free admittance of a transducer is the reciprocal of its reverse blocked impedance. (4)

REVERSE FREE IMPEDANCE. The reverse free impedance of a transducer is its output impedance when its source terminals are short-circuited. (4)

REVERSE LAY. See WIRE ROPE.

REVERSIBLE TRANSDUCER. Also Bilateral transducer. A transducer which, when connecting any energy source and an energy load, completes a system which satisfies the principle of reciprocity is known as a reversible transducer. (4)

REVERSING CURRENT. A tidal current that flows alternately in approximately opposite directions with a slack water at each reversal of direction. Currents of this type usually occur in rivers and straits where the direction of flow is more or less restricted to certain channels. When the movement is towards the shore or up a stream, the current is said to be flooding, and when in the opposite direction it is said to be ebbing. The combined flood and ebb movement including the slack water covers on an average 12.42 hours for the semidiurnal current. If unaffected by a nontidal flow, the flood and ebb movements will each last about 6 hours, but when combined with such a flow, the durations of flood and ebb may be quite unequal. During the flow in each direction the velocity of the current will vary from zero at the time of slack water to a maximum about midway between the slacks. (14)

REVERSING THERMOMETER (RICHTER REVERSING THERMOMETER). 1. A deep-sea recording thermometer. The temperature reading at the desired depth is preserved by overturning the instrument to break the mercury column.

Deep-sea reversing thermometers are delicate, but highly accurate, mercurial thermometers specially designed for recording water temperatures in situ by being reversed when the Nansen bottle is tripped by the messenger. There are two types of reversing thermometers, protected and unprotected. The temperature scale is Celsius (Centigrade) and is carefully etched on the glass stem. The scale is read with a thermometer reader, or viewer. Each thermometer actually consists of two parts: one, the reversing thermometer which is called the main; the other, a regular thermometer which is called the auxiliary. (35)

2. A mercury-in-glass thermometer which records temperature upon being inverted and thereafter retains its reading until returned to the first position. It consists of a conventional bulb connected to a capillary in which a constriction is placed so that upon reversal the mercury column breaks off in a reproducible manner. The mercury runs down into a smaller bulb at the other end of the capillary, which is graduated to read temperature. A 360°turn in a locally widened portion of the capillary serves as a trap to prevent further addition of mercury if the thermometer is warmed and the mercury expands past the break-off point.

The remote-reading potentialities of reversing thermometers make them particularly suitable for use in measuring temperatures at depths in the sea. In this application, both protected thermometers and unprotected thermometers are used, each of which is provided with an auxiliary thermometer. They are generally used in pairs in NANSEN BOTTLES. They are usually read to .01°C, and after the proper corrections have been applied, their readings are considered reliable to .02°C. Details of the correction procedure are given in Lafond's Tables. (24)

REVETMENT. A facing of stone, concrete, etc., built to protect a scarp, embankment or shore structure against erosion by wave action or currents. (11)

RFCWA. Regional Fisheries Commission for Western Africa.

RHODAMINE - B. A type of dye used in experiments concerned with determination of diffusion rates for radioactivity in the ocean. (34)

RIA. A long narrow inlet, with depth gradually diminishing inward. (11)

RICHARDSON CURRENT METER. The Richardson Current Meter is a device which measures the speed and direction of ocean currents and stores the information on 16mm film. Its chief elements are a SAVONIUS ROTOR for measurement of current speed, a vane for determining the current direction relative to the meter, a compass which fixes the position of the meter itself, a system of fiber optic light pipes which transfer the information to a camera, and the 16mm battery operated camera which can be set to run continuously or intermittently.

Under typical operating conditions, data can be recorded by this current meter for periods up to one year. (35)

RIDGE (WEDGE). 1. In meteorology, an elongated area of relatively high atmospheric pressure, almost always associated with and most clearly identified as an area of maximum anticyclonic curvature of wind flow. The locus of this maximum curvature is called the ridge line.

Sometimes, particularly in discussions of atmospheric waves imbedded in the WESTERLIES, a ridge line is considered to be a line drawn through all points at which the anticyclonically curved ISOBARS or contour lines are tangent to a latitude circle.

The most common use of this term is to distinguish it from the closed circulation of a high (or anticyclone); but a ridge may include a high (and an upper-air ridge may be associated with a surface high) and a high may have one or more distinct ridges radiating from its center. (24)

2. A long, narrow elevation of the sea floor, with steep sides and more irregular topography than a RISE. (26)

RIDGED ICE. Pressure ice having readily observed surface roughness in the form of a ridge or many ridges. (15)

RIGHT LAY. See WIRE ROPE.

RILL MARKS. Tiny drainage channels in a beach caused by the flow seaward of water left in the sands of the upper part of the beach after the retreat of the tide or after the dying down of storm waves. (11)

RING TRAVEL. Essentially a large, relatively coarse plankton net attached to a strong ring of large diameter and provided with a towing bridle.

RIP. The agitation of water caused by the interaction of water currents or by a rapid current setting in over an irregular bottom; for example, a "tide rip." See RIP CURRENTS. (24)

RIPARIAN. Pertaining to the banks of a body of water. (11)

RIPARIAN RIGHTS. The rights of a person owning land containing or bordering on a watercourse or other body of water in or to its banks, bed, or waters. (11)

RIP CURRENTS. A strong surface current of short duration flowing seaward from the shore. It usually appears as a visible band of agitated water and is the return movement of water piled up on the shore by incoming waves and wind. With the seaward movement concentrated in a limited band its velocity is somewhat accentuated. A rip consists of three parts: The feeder current flowing parallel to the shore inside the breakers; the neck, where the feeder currents converge and flow through the breakers in a narrow bank or "rip"; and the head, where the current widens and slackens outside the breaker line. A rip current is often miscalled a rip tide. (11)

RIPPLE MARKS. Small, fairly regular ridges in the bed of a waterway or on a land surface caused by water currents or wind. As their form is approximately normal to the direction of current or wind, they indicate both the presence and the direction of currents or winds. (11)

RIPRAP. A layer, facing, or protective mound of stones randomly placed to prevent erosion, scour, or sloughing of a structure or embankment; also the stone so used. (11)

RIP SURF. See CURRENT, RIP.

RISE. A long, broad elevation that rises gently and generally smoothly from the sea floor. (26)

ROAD. See ROADSTEAD.

ROADSTEAD. An area near the shore, where vessels can anchor in safety; usually a shallow indentation in the coast. One with relatively little protection may be called open roadstead. Also called road. (17)

ROARING FORTIES. The area of the oceans between 40° and 50° south latitude, where strong westerly winds prevail. See BRAVE WEST WINDS. (17)

ROBERTS RADIO CURRENT METER. The Roberts Radio Current Meter is an instrument designed specifically to record subsurface current speeds accurately and simultaneously indicate the direction of the flow. The basic components consist of a buoy from which 1 to 3 meters may be suspended, an automatic radio-transmitting system within the buoy, and a ship- or shore-based radio-receiving monitoring system which can monitor up to 15 meters. The buoys usually are anchored in bays, rivers, channels, or other relatively shallow areas. Meters have been operated successfully at depths as great as 2,500 meters from anchored ships.

The current meter is suspended at any desired depth from a buoy of special design which contains a battery-powered radio transmitter and selecting device and supports an antenna and warning lights. The meter aligns itself to the direction of the current flow. The current drives an impeller, or screw, in the nose of the meter. The impeller is connected by a magnetic drive through a watertight bulkhead to an enclosed mechanism which makes and breaks an electrical circuit by means of two contacting devices. One device makes a contact at each fifth turn of the impeller and the other every tenth turn. The frequency of the contacts serves as a measure of velocity. The first contacting device is connected with a built-in magnetic compass and the second is fixed relative to the position of the meter body. The contacting mechanisms are so arranged that when the instrument

is heading south both contacts will close at the same time. When the meter heads in any other direction the time relation between the two sets of contacts changes with the meter heading. This serves as a measure of direction. The contact makes and breaks, relating to direction and speed, are relayed via watertight electrical cable to the buoy where the transmitter is keyed to produce radio signals on a designated frequency. The operating frequency is controlled by a crystal selected for maximum results in the specific area. These signals are received, amplified, and recorded on tape by means of a chronograph at the ship- or shore-based monitoring station. Observers at the monitoring station record the signals on tape from several current meter stations by adjusting the receiver to different frequencies at timed intervals. (35)

ROCHELLE SALT AND ADP PROJECTORS. In this type projector, the plates of Rochelle salt and ADP crystals are mounted so as to utilize the length vibrations instead of the thickness vibrations. The two large faces are coated with a metal foil,

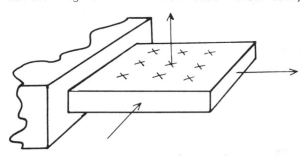

and the ac voltage is applied to the foil. The arrows indicate the deformation resulting from the indicated charge. The crystals are cemented to a single backing plate. The sound is radiated from the free ends of the crystal. The longitudinal vibration is the one desired. (30)

ROCK. (1) Engineering - A natural aggregate of mineral particles connected by strong and permanent cohesive forces. In igneous and metamorphic rocks, it consists of interlocking crystals; in sedimentary rocks, of closely packed mineral grains, often bound together by a natural cement. Since the terms "strong" and "permanent" are subject to different interpretations, the boundary between rock and soil is necessarily an arbitrary one.

(2) Geological - The material that forms the essential part of the earth's solid crust, and includes loose incoherent masses, such as a bed of sand, gravel, clay or volcanic ash, as well as the very firm, hard and solid masses of granite, sandstone, limestone, etc. Most rocks are aggregates of one or more minerals but some are composed entirely of glassy matter, or of mixtures of glass and minerals. (27)

ROLL. Athwartship (i.e., transverse) oscillation of a ship about its longitudinal axis. (12)

ROCKWEED. See FUCUS.

ROLLER. 1. SWELLS coming from a great distance and forming large breakers on exposed coasts.

They are best known on the islands of St. Helena and Ascension in the South Atlantic Ocean during the months from December to April, when they come from the northwest. They arrive, often in calm weather, with practically no warning, and are dangerous to shipping. Rollers also occur at Fernando do Noronha, Tristan da Cunha, and on the coasts of West Africa, Peru, and the East Indies. (24)

2. A long, massive wave which usually retains its form without breaking until it reaches the beach or a shoal. (17)

ROOT-MEAN-SQUARE SOUND PRESSURE. See EFFECTIVE SOUND PRESSURE.

ROPAK. A pinnacle or slab of heavy SEA ICE which has been forced to stand on edge and thus extend vertically upward. The crests may rise 25 feet above the surrounding ice. (25)

ROSSEL CURRENT. A seasonal Pacific Ocean current flowing westward and northwestward along both the southern and northeastern coasts of New Guinea, the southern part flowing through Torres Strait and losing its identity in the Arafura Sea, and the northern part curving northeastward to join the EQUATORIAL COUNTERCURRENT of the Pacific Ocean. The Rossel current is a weak branch of the SOUTH EQUATORIAL CURRENT. During the northern hemisphere winter it is replaced by an easterly-flowing current from the Indian Ocean. (17)

ROTARY CURRENT. A tidal current that flows continually with the direction of flow changing through all points of the compass during the tidal period. Rotary currents are usually found offshore where the direction of flow is not restricted by any barriers. The tendency for the rotation in direction has its origin in the deflecting force of the earth's rotation, and unless modified by local conditions the change is clockwise in the Northern Hemisphere and counterclockwise in the Southern Hemisphere. The velocity of the current usually varies throughout the tidal cycle, passing through 2 maxima in approximately opposite directions and 2 minima with the direction of the current at approximately 90° from the direction at time of maximum velocity. (14)

ROTATIONAL WAVE. See SHEAR WAVE.

ROTTEN ICE. Old ice which has become honeycombed in the course of melting and which is in an advanced stage of disintegration. Rotten ice may appear black through saturation with sea water. (Thin sheets of newly-formed, very thin ice also appear black, and may easily be confused with rotten ice when met in the ICE PACK.) (25)

RSO. Research SHIP OF OPPORTUNITY.

RUBBER ICE. A type of sludge with an elastic quality, not strong enough to bear the weight of a man. (17)

RUBBER SUIT. A partial or complete diving suit designed primarily for the purpose of insulation (preservation) of body heat. The suits are classified as "wet" and "dry". Wet suits are usually made of foam neoprene and are so designed to permit a thin insulating layer of water to contact the divers skin. The "Dry" or rubber sheet suits are designed so as to prohibit such a contact.

RUBBLE. 1. Loose angular water-worn stones along a beach.
2. Rough, irregular fragments of broken rock. (11)

RUBBLE-MOUND STRUCTURE. A mound of random-shaped and random-placed stones protected with a cover layer of selected stones or specially shaped concrete armor units. (armor units in primary cover layer may be placed in orderly manner or dumped at random.) (11)

RUM. Remote Underwater Manipulator.

RUNNEL. A corrugation (trough) of the FORESHORE (or the bottom just offshore), formed by wave and/or tidal action. Larger than the trough between RIPPLE MARKS. (11)

RUN-UP (UPRUSH). The rush of water up a structure on the breaking of a wave. The amount of run-up is the vertical height above still water level that the rush of water reaches. (11)

R/V. 1. Research Vessel
2. Reentry Vehicle.

S

SAC. Indentation in the contour lines of equal depth showing submarine relief; analogous to a gulf on the surface. The opposite is submarine peninsula. (17)

SACI. South Atlantic Cooperative Investigations.

SACLANTCEN. Supreme Allied Command for the Atlantic Center (ASW Research Center, LaSpezia, Italy.)

SADDLE. A low point on a RIDGE or between SEAMOUNTS. (26)

SALINITY. A measure of the quantity of dissolved salts in sea water. It is formally defined as the total amount of dissolved solids in sea water in parts per thousand (0/00) by weight when all the carbonate has been converted to oxide, the bromide and iodide to chloride, and all organic matter is completely oxidized. These qualifications result from the chemical difficulty in drying the salts in sea water. In practice, salinity is not determined directly but is computed from chlorinity, electrical conductivity, refractive index, or some other property whose relationship to salinity is well established.

The relationship between chlorinity Cl and salinity S as set forth in Knudsen's tables is $S = 0.03 + 1.805 \, Cl$. In 1940, however, Lyman and Fleming found that the relationship between total dissolved salts Σ and chlorinity was better expressed by $\Sigma = 0.07 + 1.811 \, Cl$. (24)

SALINITY BRIDGE. An instrument for determining salinity of water (a salinometer) by measuring electrical conductivity of the water sample with a Wheatstone bridge. (24)

SALINITY OF SEA ICE. Sea ice forms first as salt-free crystals near the surface of the sea. As the process continues, these crystals are joined together and, as they do so, small quantities of brine are trapped within the ice. On the average, new ice six inches thick contains five to ten parts of salt per thousand. With lower temperature, freezing takes place faster and a greater amount of salt is trapped in the ice.

Depending upon the temperature, the trapped brine may either freeze or remain liquid, but because its density is greater than that of the pure ice, it tends to settle down through the pure ice. As it does so the ice gradually freshens, becoming clearer, stronger, and more brittle. At an age of one year sea ice is sufficiently fresh that its melt water, if found in puddles of sufficient size, and not contaminated by spray from the sea can be used to replenish the fresh water supply of a ship. When sea ice reaches an age of about two years, virtually all of the salt has been eliminated. Icebergs contain no salt, and uncontaminated melt water obtained from them is fresh.

The settling out of the brine gives sea ice a honeycomb structure which greatly hastens its disintegration when the temperature rises above freezing. In this state, when it is called ROTTEN ICE, much more surface is exposed to warm air and water, and the rate of melting is increased. In a day's time, a floe of apparently solid ice several inches thick may disappear completely. (12)

SALINITY-TEMPERATURE-DEPTH RECORDER. The STD (Salinity-Temperature-Depth Recorder) measures temperature by means of a nickel-resistance thermometer. Utilizing the conductivity, salinity can be compiled automatically in situ. This instrument developed at Woods Hole, measures the conductivity of sea water between two platinum electrodes spaced a few inches apart. This is combined with the temperature by an electromechanical computer in the recorder to give salinity. The sensing elements are towed behind the ship while a recorder aboard ship shows the temperature, salinity, and depth. Although this instrument is not as accurate as desired, it is excellent for rapid surveys, and is adequate for surveys in estuarine waters. (35)

SALINOMETER. Any device or instrument for determining salinity, especially one based on electrical conductivity methods. (24)

SALP. See TUNICATES.

SALTATION. That method of sand movement in a fluid in which individual particles leave the bed by bounding nearly vertically and, because the motion of the fluid is not strong or turbulent enough to retain them in suspension, return to the bed at some distance downstream. The travel path of the particles is a series of hops and bounds. (11)

SALT ERROR. In determining the pH of sea water by indicators an error is introduced by the fact that neutral ions in the solution have a pronounced effect upon the color and, hence, upon the apparent pH. (13)

SALT HAZE. A haze created by the presence of finely divided particles of sea salt in the air, usually derived from the evaporation of sea spray. (12)

SAND. Loose detrital material consisting of small but easily distinguishable separate grains ranging between 0.0025 and 0.0787 inch (0.0625 and 2.0000 millimeters) in diameter. (16)

SAND REEF. Same as BAR.

SANDSTONE. A cemented or otherwise compacted detrital sediment composed predominantly of quartz grains, the grades of the latter being those of sand (See SAND). Mineralogical varieties such as feldspatic and glauconitic sandstones are recognized, and also argillaceous, siliceous, calcareous, ferruginous and other varieties according to the nature of the binding or cementing material. (Holmes, 1928) (28)

SAPROPHYTIC. Living on and obtaining food from dead or decaying matter in the soil or from the dead parts of living plants. (18)

SARGASSO. A certain type of seaweed, or more generally, a large floating mass of this seaweed. (17)

SARGASSO SEA. A region of the north Atlantic Ocean occupying the central space within a huge ellipse bounded by the GULF STREAM, the SOUTHEAST DRIFT CURRENT, the CANARIES CURRENT, and the NORTH EQUATORIAL CURRENT. It is located approximately between lat. 20°N. and 40°N. and long. 30°W. and 70°W, and is characterised by the presence of large quantities of gulf weed and the absence of any well-marked currents. (14)

SARGASSUM. A marine alga which grows attached to the bottom in tropical and subtropical waters and becomes detached to form extensive drifts, sometimes called gulfweed. (15)

SATURABLE REACTOR. See FLUX-GATE MAGNETOMETER.

SATURATION. When a person resides at sea level, his blood and all his tissues become saturated with dissolved nitrogen at a tension (partial pressure of dissolved gas) equal to the partial pressure of nitrogen in his lung ALVEOLI - about 570 mm. Hg. If the person is then exposed to a breathing medium other than air or is taken to altitude or depth, this will change the partial pressure of nitrogen in his alveoli. His blood and tissues must then either lose or take up nitrogen in order to reach equilibrium (state of balance) with the new alveolar nitrogen pressure.

SAVONIUS ROTOR. A Magnetic Pickup Rotor (having very low threshold speeds) which is used as a flow sensing device. It was introduced into Oceanography by J. M. Snodgrass in 1954.

In the Savonius Current Meter, the meter uses a magnetic compass to originate an electric signal which is proportional to direction. (35)

SCANNING SONAR. Echo-ranging system in which the ping is transmitted simultaneously throughout the entire angle to be searched, and a rapidly rotating narrow beam scans for the returning echoes. (6)

SCAR. Special Committee on Antarctic Research.

SCARP. See ESCARPMENT.

SCATTERING. Modifications of the direction in which acoustic energy is propagated caused by reflections from foreign bodies (in the medium, and including the bottom and surface interface) are said to be due to scattering. (4)

SCATTERING CROSS SECTION. The acoustic scattering cross section of an object is an area equal to 4π times the product of the mean-square sound pressure scattered by the object, averaged over a sphere of unit radius surrounding the object, and the square of the unit radius, divided by the square of the sound pressure of the plane wave incident upon the object. The unit of the cross section is the square of the unit radius. (2)

SCATTERING DIFFERENTIAL. The scattering differential is the amount by which the level of the scattered mean-square sound pressure averaged over all directions at a specified unit distance from the effective acoustic center of the object exceeds the plane-wave free-field pressure level of the sound incident upon the object. The scattering differential of an object is ten times the logarithm to the base ten of the ratio of the scattering cross section to the area of the sphere of unit radius surrounding the object. (2)

SCATTERING LOSS. Scattering loss is that part of the transmission loss which is due to scattering within the medium or due to roughness of any reflecting surfaces. (9)

SCG. Scientific Committee for Inter-Union Cooperation in Geophysics.

SCHLIEREN. (German, 'streaks', 'striae'.)
1. Regions of different density in a fluid, especially as shown by special apparatus.
2. A method or apparatus for visualizing or photographing regions of varying density in a field of flow. (31)

SCOOPFISH (UNDERWAY SAMPLER). This device consists of a sampling cup which is mounted in a hollow barrel attached to a tail-piece. When cocked ready for use, the cup protrudes about half an inch from the barrel and a hinged cover is held back by a spring. Attachment to the light towing wire is by means of a hinged arm that is folded down during descent. When ready, the sampler is gently lowered over the ship's side, but on striking the water the brake is taken off the winch drum and the cable rapidly run out. On striking bottom, a small sample is taken into the cup which at the same time is forced back into the tube. As this happens, the spring holding back the lid is released and the latter now comes over the end of the tube and prevents any loss of sample during hoisting. Simultaneously a catch is sprung which frees the after end of the towing arm so that during hoisting the towing point of the sampler is brought nearer the forward end, thus reducing drag. Although limited as to the type and amount of sediment that can be sampled this device has been very successfully used to make rapid surveys in water of depth up to 100 fathoms. (35)

SCOR. Scientific Committee on Oceanographic Research.

SCORIAE. Volcanic slag, pyroclastic ejecta; fragments of scoriae between 0.16 and 1.26 inches (4 and 32 millimeters) in size are essentially equivalent to volcanic cinders. Scoriae are classed as gravel on bottom sediment charts.

SCUBA. Self Contained Underwater Breathing Apparatus. See OPEN CIRCUIT SCUBA, CLOSED CIRCUIT SCUBA, and SEMI-CLOSED CIRCUIT SCUBA.

SEA. 1. Same as ocean.
2. A subdivision of an ocean. All seas except "inland seas" are physically interconnected parts of the earth's total salt water system. Two types are distinguished, mediterranean and adjacent. Mediterraneans are groups of seas, collectively separated from the major water body as an individual sea. Adjacent seas are those connected individually to the larger body.
3. Same as state of the sea. (See SEA STATE)
4. Sea-surface waves within their fetch; opposed to SWELL. (24)

SEA ACORNS. See BARNACLES.

SEA ANCHOR. An object towed by a vessel, usually a small one, to keep the vessel end-on to a heavy sea or surf or to reduce the drift. In its usual form it consists of a conical canvas bag with the large end open. When towed with this end forward, it offers considerable resistance. A small tripping line attached to the pointed end is used for hauling the sea anchor into the vessel. A sea anchor is sometimes improvised by using a weighted sail and spar, a bucket, a basket, a weight, or a long line. Also called drag, drogue. (17)

SEABEES. Civil Engineering Corps Division of Bureau of Yards and Docks, BuDocks Building; Washington, D. C.

SEA BREEZE. A coastal local wind that blows from sea to land, caused by the temperature difference when the sea surface is colder than the adjacent land. Therefore, it usually blows on relatively calm, sunny, summer days; and alternates with the oppositely directed, usually weaker, nighttime land breeze. As the sea breeze regime progresses, the wind develops a component parallel to the coast, owing to the coriolis deflection. (Defant, F., in Compendium of Meteorology, 1951, pp. 655-672) (24)

SEA BREEZE OF THE SECOND KIND. See COLD-FRONT-LIKE SEA BREEZE.

SEA BUOY. The outermost buoy marking the entrance to a channel or harbor. Sometimes called farewell buoy, since it is the last buoy passed by a vessel proceeding out to sea. (17)

SEACHANNEL. A long, narrow, U-shaped or V-shaped shallow depression of the sea floor, usually occurring on a gently sloping PLAIN or FAN. (26)

SEA FOG. A type of advection fog formed when air that has been lying over a warm water surface is transported over a colder water surface, resulting in cooling of the lower layer of air below its dew point. (24)

SEAGOING PLATFORM FOR ACOUSTIC RESEARCH. See SPAR.

SEA GRASS. Seed bearing marine plants, more highly organized than algae, found in shallow waters both brackish and marine, attaining lengths up to 8 feet. (15)

SEA ICE. All ice formed by the freezing of sea water. It may be classified as FAST ICE if attached in any way to the shore or to the bottom, FLOATING ICE if unattached, or it may be classified according to related features. (17)

SEA ICE SHELF. Sea ice floating in the vicinity of its formation and separated from fast ice, of which it may have been a part, by a tide crack, or a family of such cracks. (17)

SEALAB I. An underwater laboratory used in July 1964 by 4 Navy divers who lived and worked in and outside of this 192 foot deep laboratory placed at the base of ARGUS IS. The work of these divers was to participate in the Navy's first protracted physiological-engineering test to determine how men can work freely and for extended periods of time at these (192') underwater depths.

SEA LEVEL. The height or level of the sea surface (without further technical definition). It is used loosely as a synonym for MEAN SEA LEVEL, STILL-WATER LEVEL, or HALF-TIDE LEVEL. (24)

SEA LEVEL DATUM. A determination of mean sea level that has been adopted as a standard datum for heights. The sea level is subject to some variations from year to year, but as the permanency of any datum is of prime importance in engineering work, a sea level datum after adoption should in general be maintained indefinitely even though differing slightly from later determinations of mean sea level based upon longer series of observations. The sea level datum now used for the U. S. Coast and Geodetic Survey level net is officially known as the Sea Level Datum of 1929, the year referring to the last general adjustment of the net. The datum itself may be considered as an adjustment based upon tide observations taken at various tide stations along the coasts of the United States over a number of years. See also MEAN SEA LEVEL. (27)

SEAMOUNT. An elevation of the sea floor having a nearly equidimensional plan less than 60 nautical miles across the summit. (26)

SEAMOUNT CHAIN. Three or more SEAMOUNTS in a line with bases separated by a relatively flat sea floor. (26)

SEAMOUNT GROUP. Three or more SEAMOUNTS not in a line and with bases separated by a relatively flat sea floor. (26)

SEAMOUNT RANGE. Three or more SEAMOUNTS having connected bases and aligned along a RIDGE or RISE. (26)

SEA PUSS. A dangerous longshore current, a RIP CURRENT, caused by return flow, loosely the submerged channel or inlet through a BAR caused by those currents. (11)

SEA RAINBOW. See MARINE RAINBOW.

SEARCHLIGHT-TYPE SONAR. Echo-ranging system in which the same narrow beam pattern is used for transmission and reception. (6)

SEAS. Scientific Exploration for the Atlantic Shelf.

SEA-SALT NUCLEUS. A condensation nucleus of a highly hygroscopic nature produced by partial or complete desiccation of particles of sea spray or of sea-water droplets derived from breaking bubbles.
    That such nuclei are important in condensation processes over the oceans and near coasts is fairly well established; but it has not yet been demonstrated that sea-salt particles are the chief source of nuclei in condensation over continental interiors. (12)

SEASCO. Southeast Asia Science Cooperation Office.

SEASHORE. (1) Law - All the ground between the ordinary high-water and low-water mark.
        (2) The SHORE of the SEA or OCEAN. (27)

SEA SLICK. An area of sea surface, variable in size and markedly different in appearance (color and oiliness) usually caused by plankton blooms. (15)

SEASONAL CURRENT. See OCEAN CURRENT.

SEA SQUIRT. See TUNICATES.

SEA STATE. Numerical or written description of ocean surface roughness. For more precise usage sea state may be defined as the average height of the highest one-third of the waves observed in a wave train referred to a numerical code which covers an increasing range of such heights as indicated by the table below:

Code	Height (feet)
0	0
1	0 - 1/3
2	1/3 - 1 2/3
3	1 2/3 - 4
4	4 - 8
5	8 - 13
6	13 - 20
7	20 - 30
8	30 - 45
9	over 45

SEATO. South East Asia Treaty Organization.

SEA URCHINS. Echinoderms with long movable (2-15 cm long) spines radiating out from a round body about 10 cm in diameter.

SEA WALL. See JETTY.

SEA WATER. The water of the seas, distinguished from fresh water by its appreciable salinity.
    The distinction between the usage of salt water and sea water is not very sharply drawn. Commonly, sea water is used as the antithesis of specific types of fresh water, as river water, lake water, rain water, etc., whereas salt water is merely the antithesis of fresh water in general. (24)

SEA-WATER THERMOMETER. A thermometer designed for use in measuring the temperature of sea water. One form of this instrument consists of a mercury-in-glass thermometer protected by a perforated metal case. This is used to measure the temperature of a sample of sea water. Another form consists of a mercury-in-glass thermometer surrounded by a metal case which forms a well around the bulb of the thermometer. When the thermometer is raised from the water, a sample is retained in the well for temperature measurement. (24)

SECANT FUNCTION GENERATOR. A device for use with a longitude-latitude indicator to make allowance for meridian convergence toward the poles. Information of meridian curvature at the given latitude is stored in a relay system through a conducting grid on a rotating disk. As the initial position changes to another latitude, the disk is rotated proportionately by motor action reorienting the grid conductors within the relay system. The resulting new voltage, corresponding to the new meridian curvature, is relayed to the longitude indicator. Developed by Naval Air Development Center for use mainly in high-speed aircraft. (30)

SECCHI DISK. A circular plate, usually of wood, having a diameter of 30 centimeters. It is covered with a flat white paint. A ring attached at the center of the upper surface allows a graduated line to be secured. Opposite the ring on the under surface is attached a lead weight so that the disc will sink rapidly and vertically. This weight should be at least 5 pounds and may be increased when conditions of drift and current warrant. Secchi discs used on Navy surveys are provided with 5- and 7 1/2-pound weights. The line attached to the Secchi disc should be marked off in 1-meter intervals to at least 50 meters.
    The Secchi disc is designed to measure transparency and is dependent upon the available illumination which varies with the time of day, cloud formation, and amount of cloud cover. (35)

SECONDARY LOBES. See LOBES.

SEDIMENT. 1. Any material carried in suspension by water, which will ultimately settle to the bottom.
        2. Fine water-borne matter deposited or accumulated in beds. (27)

SEDIMENTO-EUSTATISM. See EUSTATISM.

SEER. Submarine Explosive Echo Ranging.

SEICHE. A stationary wave oscillation with a period varying from a few minutes to an hour or more, but somewhat less than the tidal periods. They are usually attributed to strong winds or changes in barometric pressure and are found both in enclosed bodies of water and superimposed upon the tide waves of the open ocean. The period of a seiche in an enclosed body of water is usually represented by the formula, Period $= 2L/\sqrt{gd}$ in which L is the length and d the average depth of the body of water and g is the acceleration of gravity. (14)

SEIS. Submarine Emergency Identification Signal.

SEISMICITY. The phenomenon of earth movements. (27)

SELEROPROTEIN. See SPONGIN.

SELF NOISE. See OWN-SHIP'S NOISE.

SEMIDIURNAL. Having a period or cycle of approximately one-half of a tidal day. The predominating type of tide throughout the world is semidiurnal, with two high waters and two low waters each tidal day. The tidal current is said to be semidiurnal when there are two flood and two ebb periods each day. A semidiurnal constituent has two maxima and two minima each constituent day, and its symbol is usually distinguished by the subscript 2. (14)

SENSIBLE HEAT. Heat resulting in a temperature change but not a change in state. (33)

SENSITIVITY LEVEL; (RESPONSE LEVEL, SENSITIVITY) (RESPONSE). The sensitivity (or response) level of a transducer, in decibels, is 20 times the logarithm to the base 10 of the ratio of the amplitude sensitivity to the reference sensitivity, where the amplitude is a quantity proportional to the square root of power. The kind of sensitivity and the reference sensitivity must be indicated. (1)

SENSOR. The component of an instrument that converts an input signal into a quantity which is measured by another part of the instrument. Also called 'sensing element'. (31)

SEQUENCE OF CURRENT. The order of occurrence of the four tidal current strengths of a day with special reference as to whether the greater flood immediately precedes or follows the greater ebb. (14)

SEQUENCE OF TIDE. The order in which the four tides of a day occur with special reference as to whether the higher high water immediately precedes or follows the lower low water. (14)

SERPAC. Service Forces, Pacific (USN).

SERPLANT. Service Forces, Atlantic (USN).

SESSILE. Permanently fixed, sedentary, not free-moving. (19)

SET. The direction towards which an ocean current flows. (24)

SETA. A bristle or slender, stiff bristle-like structure (evident in many marine worms). (19)

SET-UP WIND. (1) The vertical rise in the still water level on the leeward side of a body of water caused by wind stresses on the surface of the water;
(2) The difference in still water level between the windward and the leeward sides of a body of water caused by wind stresses on the surface of the water;
(3) Synonymous with wind tide. Wind tide is usually reserved for use on the ocean and large bodies of water. Wind set-up is usually reserved for use on reservoirs and small bodies of water. (11)

SEVFLT. Seventh Fleet (Pacific) (USN).

SHADING. Shading is a method of controlling the directional response pattern of a transducer through control of the distribution of phase and amplitude of the transducer action over the active face. (1)

SHADOW ZONE. Region in which refraction effects cause exclusion of echo-ranging signals (sound).

SHALLOW WATER. Commonly; water of such a depth that surface waves are noticeably affected by bottom topography. It is customary to consider water of depths less than half the surface wave length as shallow water. (11)

SHALLOW-WATER BLACKOUT. A carbon dioxide accumulation or excess in a breathing system which causes the diver to lose consciousness without the usual warning of DYSPNEA or other symptoms such as headache, nausea, dizziness or weakness. (37)

SHARKI. See KAUS.

SHEAR STRENGTH. The Ultimate Strength of a material subjected to shear loading. The maximum Shear Stress that can be sustained by a material without rupture. It may be obtained from the Torsion Test, a modified Flexure Test or the Shear Test. In the Torsion Test it is equal to Torsional Strength. In the Shear Test, it is calculated by substituting maximum sustained load for P in the punch test formula for Shear Stress. It may be calculated in the Flexure Test by substituting maximum sustained load for P in the flexure formula for Shear Stress. For Shear Stress to exceed Flexural Stress in a

Flexural Test, however, the span of a rectangular specimen must be less than half the square of its thickness, and the span of a cylindrical specimen must be less than one-third its diameter.

SHEAR STRESS. The maximum nominal biaxial stress developed by a material subjected to a specified load. In the Torsion Test, it is calculated as Torsional Stress although the assumptions underlying the formula for Torsional Stress are not valid for stresses above the Elastic Limit. In the Shear Test, Shear Stress (psi) is calculated as follows:

$$S_S = \frac{P}{dt}$$

where S_S = Shear Stress, psi
P = punch load, lb
d = punch diameter, in.
t = specimen thickness, in.
In the Flexure Test, Shear Stress (psi) may be calculated as follows:

$$S_S = \frac{0.75P}{bh} \text{ (for rectangular specimen)}$$
$$S_S = \frac{0.85P}{d^2} \text{ (for round specimen)}$$

where S_S = maximum nominal Shear Stress, psi
P = bending load, lb.
b = specimen width, psi
h = specimen thickness, psi
d = specimen diameter, psi.

SHEAR WAVE (ROTATIONAL WAVE). A shear wave is a wave, usually in a solid, which causes an element of the solid to change its shape without at the same time undergoing a change in volume. (9)

SHEET FLOW. See LAMINAR FLOW.

SHEET ICE. Ice formed in a thin, smooth layer over a water surface. This should not be confused with ICE SHEET, a continuous layer of ice covering a large land area. (17)

SHEET PILE. A PILE with a generally flat cross-section to be driven into the ground or sea bed and meshed or interlocked with like members to form a diaphragm, wall, or BULKHEAD. (11)

SHELF EDGE. A line along which there is a marked increase of slope at the outer margin of a CONTINENTAL SHELF or INSULAR SHELF. Conventionally the shelf edge has been taken at 100 fathoms. (27)

SHELF ICE. A thick ice formation with level surface extending seaward from the land but attached thereto. Shelf ice may be formed in three ways: (1) By an extension of LAND ICE onto water, (2) by the accumulation of snow upon SEA ICE which has persisted for several seasons, and (3) by a combination of (1) and (2), resulting in areas of land ice extending onto the water interspersed with areas of persistent sea ice covered with accumulations of snow.
The chief characteristics of shelf ice are: (1) A shape conforming to the boundaries of the coast, (2) a seaward edge usually floating freely in deep water, (3) vertical cliffs up to 150 feet high on the seaward edge, and (4) prominent horizontal banding and clean-cut joint faces from which TABULAR ICEBERGS are CALVED periodically. (25)

SHELL-NATRON. A commercial compound used as a carbon dioxide absorbent in diving. (37)

SHINGLE. (1) Strictly and properly, beach gravel composed of smooth, well-rounded pebbles of roughly the same size. The space between pebbles are not filled with finer materials as they are in ordinary gravel. Shingle gives out a musical note when stepped on.
(2) Loosely and commonly, any beach

gravel which is coarser than ordinary gravel, especially if consisting of flat or flattish pebbles. (27)

SHIP-BORNE WAVE RECORDER. An instrument which measures waves directly aboard ship. It combines the sea pressure at a point on the hull of the ship with the vertical displacement of this point which is obtained by double integration of the output of a vertical accelerometer. (35)

SHIP MOTION. The complex motion imparted to a ship upon encountering waves. All the motions can be regarded as combinations of three oscillations about horizontal or vertical axes (ROLL, PITCH, and YAW), and three linear displacements of the center of gravity (HEAVE, SURGE, and SWAY). (12)

SHIPS INTERNAL NAVIGATION SYSTEM. See SINS.

SHIPS OF OPPORTUNITY. These include, but are not restricted to: (1) certain U. S. Navy combatant Fleet units such as aircraft carriers, cruisers, destroyers, amphibious ships, mine sweepers, and submarines, (2) U. S. Navy Radar Picket Ships (YAGR's and DER's), (3) certain U. S. Navy auxiliary units (oilers, refrigerator ships, cargo ships, ice breakers), (4) units of Military Sea Transportation Service, (5) units of U. S. Merchant Marine, (6) U. S. Air Force Ocean Range Vessels, (7) larger units of U. S. Fishing Fleet. The installation and operation of instrument packages on these ships and vessels is predicated on a not-to-interfere basis with the ships's primary mission.

SHOAL. 1. A detached elevation of the bottom comprised of any material except rock or coral, and which may endanger surface navigation.
    2. To become shallow gradually.
    3. To cause to become shallow.
    4. To proceed from a greater to a lesser depth of water. (11)

SHOALING COEFFICIENT. The ratio of the height of a wave in water of any depth to its height in deep water with the effect of refraction eliminated. Sometimes called shoaling factor or depth factor. (11)

SHOALING FACTOR. See SHOALING COEFFICIENT.

SHORAN (SHORT RANGE NAVIGATION). A precision electronic position fixing system which uses the UHF band (200-300 megacycles) with ranges restricted to approximate line of sight distances.
    Position is determined by measuring the time required for the high frequency signal to travel from the mobile station to the transponder beacons and return. Two fixed shore stations are required and several mobile stations can use the same two fixed stations. Lines of position are concentric circles. High accuracies with ranges as much as about 40 nautical miles can be obtained depending upon the elevations available for the shore stations. The system is quite suitable for launch hydrography. High precision SHORAN is called HIRAN. (29)

SHORE. That strip of ground bordering any body of water which is alternately exposed, or covered by tides and waves. A shore of unconsolidated material is usually called a BEACH. (27)

SHOREBASED RECORDER OF LOW-FREQUENCY OCEAN WAVES. This instrument has a pressure head on the sea bottom that contains a hydraulic filter. The filter attenuates high-frequency signals caused by ordinary gravity waves and very low frequency signals caused by tides. The maximum response is for frequencies of about one cycle per 1,000 seconds. A strain-gauge transducer converts the filtered pressure fluctuations into electrical signals, which are

transmitted to shore through a cable. Two identical bellows are used in the compliant chambers, but the capillary tubes are adjusted so that their resistances to the flow of hydraulic fluid have a ratio of about four to one. (35)

SHOREFACE. The narrow zone seaward from the low tide SHORELINE permanently covered by water, over which the beach sands and gravels actively oscillate with changing wave conditions. Also called inshore. (27)

SHORE ICE. See FAST ICE.

SHORELINE. The intersection of a specified plane of water with the SHORE. The line delineating the shoreline on U. S. Coast and Geodetic Survey nautical charts and surveys approximates the mean highwater line. (27)

SHORE TERRACE. A terrace made along a coast by the action of waves and shore currents; it may become land by the uplifting of the shore or the lowering of the water. (27)

SHORT-CRESTED WAVE. An ocean wave whose crest is of finite length, i.e., the type actually found in nature. (12)

SHORT SEA. A sea in which the waves are short, irregular, and broken. (17)

SHORT WAVE. See DEEP-WATER WAVE.

SI (Smithsonian Institution). Within the National Oceanographic Program, the main responsibility of the Smithsonian Institution is the collection, preservation, and study of marine materials made by the Smithsonian Institution itself, by other Federal agencies, and by private organizations referring collections to the Institution. The Smithsonian Oceanographic Sorting Center will process specimens collected for the National Program as a service to the scientific community.

SIAM. Society of Industrial and Applied Mathematics.

SIGMA-T (SYMBOL σ_t). A conveniently abbreviated value of the density of a sea water sample of temperature t and salinity S: $\sigma_t = \left[\rho(S,t) - 1\right] \times 10^3$

where $\rho(S,t)$ is the value of the sea-water density in c.g.s. units at standard atmospheric pressure. If, for example, $\rho(S,t) = 1.02648$, then $\sigma_t = 26.48$. (24)

SIGMA-T,P. (Symbol σ_t, ρ.) SIGMA-T, corrected to the hydrostatic pressure in situ. (24)

SIGMA-ZERO (SYMBOL σ_0). SIGMA-T at $0°C$. Knudsen's tables give values of sigma-zero as a function of salinity or chlorinity, as well as corrections to be applied to obtain sigma-t. (24)

SIGNAL. See SIGNAL WAVE.

SIGNAL-TO-INTERFERENCE RATIO. The magnitude of a signal wave relative to the magnitude of a wave which interferes with its reception may properly be described as the signal-to-interference ratio. (4)

SIGNAL-TO-NOISE RATIO. See SIGNAL-TO-INTERFERENCE RATIO.

SIGNAL TRANSMISSION LEVEL. The signal transmission level in a transmission system is the signal level (of a kind to be specified) at a designated position in the system. (2)

SIGNAL WAVE. Any sound wave upon which it is

required to make an observation of any kind is known as a signal wave, or more often, simply as a signal. (4)

SIGNIFICANT WAVE. A statistical term denoting waves with the average height and period of the 1/3 highest waves of a given wave group. The composition of the higher waves depends upon the extent to which the lower waves are considered. Experience so far indicates that a careful observer who attempts to establish the character of the higher waves will record values which approximately fit the definition. A wave of SIGNIFICANT WAVE PERIOD and SIGNIFICANT WAVE HEIGHT. (11)

SIGNIFICANT WAVE HEIGHT (CHARACTERISTIC WAVE HEIGHT). The average height of the one-third highest waves of a given wave group. Note that the composition of the highest waves depends upon the extent to which the lower waves are considered. In wave record analysis, the average height of the highest 1/3 of a selected number of waves, this number being determined by dividing the time of record by the significant period. (11)

SIGNIFICANT WAVE PERIOD. An arbitrary period generally taken as the period of the 1/3 highest waves within a given group. Note that the composition of the highest waves depends upon the extent to which the lower waves are considered. In wave record analysis, this is determined as the average period of the most frequently recurring of the larger well-defined waves in the record under study. (11)

SIKUSSAK. Very old SEA ICE trapped in FIORDS. Sikussak resembles GLACIER ICE since snowfall and snow drifts contribute to its formation. (25)

SILICIOUS. Containing more than 30 per cent of silicon-based material. Diatom and radiolarian oozes are silicious. (27)

SILL. A RIDGE or RISE separating partially closed BASINS from one another or from the adjacent sea floor. (26)

SILL DEPTH. The greatest depth over a SILL. (26)

SILT. A clastic deposit of an inorganic granular material with median diameters approximately between 0.005 mm and 0.05 mm. It is thus between sand and clay in size. The Corps of Engineers defines silt as soil having a liquid limit of 27 or less, and a plasticity limit (based on -40 fraction) of 6 or greater. (27)

SIMPLE HARMONIC MOTION. A simple harmonic motion is a motion such that the displacement is a sinusoidal function of time. (2)

SIMPLE SOUND SOURCE. A simple sound source is a source that radiates sound uniformly in all directions under free-field conditions. (2)

SINGLE SHOT UNDERWATER CAMERA. See UNDERWATER CAMERAS.

SINKING CENTER. Subartic region where strongly saline surface water of tropical origin sinks through the colder, but less saline underlying layers.

SINS (SHIPS INTERNAL NAVIGATION SYSTEM). A precise dead reckoning method which establishes the navigation coordinates through measurements made by its gyroscopes and accelerometers. SINS uses two accelerometers, one oriented north-south and the other east-west, to determine ship travel over the earth. The effects of gravity accelerations and ships roll and pitch are eliminated by use of three gyroscopes. By integration, present latitude and longitude, velocity and heading can be determined. (34)

SIO. Scripps Institution of Oceanography.

SIROCCO. A warm wind of the Mediterranean area, either a foehn or a hot southerly wind in advance of a low pressure area moving from the Sahara or Arabian deserts. Called leveche in Spain. (17)

SIXFLT. Sixth Fleet (Atlantic) (USN).

SKIN DIVING. Diving without the use of SCUBA or artificial breathing apparatus.

SLACK WATER. The state of a tidal current when its velocity is near zero, especially the moment when a reversing current changes direction and its velocity is zero. The term is also applied to the entire period of low velocity near the time of turning of the current when it is too weak to be of any practical importance in navigation. The relation of the time of slack water to the tidal phases varies in different localities. In some places slack water occurs near the times of high and low water, while in other localities the slack water may occur midway between high and low water. (14)

SLEEPER. See ETESIANS.

SLICK. A smooth area of water, as one caused by the sweep of a vessel's stern during a turn, or by a film of oil. (17)

SLIP. 1. A berthing space between two piers. Also called DOCK.
    2. The difference between the distance a propeller would travel longitudinally in one revolution if operating in a solid and the distance it travels through a fluid. (17)

SLOPE. The degree of inclination to the horizontal. Usually expressed as a ratio, such as 1:25, indicating one unit rise in 25 units of horizontal distance; or in a decimal fraction (0.04); degrees (2°18'); or per cent (4%). It is sometimes expressed by such adjectives as steep, moderate, gentle, mild, flat, etc. Also called GRADIENT. (27)

SLOPE AMPLIFICATION. Amplification, in an FM sonar receiver amplifier, which increases uniformly with increasing frequency. (5)

SLOUGH. 1. A small muddy marshland or tidal waterway which usually connects other tidal areas.
    2. A tide-land or bottom-land creek. (11)

SLUDGE FLOE. See FLOE.

SLUSH. 1. Partly melted, wet snow.
    2. Partly frozen sea water, when its consistency is soupy. Called snow slush or snezhura when formed from snow that has fallen into water that is at a temperature below that of the snow. (17)

SMALL FLOE. See FLOE.

SMITH-MCINTYRE MUD SAMPLER. With this device the digging and hoisting mechanisms are separated. This fact improves overall performance even under

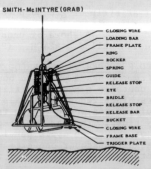

SMITH-McINTYRE (GRAB)

CLOSING WIRE
LOADING BAR
FRAME PLATE
RING
ROCKER
SPRING
GUIDE
RELEASE STOP
EYE
BRIDLE
RELEASE STOP
RELEASE BAR
BUCKET
CLOSING WIRE
FRAME BASE
TRIGGER PLATE

bad working conditions. The sampler consists of a spring-loaded bucket actuated only after the device rests squarely on the bottom. The bucket is carried on a heavy metal bridle which slides on a guide tube, and two heavy springs on the frame bear on the movable bridle. In the set position the springs are held by two catches which fit into a pair of holders and these are triggered when the device strikes bottom. On release, the springs bear on the bridle and push the bucket down into the sediment. At the same time as these are triggered, a release bar moves so that on hoisting the weight goes on the wire and the two halves of the bucket are drawn together taking a sample of the sediment. (35)

SN. 1. Secretary of the Navy;
2. Signal-to-Noise ratio.

SNAP. Systems for Nuclear Auxiliary Power, developed by AEC. Compact devices to supply power for space, terrestrial and underwater uses. System is based on conversion of heat to energy. Heat is obtained either from a small nuclear reactor or from the decay of radioisotopes. Characteristics: long life (5-10 years); reliability of power source; independence from environmental conditions; high cost. Power ranges 1-500 milliwatts, 10-200 watts, others in development. (30)

SNAPPING SHRIMP. Species of shrimp which produce sharp cracking sounds through the rapid closure of the large pincer claw. Greatest populations of snapping shrimp are found in shallow temperate and tropic waters on shell, rock, coral, and sponge bottoms. The noise produced ranges in frequency from 1.5 to 45 kilocycles, and interferes with sound ranging. (15)

SNEZHURA. See SLUSH.

SNORKEL. A tube used by skin divers which permits breathing without raising the nose or mouth out of the water when swimming face down on the surface of the water. One end of the tube is held in the mouth of the swimmer while the other end protrudes above the surface.

SNOWBLINK. See SKY MAP.

SNOW SLUSH. See SLUSH.

SOFAR. (Sound Fixing and Ranging)
In most parts of the oceans there exists a natural sound channel, which extends from very near the surface to a depth of approximately 12,000 feet. This channel has an acoustical center, or axis, which is generally between 1,500 to 4,000 feet below the surface. The sound from a small bomb detonated near this axis can be received by a monitoring station at ranges up to 3,000 miles. The depth of the sound channel axis varies in different oceans and latitudes, but for any particular location its depth remains fairly constant.
The Sofar system consists of several widely separated shore-based listening stations (each connected by electric cable to an underwater HY-DROPHONE at the depth of the sound channel axis for that location). Sounds from a correctly set distress signal bomb can be heard by several SOFAR stations at very great ranges, if not shadowed by a land mass.
The listening stations used in SOFAR are precisely synchronized in time by radio. Therefore, since underwater sound radiates in all directions at a nearly uniform rate, it is possible to compute the location of the sound source by comparing the times when the signal is received at the various listening stations. Thus, when such a signal is received, the approximate location of the signal source can be determined within a few minutes. (29)

SOLENOID. A tube formed in space by the intersection of unit-interval isotimic surfaces of two scalar quantities. The number of solenoids enclosed by a space curve is therefore equal to the flux of the vector product of the two gradients through a surface bounded by the curve, or

$$\int\int_A (\nabla \phi_1 \times \nabla \phi_2) \cdot ds = \oint \phi_1 d\phi_2,$$

where ds is the vector element of area of a surface bounded by the given curve.
Solenoids formed by the intersection of surfaces of equal pressure and density are frequently referred to in meteorology. A barotropic atmosphere implies the absence of solenoids of this type, since surfaces of equal pressure and density coincide. (24)

SOLION. Solion is a contraction of the phrase, solution of ions. It refers to a class of liquid state electrochemical devices which can be used as signal processing systems and transducers.
The solion electrochemical system is similar to an electrolysis system. However, the former have the advantage of indefinite life expectancy since the chemicals used are regenerated.

SOLITARY WAVE. A wave of translation consisting of a single crest rising above the undisturbed water level without any accompanying trough. The rate of advance of a solitary wave depends upon the depth of the water and is usually expressed by the formula: $r = \sqrt{g(d + h)}$, in which r is the rate of advance, g the acceleration of gravity, d the depth of water, and h the height of wave, the depth and height being measured from the undisturbed water level. (14)

SOLSTITIAL TIDES. Tides occurring near the times of the solstices. The tropic range may be expected to be especially large at these times. (14)

SOMALI CURRENT. An ocean current flowing southwestward along the coast of Somaliland (East Africa) as a continuation of the NORTH EQUATORIAL CURRENT. In summer (Northern Hemisphere), when the north equatorial current and the EQUATORIAL COUNTERCURRENT are replaced by an eastward flowing monsoon current, the Somali current reverses its direction and flows north from about $10°S$. (24)

SONAR. Sonar is the method or equipment for determining, by underwater sound, the presence, location, or nature of objects in the sea. The word "sonar" is an acronym derived from the expression "SOund NAvigation and Ranging." (1)

SONAR BACKGROUND NOISE. Sonar background noise is the total noise that interferes with the reception of the desired signal. The noise is that presented to the final receiving element, such as a recorder or the ear of a listener. (1)

SONAR BOOMER TRANSDUCER. This transducer consists of a flat, epoxy-encapsulated coil with a spring-loaded aluminum face plate. When the capacitor bank from which the energy is obtained is discharged into the coil of the transducer, eddy currents generated in the aluminum disk create a strong magnetic field that is opposed to that in the coil. Because the opposed magnetic fields cause the aluminum disk to be driven away from the coil with tremendous force, a large pressure wave is generated in the surrounding water. (30)

SONAR DOME INSERTION LOSS. The sonar dome insertion loss caused by the addition of a sonar dome is the increase in transmission loss between the electrical terminals of a specified transducer and an external field point at which transmission or reception of sound occurs. (1)

SONAR DOME LOSS PATTERN. The sonar dome loss pattern of a specified sonar dome, in conjunction with a specified sonar transducer enclosed by it, is a description, often presented graphically, of the dome insertion loss as a function of the direction of sound transmission relative to the dome's reference axes. (1)

SONAR PINGER SYSTEM. A system used to precisely determine the distance of equipment above the ocean floor. Two types of systems have been used successfully; one for depths to 6,500 feet and the other for depths to 37,500 feet. The system has been partially successful in positioning underwater cameras at a given distance off the bottom. However, it also can be applied to NANSEN BOTTLE casts, bottom coring operations, etc.

A transducer, located with the subsurface equipment, emits short bursts of high frequency energy (12 kilocycles) at one-second intervals. The transmitted pulse travels directly to the surface and also is reflected from the bottom. The converted time difference between the direct signal and the reflected signal gives the distance from the transducer to the bottom. Any sonar receiver or cathode-ray tube display can be used to pick up and display the pulses. An echo-sounding recorder is preferred as it gives a graphic picture of the location of the transducer with respect to the bottom and enables maintenance of a constant distance off the bottom. (35)

SONAR THUMPER SEISMIC SYSTEM. A complete continuous seismic profiling system consists of the Sonar Thumper unit, Sonar Recorder, transducer fish, receiving hydrophone, preamplifier if necessary and variable filter. Sonar Thumper units are available from 1000 watt-sec models up to 13000 watt-sec (experimental models). The standard thumper consists of a power supply, capacitor bank and transducer. Thumpers are used for marine geological studies and dredging surveys. The power supply output is fed to the capacitor bank which is discharged into the transducer producing a precisely repeatable pressure pulse in the water. (30)

SONIC. Pertaining to the range of audible frequencies, sometimes taken as from 0.02kc to 15kc. (7)

SONIC MARINE ANIMALS. Species of fishes, marine mammals, and crustaceans which may produce noise of sufficient intensity and frequency to interfere with sound ranging operations and acoustic mines. (15)

SONOAN. Sonic Noise Analyzer.

SONOBUOY. The Passive Sonobuoy is a remote "listening" post in the ocean capable of detecting undersea sounds and relaying them via radio to remote observers. In its primary application, it is used to enable aircraft to probe the sea in search of submarines and, so used, is one of the principal means of ocean surveillance and localization for ASW Targets. It is activated and operates automatically after water impact, floats to support the listening hydrophone and keep the antenna well above the water, converts sound signals in the sea to electrical signals for amplification and transmission by a self-contained transmitter and antenna to patrol aircraft, supplies its own power. It can be launched from aircraft and can be located from the air in day or night. (30)

SOOP. Submarine Oceanographic Observation Program (NAVOCEANO).

SORTING COEFFICIENT. A coefficient used in describing the distribution of grain sizes in a sample of unconsolidated material. It is defined as

$S_o = \sqrt{Q_1/Q_3}$ where Q_1 is the diameter which has 75% of the cumulative size-frequency (by wt.) distribution smaller than itself and 25% larger than itself,

and Q_3 is that diameter having 25% smaller and 75% larger than itself. (11)

SOUND. 1. A wide waterway between the mainland and an island, or a wide waterway connecting two sea areas.
2. A relatively long arm of the sea or ocean forming a channel between an island and a mainland or connecting two larger bodies, as a sea and the ocean, or two parts of the same body; usually wider and more extensive than a strait.
3. To measure or ascertain the depth of water as with a SOUNDING LINE. (11)
4. An oscillation in pressure, stress, particle displacement, particle velocity, etc., in a medium with internal forces (e.g., elastic, viscous), or the superposition of such propagated oscillations. (1)

SOUND ABSORPTION. Sound absorption is the change of sound energy into some other form, usually heat, in passing through a medium or striking a surface. (2)

SOUND BUOY. A buoy equipped with a characteristic sound signal, such as a bell, whistle, etc. (17)

SOUND CHANNEL. A horizontal layer which is bounded by levels at which the velocity of propagation is greater than at any depth within the layer is known as a sound channel. (4)

SOUND ENERGY. The sound energy of a given part of a medium is the total energy in this part of the medium minus the energy which would exist in the same part of the medium with no sound waves present. (2)

SOUND-ENERGY DENSITY. The sound-energy density at a point in a sound field is the sound energy contained in a given infinitesimal part of the medium divided by the volume of that part of the medium. (2)

SOUND-ENERGY FLUX. The sound-energy flux is the average rate of flow of sound energy for one period through any specified area. (2)

SOUND-ENERGY FLUX DENSITY. See SOUND INTENSITY.

SOUND FIELD. A sound field is a region containing sound waves. (1)

SOUNDHEAD (FM). A cylinder containing the transmitting projector and the receiving hydrophone. (5)

SOUNDING DATUM. The datum (REFERENCE PLANE) to which soundings are referred. (27)

SOUNDING LINE (LEAD LINE). The line attached to a sounding lead. (17)

SOUND INTENSITY. The sound intensity in a specified direction at a point is the average rate of sound energy transmitted in the specified direction through a unit area normal to this direction at the point considered. (2)

SOUND-POWER DENSITY. See SOUND INTENSITY.

SOUND POWER OF A SOURCE. The sound power of a source is the total sound energy radiated by the source per unit of time. (2)

SOUND PRESSURE. The sound pressure at a point in a medium is the instantaneous pressure at that point in the presence of a sound wave, minus the static pressure at that point. (9)

SOUND PRESSURE LEVEL. The sound pressure level, in decibels, of a sound is 20 times the logarithm to the base 10 of the ratio of the pressure of this sound to the reference pressure. The reference pressure shall be explicitly stated. (1)

SOUND RAY. See RAY PATH.

SOURCE ADMITTANCE. The source admittance of a transducer may be defined as the quotient obtained by dividing the phasor representing the short-circuited source current by the phasor representing the open-circuited source voltage. (4)

SOURCE CURRENT. The source current of an energy source is the rms current which would be measured at the terminals of that source if they were short-circuited. (4)

SOURCE POWER. The source power of an energy source is the available power of that source. (4)

SOURCE TRANSITION LOSS. The source transition loss at the junction between an energy source and a transducer connecting that source to an energy load is the transmission loss measured by the ratio of the source power of the source to the input power of the transducer. (4)

SOURCE VOLTAGE. The source voltage of an energy source is the rms voltage which would be measured at the terminals of that source if they were open-circuited. (4)

SOUTH ATLANTIC CURRENT. An Atlantic Ocean current flowing eastward from south of Rio de Janeiro to west of the Cape of Good Hope, and then curving northward along the west coast of South Africa and continuing as the BENGUELA CURRENT. The South Atlantic current is formed by the merging of the BRAZIL CURRENT and the FALKLAND CURRENT and forms the southern part of the general counterclockwise oceanic circulation of the South Atlantic Ocean. (17)

SOUTHEAST DRIFT CURRENT. A North Atlantic Ocean current flowing southeastward and southward from a point west of the Bay of Biscay toward southwestern Europe and the Canary Islands, where it continues as the CANARY CURRENT. The Southeast Drift Current is the continuation of the southern branch of the NORTH ATLANTIC CURRENT, and forms the northeastern and eastern parts of the general clockwise oceanic circulation of the North Atlantic Ocean. (17)

SOUTH EQUATORIAL CURRENT. In the Atlantic the south equatorial current starts off the west coast of Africa, south of the Gulf of Guinea, and flows in a generally westerly direction at an average speed of about 0.6 knots. However, the speed gradually increased until it may reach a value of 2.5 knots or more off the east coast of South America. As the current approaches Cabo de Sao Roque, the eastern extremity of South America, it divides, the southern part curving toward the south along the coast of Brazil, and the northern part being deflected by the continent of South America toward the north. In the Pacific the south equatorial current flows westward in the region of the southeast trades and is present on both sides of the Equator. Off South America the flow is directed more or less parallel to the coast line, turning gradually west when approaching the Equator. (12,13)

SPAR (SEAGOING PLATFORM FOR ACOUSTIC RESEARCH). SPAR is a 354 foot cylindrical vessel which is 16 feet in diameter and has a uniform circular cross section throughout its length (with the exception of the ends which are modified cones) with the bow shaped to minimize resistance when under tow in the horizontal attitude and the stern shaped to conform to good vessel design. The weight of the structure with zero liquid load is 587 tons. In the horizontal attitude with this liquid loading the vessel has a mean draft of 11 feet, being trimmed 4 feet by the stern. When in the vertical attitude the displacement of the SPAR, including the free flooding water, is 1720 tons with a draft of 300 feet. (35)

SPC. South Pacific Commission.

SOUTH PACIFIC CURRENT. An eastward flowing current of the South Pacific Ocean that is continuous with the northern edge of the ANTARCTIC CIRCUMPOLAR CURRENT. (24)

SPAR. Any log or built-up section of wood or metal shaped to serve as a mast, yard, boom, SPAR BUOY, etc. (17)

SPAR BUOY. A buoy made of a tapered log or of metal shaped like a tapered log, and secured so as to float in an approximately vertical position. (17)

SPECIFIC ACOUSTIC IMPEDANCE. The quotient obtained by dividing (1) the maximum value of the sinusoidally varying acoustic pressure at a point on a plane surface in a fluid medium due to plane waves of acoustic energy propagated in a direction perpendicular to that surface, by (2) the maximum value of the accompanying sinusoidally varying volume velocity per unit area through the surface at that point. (4)

SPECIFIC GRAVITY. The ratio of the density of a given substance to that of distilled water at 4^oC and at a pressure of 1 atmosphere.

SPECIFIC HEAT. The number of calories required to raise the temperature of 1 g. of a substance 1^oC. Specific heat decreases with increasing salinity. Temperature and pressure effects are the same as those for pure water.

SPECTRUM. (1) The spectrum of a function of time is a description of its resolution into components, each of different frequency and (usually) different amplitude and phase. (2) "Spectrum" is also used to signify a continuous range of components, usually wide in extent, within which waves have some specified common characteristics; e.g., "Audio-Frequency Spectrum." (2)

SPECTRUM CHARACTERISTIC. When the power per unit band of a wave having a continuous spectrum is plotted as a function of frequency, a curve is obtained which represents the manner in which the energy of that wave is distributed in frequency. Such a curve may be called a spectrum characteristic. (4)

SPECTRUM DENSITY. The spectrum density of an oscillation is the mean-square amplitude of the output of an ideal filter with unity gain responding to the oscillation, per unit bandwidth; i. e., the limit for vanishingly small bandwidth of the quotient of the mean-square amplitude divided by the bandwidth. (2)

SPECTRUM INTERVALS. Frequency bands represented by intervals on either a linear or a logarithmic frequency scale are sometimes spoken of as spectrum intervals. (4)

SPECTRUM LEVEL. The spectrum level of a specified signal at a particular frequency is the level of that part of the signal contained within a band one cycle per second wide, centered at the particular frequency. Ordinarily this has significance only for a signal having a continuous distribution of components within the frequency range under consideration. The phrase "spectrum level" cannot be used, but must appear in combination with a modifier, as, for example, pressure, velocity, voltage, etc. (9)

SPECTRUM LEVEL CHARACTERISTIC. The graph obtained by plotting spectrum level as a function of frequency is known as a spectrum level characteristic. (4)

SPECTRUM PATTERN. A graph showing the relative

response of a sonar transducer as a function of frequency for some specified bearing may be described as a spectrum pattern. (4)

SPEED OF SOUND IN SEA WATER. Three variables govern the speed (S) of sound in a fluid. They are density (ρ), compressibility (β), and the ratio between the specific heats of the fluid at constant pressure and at constant volume (γ). The following formula is applicable:

$$s = \sqrt{\frac{\gamma}{\rho\beta}}$$

For atmospheric pressure 29.92 inches of mercury, temperature 60 degrees F, and salinity 34.85 parts per thousand, the density of sea water is 64 pounds per cubic foot and the compressibility approximately 0.0000435 per atmosphere. Using these values and 32.174 feet per second (the acceleration of gravity at latitude 45 degrees) and 144 square inches per square foot, and taking γ equal to unity, the speed of sound in sea water is computed to be 4945 ft/sec.

An increase in temperature decreases both density and compressibility, resulting in an increase in the speed of sound. In sea water, an increase in pressure or salinity produces a slight increase in density and a larger decrease in compressibility, resulting in a net increase in the speed of sound. Thus, in sea water, an increase in temperature, pressure, or salinity results in greater speed of sound. Of the three, temperature has the greatest influence on the speed of sound in sea water. The pressure effect is slight, and the change of salinity is not sufficiently great to exercise a marked influence on the speed. (12)

SPHERICAL BUOY. A buoy, the above-water part of which, is hemispherical in shape. (17)

SPHERICAL WAVE. A spherical wave is a wave in which the wave fronts are concentric spheres. (9)

SPICULE. The tissue of various invertebrates, such as some of the sponges, radiolarians, holothurians, etc., are supported by minute chrystal-like spicules consisting of either silica or calcium carbonate. Varying complexity in construction leads to spicules being classified as: (1) Monaxons - having a single axis, (2) Triaxons - having three axes crossing at right angles, (3) Tetraxons - having four axes not in the same plane, which diverge from a common point, (4) Polyaxons - having several equal rays diverging from a point, and (5) Desmas - characterized by seeming lawlessness of structural plan since divergent main members commonly bear spiny or warty excrescences growing in all directions.

Spicules contribute to the fossil record and to marine sediments since the siliceous ones in particular are preserved upon decomposition of the animals soft parts. (21,19)

SPILHAUS-MILLER SEA SAMPLER. An instrument resembling the BATHYTHERMOGRAPH and operating in a similar fashion, with the additional ability of obtaining water samples at discrete depths within the limit of operation. Basically a bathythermograph to which 12 small sea water sampling bottles are attached, it performs the same functions as a cast of Nansen bottles and REVERSING THERMOMETERS to limited depths, but with less accuracy. It is useful for studies of shallow water areas, bays, and estuaries, where rapidity of sampling is of greater importance than the degree of accuracy of temperatures.

The sea sampler is operated in much the same manner as the bathythermograph, and is lowered from a bathythermograph winch. The temperature is recorded both during lowering and hoisting on a smoked-glass slide. The water sampling bottles have valves at each end and are sent down open. They are closed at predetermined depths while the sampler is rising to the surface. (35)

SPIN ECHO STORAGE. The utilization of electron spin resonance to store data processing information for very-high-speed access.

SPIT. A low tongue of land, or a relatively long, narrow shoal extending from the shore. (17)

SPITSBERGEN CURRENT. An ocean current flowing northward and westward from a point south of Spitsbergen, and gradually merging with the EAST GREENLAND CURRENT in the Greenland Sea. The Spitsbergen current is the continuation of the northwestern branch of the NORWEGIAN CURRENT. (17)

SPLASHNIK. A Navy buoy for measuring waves by telemetering vertical motions of the buoy to a ship via an FM radio transmitter. See TELEMETERING WAVE BUOY.

SPLIT TRANSDUCER. A split transducer is a directional transducer in which electroacoustic transducing elements are so divided and arranged that each division is electrically separated. (1)

SPOIL GROUND BUOY. A buoy marking the discharge area for dredged material. The expression is not generally used in United States waters. (17)

SPONGES. Sessile invertebrates which inhabit fresh, brackish, or salt water and occur from tropic to polar areas. They attach to submerged objects and, in warm waters, afford shelter for great concentrations of snapping shrimp. Sponges vary in size from very minute to several feet in diameter. (15)

SPONGIN. Some of the sponges (Class Demospongiae) secrete a skeletal material called spongin, which is a sulphur-containing protein (seleroprotein) that is insoluble, inert chemically, and resistant to protein-digesting enzymes. Commonly known as the "bath sponge". (19)

SPONTANEOUS PNEUMOTHORAX. This disease or accident refers to the forceful entry of air into the chest cavity. It results from an over expansion of air in the lungs.

SPORANGIUM. A SPORE case within which spores are formed. (18)

SPORE. A minute reproductive body produced by plants. Usually unicellular, but sometimes multicellular. The spore is not a reproductive body in bacteria. (18)

SPOROPHYTE. See ALTERNATION OF GENERATIONS.

SPREADING. The reduction in acoustic intensity due to an increase in the area over which a given acoustic energy is distributed is said to result from spreading. (4)

SPREADING ANOMALY. That part of the propagation anomaly which may be identified with the geometry of the ray paths. (4)

SPRING RANGE (Sp). The mean semidiurnal range of tide when spring tides are occurring; the mean difference in height between spring high water and spring low water. (17)

SPRING TIDES OR TIDAL CURRENTS. Tides of increased range or tidal currents of increased velocity occurring semimonthly as the result of the moon being new or full. The spring range of tide is the average semidiurnal range occurring at the time of spring tides and is most conveniently computed from the harmonic constants. It is larger than the mean range where the type of tide is either semidiurnal or mixed, and is of no practical significance where the type of tide is diurnal. The average height of the high waters of the spring tides is called spring high water or high water springs and the average height of the corresponding low waters is called spring low water or low water springs. (14)

SPUR. A subordinate RIDGE or RISE projecting outward from a larger feature of elevation. (26)

SQUALL. A wind of considerable intensity caused by atmospheric instability. It comes up and dies down quickly, and is often accompanied by thunder, lightning, and precipitation, when it may be called a thundersquall. An arched squall is one relatively high in the center, tapering off on both sides. A bull's eye squall is one formed in fair weather, characteristic of the ocean off the coast of South Africa. A squall occurring along a front, usually one of a series of severe squalls and thunderstorms extending for a considerable distance, is called a line squall. A front along which this takes place is sometimes called squall line. (17)

SQUALL LINE. See SQUALL.

SQUEEZE. Squeeze in diving is due to the effect of increasing external pressure upon the ears and sinuses, the FACE PLATE or the swim suit uncompensated by an equal increase in pressure from within. The incidence of squeeze is low. It is recognized by beginning pain in the ears and sinus areas, or by a feeling of tightness within the face covering, usually within the first few feet of descent. This pressure differential decreases with increased depth. Face squeeze can easily be prevented by exhaling into the face plate. Equalization of the internal ear pressure can be accomplished in several ways. The most effective method is to close the nose and mouth and force air into the back of the throat. Deliberate yawning may help if mouth piece is not being used. Preliminary inflation of the ears just before entering the water is very helpful and should be practiced routinely. The swimmer with an acute head cold or throat infection should not enter the water. If pain does occur at any depth the swimmer should ascend a few feet before again trying to readjust the internal pressure.

Serious consequences of squeeze are unlikely. Nosebleed, hemorrhage in the conjunctiva, sinuses or middle ear, and ruptured eardrums can occur if the symptoms are ignored. (37)

SS. U. S. Navy designation for a Submarine.

SSB. U. S. Navy designation for a Fleet Ballistic Missile Submarine.

SSG. U. S. Navy designation for a Guided Missile Submarine.

SSK. U. S. Navy designation for a Killer Submarine.

SS LORAN. Sky-wave synchronized loran, or loran in which the sky wave rather than the ground wave from the master controls the slave. SS loran is used with unusually long base lines. (17)

SSO. U. S. Navy ship designation for an Oiler.

SSR. U. S. Navy designation for a Radar Picket Submarine.

SST. 1. U. S. Navy designation for a Target Submarine.
2. Sea surface temperature.

STABILITY. The resistance to overturn or mixing of the water column, resulting from the presence of a density gradient.

STAMUKHA (pl. STAMUKHAS). A fragment of ice stranded on a shoal.

STANDARD DEPTH. A depth below the sea surface at which water properties should be measured and reported, either directly or by interpolation, according to the proposal by the International Association of Physical Oceanography in 1936; analogous to the mandatory levels of meteorological upper-air observations. (12)

STANDARD MERIDIAN PLANE. See LONGITUDE.

STANDING WAVE. A type of wave in which the surface of the water oscillates vertically between fixed points, called nodes, without progression. The points of maximum vertical rise and fall are called antinodes or loops. At the nodes, the underlying water particles exhibit no vertical motion but maximum horizontal motion. At the antinodes the underlying water particles have no horizontal motion and maximum vertical motion. They may be the result of two equal progressive wave trains travelling through each other in opposite directions. Sometimes called STATIONARY WAVE. (11)

STAND OF TIDE. An interval at high or low water when there is no sensible change in the height of the tide. The water level is stationary at high and low water for only an instant but the change in level near these times is so slow that it is not usually perceptible. In general the duration of the apparent stand will depend upon the range of tide, being longer for a small range than for a large range, but where there is a tendency for a double tide the stand may last for several hours even with a large range of tide. (14)

STARBOARD. The right side of a craft, facing forward. The opposite is PORT. (17)

STAR (SHIP TENDED ACOUSTIC RELAY). An acoustic navigation system employing ocean bottom TRANSPONDERS. In Star, the principle of operation involves a pulsed signal which is transmitted from an acoustic transducer towed from or mounted below the hull of the ship. This signal is received, filtered and amplified by suitable circuits at the transponder; it then triggers a pulsed acoustic reply at a different frequency or frequencies. The reply is received and recorded on board the attendant ship, and the time interval between transmission and reception is measured. Time is converted to range with an accuracy limited only by the accuracy of the average sound velocity between surface and bottom used in the calculation. The system is the same for the MARS (Mobile Atlantic Range Station). (35)

STAR TRANSPONDER

Command frequency (transmitted from shipboard equipment)	1.4 to 2.4 kc (Frequency coded)
Reply frequency	5 frequencies available between 3 kc and 12 kc
Transmitter power	< 200 watts
Angle of coverage in vertical plane	+90 from vertical
Life	2 X 10 interrogations or > 1 year
Depth	> 20,000 ft
Power supply	lead-acid batteries
Range	15 miles
Range accuracy	0.1% of range + 20 ft
Readout	Digital counters, recorders.

STATIC PRESSURE. The static pressure at a point is the pressure that would exist at that point in the absence of sound waves. (1)

STATION. In oceanography, the geographic location at which any set of oceanographic observations was taken; also, the observations recorded at the location. The appropriate verbal phrase is "occupy a station". (12)

STATIONARY WAVE. A wave that oscillates about an axis without progressing. Such a wave may be illustrated by the oscillation of the water in a pan that has been tilted. Near the axis, which is called the node or nodal line, there is little or no vertical rise and fall of the water. The ends of the waves are called LOOPS and at these places the vertical rise and fall is a maximum. The period of a stationary wave depends upon the length and depth of the body of water and may be expressed by the formula, $P = 2L/\sqrt{gd}$, in which P is the period, L the length, d the depth and g the accelleration of gravity on the earth's surface. A stationary wave may be resolved into two progressive waves of equal amplitude and equal speeds moving in opposite directions, the length of each PROGRESSIVE WAVE measured from crest to crest being twice as great as the resultant stationary wave measured from loop to loop. (14)

STATIONARY-WAVE THEORY. An assumption that the basic tidal movement in the open ocean consists of a system of stationary wave oscillations, any PROGRESSIVE WAVE movement being of secondary importance except as the tide advances into tributary waters. The continental masses divide the sea into irregular basins, which, although not completely enclosed, are capable of sustaining oscillations which are more or less independent. The tide-producing force consists principally of two parts, a semidiurnal force with a period approximating the half day and a diurnal force with a period of a whole day. In so far as the free period of oscillation of any part of the ocean, as determined by its dimensions and depth, is in accord with the semidiurnal or diurnal tide-producing force, there will be built up corresponding oscillations of considerable amplitude which will be manifested in the rise and fall of the tide. The diurnal oscillations, superimposed upon the semidiurnal oscillations, cause the inequalities in the heights of the two high and the two low waters of each day. Although the tidal movement as a whole is somewhat complicated by the overlapping of oscillating areas, the theory is consistent with observational data. (14)

STATION BUOY. A buoy used to mark the approximate position of an important buoy or lightship should it be carried away or temporarily removed. Also called marker buoy, watch buoy. (17)

STAVE. Individual longitudinal elements, a number of which make up a sonar transducer. (7)

STD. An instrument for continuously measuring the temperature, electrical conductivity and depth. It automatically determines water salinity from the temperature-conductivity-salinity relationships.

STEADY-STATE VIBRATION. Steady-state vibration exists in a system if the velocity of each particle is a continuing periodic quantity. (2)

STENOHALINE. Term used to indicate a narrow range of salinity values, and is frequently used to describe marine organisms which are sensitive to small changes in salinity. Stenohaline animals are especially characteristic of deep water and of the open sea where the salinity ranges only between about 34 to 36 0/00. It should not be understood, however, that stenohaline animals are confined to the open sea or the above salinity range. The term euryhaline is used to indicate those organisms which have a great degree of tolerance to wide range of salinity. The euryhaline animals are naturally characteristic inhabitants of the coastal regions and of estuaries, but due to their tolerance are represented in the open sea as well. Along this same line stenothermic and eurythermic animals are those capable of tolerating narrow or wide ranges of temperature respectfully. Among the stenothermic animals their are those which are cold-limited (phychrophile) and those which are warmth-limited (thermophile). Although some animals are either stenothermic or eurythermic throughout life, many others are eurythermic with respect to one phase of the life cycle and stenothermic at another phase. For the latter type it is necessary to distinguish between reproductive euryhaline or stenohaline during spawning periods or during the egg or larval developmental stages, and vegetative euryhaline or stenohaline during all other periods of life. (13)

STENOTHERMIC. See STENOHALINE.

STILL WATER LEVEL (UNDISTURBED WATER LEVEL). The surface of the water if all wave and wind action were to cease. In deep water this level approximates the midpoint of the wave height. In shallow water it is nearer to the trough than the crest. (27)

STOKESIAN WAVE. See DEEP-WATER WAVE.

STOKES'S LAW. A relation which gives the terminal fall velocity reached by a small sphere falling freely under gravity in a viscous medium. The relation between the terminal velocity of the sphere v_T and the frictional force f arising from the viscosity of the medium is given by $f = 6\pi\mu r v_T$, where μ is the dynamic viscosity and r is the radius of the sphere. Stokes's law holds with fair accuracy for motion in air provided that the diameter of the sphere does not exceed about 0.008 cm. It fails completely for larger bodies, such as raindrops, which require consideration of the turbulence induced in the medium by the passage of the drops.

When the frictional force is equated to the force due to gravity, the resulting expression for the terminal velocity is $v_T = \frac{2}{9} r^2 g (\rho - \rho_0)/\mu$, where g is the acceleration of gravity and ρ and ρ_0 are the density of the sphere and of the medium, respectively. For sufficiently small spheres, this velocity is so small that the particle may be said to be in suspension. (24)

STONES. Detached particles of rock usually smaller than 10 inches (256 millimeters) in diameter. Stones are classed as gravel on bottom sediment charts.

STOR. Scripps Tuna Oceanographic Research.

STORAGE SYSTEM. Scanning system in which the received signal from each direction is integrated in the capacitors associated with each of many directional channels for later sampling. (7)

STORIS. The largest pieces of polar ice drifting along the Greenland coast from the Arctic Ocean. (17)

STORM ICE FOOT. An ice foot produced by the breaking of a heavy sea or the freezing of wind-driven spray. (17)

STORM WAVES (STORM SURGES). Severe storms may be accompanied by exceptionally high water called storm waves or storm surges. Three effects in a storm induce a rise in sea level. The first is wind stress on the sea surface, which results in a piling-up of water. The second effect is the convergence of wind-driven currents, which elevates the sea surface along the convergence line. In shallow water, bottom friction and the effects of local topography cause this elevation to persist and may even intensify it. The low atmospheric pressure that accompanies severe storms causes the third effect, which is sometimes referred to as the "inverted barometer". An inch of mercury is equivalent to about 13.6 inches of water and the adjustment of the sea surface to the reduced pressure can amount to several feet at equilibrium. All three of these causes act independently, and if they happen to occur simultaneously, their effects are additive. In addition, the wave can be intensified or amplified by the effects of local topography. Storm waves may reach heights of 20 feet or more, and it is estimated that they cause three-fourths of the deaths attributed to hurricanes. Like TSUNAMIS, storm waves or storm surges are often called TIDAL WAVES although they have nothing to do with the tides. (12)

STRAIN. A measure of the change in size or shape of a body, due to force, referred to its original size or shape. Strain is a non-dimensional quantity, but it is sometimes expressed in inches per inch, etc.

STRAIN GAGE. The strain gage is an electromechanical device which transforms small displacements to changes in resistance which are proportional to the displacement.
   Strain gages are used in ocean bottom pressure measuring equipment. (35)

STRAIT. A relatively narrow waterway between two larger bodies of water. (11)

STRANDED FLOE ICE FOOT. See STRANDED ICE FOOT.

STRANDED ICE. See FAST ICE.

STRANDED ICE FOOT. An ice foot formed by the stranding of floes or small icebergs along a shore. It may be built up by freezing spray or breaking seas. Also called stranded floe ice foot. (17)

STRATH. A broad elongated depression with relatively steep walls located on a CONTINENTAL SHELF. The longitudinal profile of the floor is gently undulating with the greatest depths often found in the inshore portion. (26)

STRATOCUMULUS. Low clouds (mean upper level below 6,500 feet) composed of a layer or patches of globular masses or rolls. The smallest of the regularly arranged elements are fairly large, and are soft and gray, with darker parts. (17)

STRATUS. A low cloud (mean upper level below 6,500 feet) in a uniform layer, resembling fog but not resting on the surface. (17)

STRAY CURRENT CORROSION. The type of corrosion that occurs when electrical current from some external source reaches a metal at one point and leaves it at another. This causes accelerated corrosion where the areas at which the current leaves the metal are in contact with a corrosive solution or substance, such as the earth, wet wood, etc.

STRAY LINE. Ungraduated portion of line connected with the CURRENT POLE used in taking current observations. The stray line is usually about 100 feet long and permits the pole to acquire the velocity of the current at some distance from the disturbed waters in the immediate vicinity of the observing vessel before the current velocity is read from the graduated portion of the CURRENT LINE. (14)

STREAM CURRENT. See OCEAN CURRENT.

STREAMING, ACOUSTIC. Acoustic streaming is the name given to unidirectional flow currents in a

STREAMLINE. A line whose tangent at any point in a fluid is parallel to the instantaneous velocity of the fluid at that point. The differential equations of the streamlines may be written $drxv = 0$, where dr is an element of the streamline and v the velocity vector; or in Cartesial coordinates, $dx/u = dy/v = dz/w$, where u, v, w, are the fluid velocities along the orthogonal x, y, z axes, respectively. In steady-state flow the streamlines coincide with the trajectories of the fluid particles; otherwise the streamline pattern changes with time. (12)

STREAMLINE FLOW. See LAMINAR FLOW.

STRENGTH OF A SOUND SOURCE. The strength of a sound source is the maximum instantaneous rate of volume displacement produced by the source when emitting a wave with sinusoidal time variation. (2)

STRENGTH OF CURRENT. Phase of tidal current in which the velocity is a maximum; also the velocity at this time. Beginning with the slack before flood in the period of a reversing tidal current, the velocity gradually increases to the flood strength and then diminishes to another slack, after which the current turns in direction, the velocity increasing to the ebb strength and then diminishing to the slack before flood thus completing the cycle. If it is assumed that the velocity throughout the cycle varies as the ordinates of a cosine curve, it can be shown that the average velocity for an entire flood or ebb period is equal to $2/\pi$ or 0.6366 of the velocity of the corresponding strength of current. (14)

STRESS. The load on a material divided by the original area of the cross-section through which it acts. Units: psi. Stress, as defined above

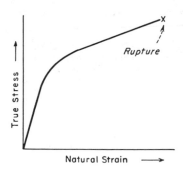

and commonly used in connection with routine mechanical tests, is not a true stress. A true stress represents intensity of the internal distributed forces which resist a change in the form of a material, and is equal to the load on the material divided by the instantaneous area of the cross-section through which it acts.

STRESS CORROSION. Corrosion which is accelerated by stress either residual internal stress or externally applied stress.

STRESS CORROSION CRACKING. That cracking which takes place in a metallic structure due to the combined effect of tensile stresses and corrosive action.

STRESS-STRAIN DIAGRAM. A graph on which is plotted stress vs. strain. Such a graph may be constructed in any test during which frequent or continuous measurements of both stress and strain are made. It is commonly constructed for the Compression, Tension and Torsion Tests. It is usually necessary for the determination of Deformation Energy, Elastic Limit, Modulus of Elasticity, Modulus of Rigidity, Proportional Limit and Yield Strength. It is often useful in determination of Elongation, Modulus of Rupture, Ultimate Strength and other related properties.

STRONG GALE. See GALE.

SUB-BOTTOM DEPTH RECORDER. The SDR is a compact seismic equipment which is capable of providing continuous soundings of sub-bottom strata. The sound energy source is an electrical spark discharge in water. An intense spark discharge, confined to a very small volume of water, will vaporize the water and produce high-pressure bubbles whose expansion and contraction radiate acoustic energy. The SDR utilizes the low frequency energy output of the spark discharge source to obtain continuous records of bedrock lying more than 450 feet of sediment. The transmitter section works in conjunction with a recorder and float assembly which is towed astern by means of the hydrophone and electrode cables. The hydrophone which detects the incoming signal is housed within the float structure. (30)

SUBCUTANEOUS EMPHYSEMA. See EMPHYSEMA.

SUBHARMONIC. A subharmonic is a sinusoidal quantity having a frequency that is an integral submultiple of the fundamental frequency of a periodic quantity to which it is related. (2)

SUBMARINE CANYON. See CANYON.

SUBMARINE FREE COMMUNICATION EFFECT. Free communication effect is the effect caused by a partly filled tank that is open to the sea as in the case of a ballast tank with open vents. In this case not only does the water in the tank shift with roll or pitch, but water may actually enter or leave the tank through the opening to sea causing a change in weight and therefore a shift in the center of gravity. (33)

SUBMARINE FREE SURFACE EFFECT. Free surface effect is that effect caused by free surface of a liquid in a partly filled tank which reduces stability because the liquid is free to shift within the tank boundaries in the direction of the roll or pitch of the vessel. (33)

SUBMARINE ISTHMUS. A submarine elevation joining two land areas and separating two basins or depressions by a depth less than that of the basins. (17)

SUBMARINE PENINSULA. An elevated portion of the submarine relief resembling a peninsula. The opposite is SAC. (17)

SUBMARINE PHOTOMETER. A device which detects and records directly, in foot-candles, the light existing at the surface of the ocean and all depths down to approximately 150 meters. Through the use of filters, observations are made in the infrared ultra-violet ranges of the spectrum. The instrument consists of two 2-pen Brown potentiometer recorders and a detecting unit of 3 photoelectric cells and a Statham STRAIN GAGE.

In connection with studies of PHYTOPLANKTON, biological oceanographers are generally interested in light penetration. The submarine photometer used in these studies is a WESTON PHOTOELECTRIC CELL enclosed in a watertight housing which is lowered on a two-conductor cable. The amount of light detected by the weston cell is read on a microammeter. (35)

SUBMARINE PIT. A cavity on the bottom of the sea. Also called submarine well. (17)

SUBMARINE SPRING. A spring of water issuing from the bottom of the sea. (17)

SUBMARINE WAVE RECORDER. A wave recorder which uses the submarine as a hovering, submerged, stable platform from which to measure oceanographic variables. In this method essentially an inverted echo sounder mounted on the deck of a hovering submerged submarine is used plus the travel time required for the vertical sound beam to go from the submarine to the height of the water above the submarine. Thus, changes in water height above the submarine are recorded as changing wave height. (35)

SUBTROPICAL ANTICYCLONE. See SUBTROPICAL HIGH.

SUBTROPICAL HIGH (SUBTROPICAL ANTICYCLONE, OCEANIC ANTICYCLONE, OCEANIC HIGH). One of the semi-permanent highs of the SUBTROPICAL HIGH-PRESSURE BELT. They appear as centers of action on mean charts of surface pressure. They lie over oceans, and are best developed in the summer seasons. (14)

SUBTROPICAL HIGH-PRESSURE BELT (SUBTROPICAL RIDGE). One of the two belts of high atmospheric pressure that are centered, in the mean, near $30^{\circ}N$ and $30^{\circ}S$ latitudes. These belts are formed by SUBTROPICAL HIGHS. (14)

SUBTROPICAL RIDGE. See SUBTROPICAL HIGH-PRESSURE BELT.

SUESTADO. A storm with southeast gales, caused by intense cyclonic activity off the coasts of Argentina and Uruguay, which affects the southern part of the coast of Brazil in the winter. (17)

SUGAR ICEBERG. An ICEBERG composed of the most porous type of GLACIER ICE. Such ice is formed at very low temperatures, is loosely constructed, and falls apart easily. (25)

SUGG. To roll with the action of the sea when aground. (17)

SULPHUR-BOTTOM. A descriptive term frequently applied to the blue whale, and arising from the fact that after feeding for some time in antarctic waters the under portion of their bodies may become incrusted with yellow diatoms (Cocconeis citicola). (13)

SUMATRA. A squall with violent thunder, lightning, and rain, which blows at night in the Malacca Straits, especially during the southwest monsoon. It is intensified by strong mountain breezes. (17)

SUPERHEAT. Sensible heat in a gas above the amount needed to keep it a gas. (33)

SUPERSONIC FREQUENCY. See ULTRASONIC FREQUENCY.

SURF. The wave activity in the area between the shore line and the outermost limit of breakers. (11)

SURFACE REVERBERATION. See REVERBERATION.

SURFACE THERMOMETER. In oceanography, a thermometer used in a bucket of sea water to measure sea surface temperature. (24)

SURF BEAT. Irregular oscillations of the nearshore water level, with periods of the order of several minutes. (11)

SURGE. (1) The name applied to wave motion with a period intermediate between that of the ordinary wind wave and that of the tide, say from 1/2 to

60 minutes. It is of low height; usually less than 0.3 foot. (2) in fluid flow, long interval variations in velocity and pressure, not necessarily periodic, perhaps even transient in nature. (11)

    3. The fore and aft movement of the center of gravity of a ship.

    4. Water transported up a beach by breaking waves. (12)

SURGE, STORM. That rise above normal water level on the open coast due only to the action of wind stress on the water surface. Storm surge resulting from a hurricane also includes that rise in level due to atmospheric pressure reduction as well as that due to wind stress. (11)

SUSPENSION CURRENT. See TURBIDITY CURRENT.

SVTP. Sound Velocity, Temperature, and Pressure. A measuring instrument which measures sound velocity by a velocimeter, temperature via a Wien bridge and pressure by means of a VIBRATRON.

SWAFAC. Southwest Atlantic Fisheries Advisory Commission.

SWALLOW-TYPE NEUTRAL FLOATS. These floats are objects that can be "trimmed" to make them settle at any depth in the ocean. Equipped with sound pingers they can be "followed" to investigate the flow of deep water. The float consists of an o-ring sandwiched between two commercial pipecap forgings. The instrumentation within a float is designed to measure the position and acceleration of the shell and to obtain the temperature of the surrounding water.
A neutrally buoyant float is stable at a given depth, if it is less compressible than water and has the same density as the water at that depth. A settled float will follow horizontal water motion because it is subjected to the same horizontal driving forces as an equivalent volume of water. The neutrally buoyant cans will follow horizontal motions fairly closely at all depths, and probably can be used to measure the horizontal displacements associated with deep internal waves. (30)

SWASH CHANNEL. 1. On the open shore, a channel cut by flowing water in its return to the parent body (e.g. a rip channel).
    2. A secondary channel passing through or shoreward of an inlet or river bar. (11)

SWASH MARK. The thin wavy line of fine sand, mica scales, bits of seaweed, etc., left by the UPRUSH when it recedes from its upward limit of movement on the beach face. (11)

SWAY. Lateral movement of the center of gravity of a ship. (12)

SWELL. A long and relatively symmetrical wave having a period in the order of 10 seconds produced by winds and storms at some distance from the point of observation.

SWIM FINS (FLIPPERS). Any device designed to be attached to the feet of a swimmer or SCUBA diver to increase the power and control of the swimmer.

SWINGING BUOY. A buoy placed at a favorable location to assist a vessel to adjust its compass or swing ship. The bow of the vessel is made fast to one such buoy and the vessel is swung by means of lines to a tug or to additional buoys. (17)

SYMBIOSIS. The living together of two or more organisms in an association which is mutually advantageous. (18)

SYNODICAL MONTH. The average period of the revolution of the moon around the earth with respect to the sun, or the average interval between corresponding phases of the moon. The synodical month is approximately 29.530588 days in length. (14)

SYNOPTIC. In general, pertaining to or affording an overall view.
    In meteorology, this term has become somewhat specialized in referring to the use of meteorological data obtained simultaneously over a wide area for the purpose of presenting a comprehensive and nearly instantaneous picture of the state of the atmosphere. Thus, to a meteorologist, "synoptic" takes on the additional connotation of simultaneity. (24)

SYSTOPHE. The condition whereby the chromatophores, usually scattered, are collected into a group when exposed to strong light. Observed in some algae. (13)

SYZGY. Position of the moon when it is new or full. (14)

T

TABLEMOUNT. A SEAMOUNT rising more than 500 fathoms from the sea floor and having a comparatively smooth, flat top with minor irregularities. (26)

TABULAR ICEBERG. A mass of ice calved from an ice shelf in the Antarctic, having a flat upper surface, and at least the upper portion being composed of stratified snow or NEVÉ. Tabular icebergs are characterized by their vast size (often measured in miles), rectangular block cleavage, relatively large air content, and white color and lustre. When a tabular iceberg becomes unbalanced, so that the flat, level top is inclined, it is called a Tilted iceberg. Large tabular icebergs and somewhat similar formations in the arctic are called Ice islands. Also called Barrier Iceberg. (17)

TAFFRAIL LOG. A log consisting essentially of a rotator towed through the water by a braided log line attached to a distance registering device usually secured at the taffrail, the railing at the stern. Also called patent log. (17)

TAPE GAGE. A tide gage which consists essentially of a float attached to a tape and counterpoise. The float operates in a vertical box or pipe which dampens out short-period wind waxes while admitting the slower tidal movement. For the standard installation, the tape is graduated with numbers increasing toward the float and is arranged with pulleys and counterpoise to pass up and down over a fixed reading mark as the tide rises and falls. (14)

TARGET LENGTH. The distance, measured along the direction of propagation, between the first point and the last point, on a given target, to return detectable echo signals to the source is known as the target length. (4)

TARGET STRENGTH. Measure of reflecting power of the target. Ratio, in decibels, of the target echo to the echo from a six-foot diameter perfectly reflecting sphere at the same range and depth. (7)

TECTIN. The organic material in skeletons of some PROTOZOANS; pseudochitin. (19)

TECTOGEN. The down-buckled root of a geosynclinal trough. See also GEOSYNCLINE. (27)

TECTONIC. An adjective pertaining to or designating structures resulting from deformation of the earth's crust. (27)

TECTONO-EUSTATISM. See EUSTATISM.

TEHUANTEPECER. A violent north wind frequent in the winter in the region around the Gulf of Tehuantepec in Mexico. (17)

TELECHIRIC. A word formed by two Greek words, tele, meaning distant and kheir which means, hand.
    Telechiric is used to mean the technology of manipulation at a distance and with no direct connection between the operator and his machine or tools. Such fully controlled uninhabited mechanical devices can be effectively used in oceanographic and OCEAN ENGINEERING work.

TELEGRAPH BUOY. A buoy used to mark the position of a submarine telegraph cable. (17)

TELEMETERING THERMOMETER. This is a temperature TRANSDUCER for temperature measurement at depth, working in conjunction with a radio telemetering link from a drift buoy, allowing identification of the body of water in which the buoy rests at the time of observation. Sometimes used to determine whether the buoy has remained with the water mass in which it was deposited or conversely to know some parameter of the water immediately under it. The normal design depth is 200 meters where surface disturbances are not felt. (30)

TELEMETERING WAVE BUOY (SPLASHNIK). A device similar to the floating ACCELEROMETER with one significant difference. This unit transmits its vertical acceleration signals back to a ship by radio, eliminating any ship motion from being imparted to the buoy. The system consists of a buoy assembly containing a transducer and transmitter, a wideband FM receiver, an electronic low-pass filter, and a recorder. The transmitter sends a signal that varies in frequency proportional to the acceleration experienced by the buoy assembly. This signal is received by an antenna mounted on a ship and is fed into the FM receiver. In the receiver the frequency changes are converted to a varying d.c. voltage which is proportional to the acceleration. The d.c. voltage is placed on the input of the adjustable low-pass filter which cuts off the signals produced by the surface chop of the sea, but passes unaltered the lower-frequency signals produced by the larger and longer waves. The output of the filter unit then is recorded either on magnetic tape or on a direct-writing recorder. The surface wave record is obtained by a double integration of this output.
    This wave buoy was not designed to be a refined instrument; the cost has been kept at around $100 to $200, and it probably could be brought lower by mass production. Thus the buoy can be considered as expendable if necessary. The transmitter is subject to some frequency drift, and the tuner needs occasional retuning. An error exists in the acceleration information obtained, because the lever arm of the accelerometer does not remain horizontal as the float assembly rides up and down the waves. (35)

TELEMETRY. The science involved with measuring a quantity or quantities, transmitting this value to a station, and there interpreting, indicating, or recording the quantities.

The oceanographer may utilize radio and acoustic links or electrically insulated wire devices to transmit telemetered information.

TELERECORDING BATHYTHERMOMETER. The bathythermometer is a 2-unit transistorized system, operated like a BT, which gives a plot of temperature vs depth. The absolute accuracy in depth reportedly is better than $+0.25$ per cent, or $+2.5$ feet in 1000 feet, temperature sensitivity is $0.05^{o}C$. A vibrating wire transducer (Vibrotron) and thermistor Wien-bridge oscillator provide for depth and temperature respectively. This device, developed by Snodgrass and Cawley employs a thermistor as temperature-sensing element. The data are telemetered from depth over a single polyethylene-insulated wire to a ship. This method can be used to telemeter additional information. (35)

TELERECORDING CURRENT DIRECTION TRANSDUCER. The underwater unit of this instrument transmits ocean current direction to the surface over a single conductor insulated cable, sea-return system. Eight underwater units may be suspended and operated simultaneously over a single conductor cable. Basic underwater data is photoelectric position information obtained from a precision mounted, viscous damped magnetic compass element. Data transmission is P.D.M. (Pulse Duration Modulation) by F.S.K. (Frequency Shift Keyed) on standard channels 6 through 13. Power is supplied to 4 surface modules and the underwater unit. Each plug-in module contains a hand pass filter, limiter, discriminator, and P.D.M. data conversion circuits. A meter on each module indicates current direction. (30)

TELLUROMETER. The Tellurometer is a phase comparison base line measuring system which was developed in the Union of South Africa and is now widely used over the world for geodetic surveying. Radar frequencies are used to carry the distance information and the system used 10 megacycles as the basic measure-frequency so that the line width is approximately 15 meters. (35)

TEMPERATURE-CHLORINITY-DEPTH RECORDER. The three quantities are recorded sequentially by a single-pen strip chart recorder, each quantity being recorded for five seconds at a time. The underwater unit is suspended by means of an armored steel cable which has a single electrically insulated core. This core carries power down to the underwater unit and brings up the signals from the measuring elements. A simple frequency modulation method of telemetering is used.
    Chlorinity is measured by means of a conductivity cell with platinized electrodes. The effect of temperature on conductivity is compensated by using a THERMISTOR. (35)

TEMPERATURE OF THE OCEAN (General). Temperature in the ocean varies widely, both horizontally and with depth. Maximum values of about 90 degrees F are encountered in the Persian Gulf in summer, and the lowest possible values of about 28 degrees F (the usual minimum freezing point of sea water) occur in polar regions.
    The vertical distribution of temperature in the sea nearly everywhere shows decrease of temperature with depth. Since colder water is denser, it sinks below warmer water. This results in a temperature distribution just opposite to that in the earth's crust, where temperature increases with depth below the surface of the ground.
    In general, in the sea there is usually a mixed layer of isothermal water below the surface, where the temperature is the same as that of the surface. This layer is best developed in the trade-wind belts, where it may extend to a depth of 100 fathoms; in temperate latitudes in the spring, it may disappear entirely. Below this layer is a zone of rapid temperature decrease, called the THERMOCLINE, to the temperature of the

deep oceans. At a depth greater than 200 fathoms, the temperature everywhere is below 60 degrees F, and in the deeper layers, fed by cooled waters that have sunk from the surface in the arctic and antarctic, temperatures as low as 33 degrees F exist.

It is only in the deepest ocean basins, at depths greater than 2,000 fathoms, that the heat of the earth's crust influences the water temperature. In such basins the temperature shows a slight increase with depth, seldom amounting to more than 1 degree F. (12)

TEMPERATURE PROFILE RECORDER (TPR). The Temperature Profile Recorder is a portable unit consisting of a thermistor sensing element, 6-volt power supply, amplifier, and a recorder. The recorder is geared to a drum containing an electrical cable to which the bead is fastened. When the bead is lowered into the water, the paper on the recorder is moved accordingly. Depth is measured by the amount of wire paid out. This device is used in shallow water, particularly in lakes. (35)

TEMPERATURE-SALINITY DIAGRAM. (Abbreviated T-S diagram.) A graph with temperature as ordinate and salinity as abscissa, on which the points observed at a single oceanographic serial station are joined by a curve (the T-S curve). (24)

TEMPORARY PLANKTON. See MARINE LIFE.

TENOC. Ten-year oceanographic program (Navy).

TENSILE MODULUS OF ELASTICITY. Also called Modulus of Elasticity in Tension and often merely Modulus of Elasticity. The tangent or secant Modulus of Elasticity of a material in the Tension Test. The relationship between Tensile Stress and Tensile Strain.

TENSILE STRENGTH. The Ultimate Strength of a material subjected to tensile loading. The maximum Tensile Stress developed by a material in the Tension Test. It is calculated by determining the Tensile Stress corresponding to the maximum load observed in the Tension Test. For ductile metals Tensile Strength of a material is usually greater than its Breaking Strength, but is well below the maximum true stress developed by the material. Tensile Strength is a common index for strength comparison of materials. It may be directly useful in design where some plastic deformation is permitted, but Yield Strength is the common basis for elastic design. Tensile Strength may also be some indication of allowable severity of hot and cold working processes.

TENSILE STRESS. Sometimes called Modulus. The nominal stress developed by a material subjected to a specified stretching load, as in the Tension Test. Above the Elastic Limit, nominal Tensile Stress is considerably lower than the true stress because it does not reflect the decrease in cross-section area accompanying continued deformation.

TENTED ICE. A type of pressure ice created when ice is displaced vertically upward, forming a flat-sided arch with a cavity between the raised ice and the water underneath. (17)

TENTING. The vertical displacement upward of ice under pressure to form a flat-sided arch with a cavity beneath. (17)

TERDIURNAL. Having three periods in a constituent day. The symbol of a terdiurnal constituent is usually distinguished by the subscript 3. (14)

TERRACE. A bench-like feature bordering an elevation of the sea floor. A terrace does not include the CONTINENTAL SHELF or ISLAND SHELF, but may include bench-like features on the shelf. (26)

TERRIGENOUS. Of the land. When applied to ocean bottom deposits, it denotes those that are composed predominently of material brought from the land. The continental shelves are covered almost entirely by terrigenous deposits. (27)

TETRASPORE. One of the haploid asexual spores in the red algae developed meiotically and commonly in groups of four from the diploid tetrasporangia and germinating to produce the haploid gametophytic plants. (20)

TETRAXON. See SPICULE.

THALLUS. A type of plant body which is undifferentiated into root, stem, or leaf. (18)

THALWEG. 1. The line joining the lowest points of a valley or a submarine valley.
2. The center line of the principal navigational channel of a waterway constituting a boundary between political subdivisions. (17)

THEODOLITE. An optical micrometer-reading instrument in which two diametrically opposed axes are brought to coincidence and read through a microscopic eyepiece. This angle and distance measuring instrument is used, for example, in certain types of geodetic field survey work. (29)

THERMAL EXHAUSTION. The underwater swimmer is extremely sensitive to moderate changes in water temperature in both directions because water is a much better heat conductor than air. At present there is no equipment to protect a man against moderately warm water. Heat prostration may occur during exercise in water around 86°F. and at rest in water around 96°F.

A much commoner stress is water colder than 65° to 72°F. Many types of clothing have been devised to protect against cold water. Unfortunately most have obvious handicaps such as loss of protection when wet inside, limitation of motion, SQUEEZE and chafing at depths, marked buoyancy changes at depth and lack of a mechanism to rid oneself of sweat and excreta. (37)

THERMAL NOISE. Even if it were possible to isolate a sample of water completely from all external influences there would still be minute movements of the molecules, due to thermal agitation, accompanied by the release of acoustic energy. This molecular agitation, which is proportional to the absolute temperature of the water, is spoken of as thermal noise. (4)

THERMAL PROBE. A device used for measuring the heat flow out of ocean bottom SEDIMENT.

THERMISTOR. An electrical resistor made of a material whose resistance varies sharply in a known manner with the temperature.

Thermistors are commonly used for shipboard oceanographic temperature measurements because of their percentage response to unit temperature change and their great sensitivity.

THERMOCLINE. A vertical temperature gradient in some layer of a body of water, which is appreciably greater than the gradients above and below it; also a layer in which such a gradient occurs. The principal thermoclines in the ocean are either seasonal, due to heating of the surface water in summer, or permanent. (24)

THERMOMETER FLOAT. This instrument is used for studying the temperature structure in the upper 10 meters of water. The instrument is in two sections; a float which contains a spooling winch from which the sensing unit is lowered, and an indicator case which contains the remote indicating equipment and remote control system. The two sections are connected by an electric cable and flexible shaft, supported by net floats. The indicator case is clear lucite. It contains the indicating meter and electric circuitry for temperature determination. It also contains a Veeder-Root counter which indicates directly in centimeters the depth at which the sensing unit is located. This instrument makes it possible to read temperature to within 0.1 degree centigrade and to know the depth of the sensing unit to within plus-or-minus 0.5 centimeter. It is intended to be used at sea from a skiff or tender rather than from the research vessel itself. (30)

THERMOPHILE. See STENOHALINE.

THEVENIN'S THEOREM. Thevenin's theorem states that, if an impedance be connected between any two points of a circuit the resulting steady-state current through that impedance will be such that its phasor is the quotient obtained by dividing (1) the phasor of the potential difference between the two points prior to the connection by (2) the sum of the phasors of the connected impedance and the impedance of the circuit measured between the two points prior to the connection. (4)

THIXOTROPHY. The property of a material that enables it to stiffen in a short time upon standing but upon agitation to change to a very soft consistency or to a fluid of high viscosity. The process is completely reversible.

TIDAL CURRENTS. See APOGEAN TIDES.

TIDAL FLAT. A flat, soggy area which emerges during low tide, that is characterised by the simultaneous deposition of clay and sand by tidal waters. (15)

TIDAL INLET (TIDAL OUTLET). 1. A natural inlet maintained by tidal flows.
2. Loosely any inlet in which the tide ebbs and flows. (11)

TIDAL OUTLET. See TIDAL INLET.

TIDAL PLATFORM ICE FOOT. An ice foot between high and low water levels, produced by the rise and fall of the tide. (17)

TIDAL PRISM. The total amount of water that flows into the harbor or out again with movement of the tide, excluding any fresh water flow. (11)

TIDAL STREAM. In British usage the expression is applied to a tidal current, their use of the word "current" being confined exclusively to the non-tidal horizontal flow of water. (14)

TIDAL VOLUME. In physiology - the volume of air moved in and out during a single normal respiratory cycle. During rest, the tidal volume generally averages about one-half liter. Tidal volume increases considerably during physical exertion. It naturally cannot exceed the vital capacity. (37)

TIDE. The periodic rising and falling of the water that results from the gravitational attraction of the moon and sun acting upon the rotating earth. Although the accompanying horizontal movement of the water resulting from the same cause is also sometimes called the tide, it is preferable to designate the latter as TIDAL CURRENT, reserving the name tide for the vertical movement. (14)

TIDE GAGES. Devices used to measure the rise and fall of the tide. They may be divided into two classes; nonregistering gages which require the observer to record the heights of the tide and self registering or recording gages which are equipped to automatically plot the rise and fall of the tide.
Nearly all the tide gages of which there are

several designs are operated in the U. S. by the U. S. Coast and Geodetic Survey. See also BOX GAGE, PRESSURE GAGE, TAPE GAGE and TIDE STAFF. (35)

TIDE INDICATOR. A form of tide gage designed for the purpose of clearly indicating on a suitable scale the height of the tide at any time as referred to the plane of reference. Such an indicator may be located in the immediate vicinity of the tidal water or at a distance with electrical connection. (14)

TIDE-PREDICTING MACHINE. An instrument that predicts the tide by mechanically summing the harmonic constituents of which it is composed. The tide-predicting machine used by the Coast and Geodetic Survey in the preparation of its annual Tide Tables is described in detail in Coast and Geodetic Survey Special Publication No. 98, "Manual of Harmonic Analysis and Prediction of Tides". (14)

TIDE RACE. A very rapid tidal current in a narrow channel or passage. (15)

TIDE RIPS. A turbulent water body produced by opposition to tidal currents. (See RIP CURRENTS) (15)

TIDE STAFF. A tide gage consisting of a vertical graduated staff from which the height of the tide can be read directly. It is called a fixed staff when it is secured in place so that it cannot be easily removed. A portable staff is one that is designed for removal from the water when not in use. For such a staff a fixed support is provided, and the staff itself has a metal stop secured to the back so that it will always have the same elevation when installed for use. (14)

TIDEWATER. Water affected by tides or sometimes that part of it which covers the tideland. The term is sometimes used broadly to designate the seaboard. (17)

TIDE WAVE. The ridge of water raised by tidal action, resulting in tides at various places around the world. Also called tidal wave. (17)

TILLITE. An ancient consolidated till or boulder clay, deposited directly from a GLACIER or an ICE-SHEET. It is an unsorted deposit, often containing striated stones set in a clay matrix. (27)

TINRO. Pacific Research Institute of Fisheries and Oceanography (USSR).

TOMBOLO. An area of unconsolidated material, deposited by wave action or currents, that connects a rock or island, etc., to the mainland or to another island. (11)

TONGUE. A projection of FLOATING ICE caused by wind and current. The extent of a tongue may be several miles. (25)

TOPMARK BUOY. A buoy with a topmark, or characteristic shape secured at the top to aid in its identification. (17)

TOPOGRAPHY. The general configuration of the land surface (or the ocean bottom); the sum total of the results of erosion and deposition on the physiographic features of a region. (27)

TOROID CONDUCTIVITY CELL. The toroid conductivity cell is a device used to measure the electrical conductivity of sea water by relating a signal voltage to the resistance of the electrical path in the water. (35)

TOTAL ICE SEASON, MAXIMUM. The longest ice season recorded over a period of years in an area. See ICE PERIOD.

TOTAL ICE SEASON, MINIMUM. The shortest ice season recorded over a period of years in an area. See ICE PERIOD.

TOTAL LUNG CAPACITY. The total volume of air that the lungs can hold when filled to capacity. It is normally between 5 and 6 liters. (A liter is about the same as a quart. It is the standard unit of volume in the metric system, which is generally used in physiological measurements. (37)

TOTO. Tongue of the Ocean. See AUTEC.

TOWING HAWSER. See WIRE ROPE.

TRADES. See TRADE WINDS.

TRADE WINDS (TRADES). The wind system, occupying most of the tropics, which blows from the SUB-TROPICAL HIGHS toward the EQUATORIAL TROUGH; a major component of the general circulation of the atmosphere. The winds are northeasterly in the Northern Hemisphere and southeasterly in the Southern Hemisphere; hence they are known as the northeast trades and southeast trades, respectively.
  The trade winds are best developed on the eastern and equatorial sides of the great subtropical highs, especially over the Atlantic. In the Northern Hemisphere they begin as north-northeast winds at about latitude 30° in January and latitude 35° in July, gradually veering to northeast and east-northeast as they approach the equator. Their southern limit is a few degrees north of the equator. The southeast trades occupy a comparable region in the Southern Hemisphere, and similarly change from south-southeast on their poleward side to southeast near the equator. In the Pacific, the trade winds are properly developed only in the eastern half of that ocean; and in the Indian Ocean, only south of about 10°S. They are primarily surface winds, their usual depth being from 3000 to 5000 feet, although they sometimes extend to much greater altitudes. They are characterized by great constance of direction and, to a lesser degree, speed; the trades are the most consistent wind system on earth. (14)

TRAFFIC NOISE. By traffic noise is meant the general disturbance due to ships which is not associated with a specific vessel, or what is more significant, which has no definite directional distribution relative to a given observation point and which shows little change in intensity with change in position. (4)

TRAINING WALL. See JETTY.

TRAMONTANA. A northeasterly or northerly wind occurring in winter off the west coast of Italy. It is a fresh wind of the fine weather mistral type. (17)

TRANSDUCER. Any device for converting energy from one form to another (electrical, mechanical, or acoustic). In sonar, usually combines the functions of a hydrophone and a projector. (5)

TRANSDUCER LOSS. The transducer loss of a transducer connecting an energy source and an energy load is the transmission loss measured by the ratio of the source power of the source to the load power of the load. (4)

TRANSFER ADMITTANCE. The transfer admittance of a network made up of an energy source and an energy load connected by a transducer is the quotient obtained by dividing the phasor representing the source current of the source by the phasor representing the load voltage of the load. (4)

TRANSFER IMPEDANCE. The transfer impedance of a network made up of a given source and a given load connected by a given transducer is the quotient obtained by dividing the phasor representing the source voltage of the source by the phasor representing the load current of the load. (4)

TRANSIENT VIBRATION. Transient vibration is temporarily sustained vibration of a mechanical system. It may consist of forced or free vibration or both. (2)

TRANSIT. Program to develop and establish in being a system of near-earth satellites to provide a means for establishing locations (navigating) anywhere on the surface of the earth. (35)

TRANSITIONAL WATER (TRANSITIONAL ZONE). In regard to progressive gravity waves, water whose depth is less than 1/2 but more that 1/25 the wave length. Often called SHALLOW WATER. (11)

TRANSITION LOSS. The transition loss at the junction between an energy source and an energy load is the transmission loss measured by the ratio of the source power of that source to the load power of that load. (4)

TRANSMISSIBILITY. Transmissibility is a term which is used to describe the ability of a system either to amplify or to suppress an input vibration. More technically, it is the ratio of the response amplitude of the system in steady-state forced vibration to the excitation amplitude. The ratio may be between forces, displacements, velocities, or accelerations. (9)

TRANSMISSION ANOMALY. The difference (in decibels) between the total transmission loss in intensity and the reduction in intensity due to an assumed inverse square divergence. (5)

TRANSMISSION GAIN. Whenever the TRANSMISSION FACTOR is a number greater than unity, as it is in the case of an amplifier, the transmission loss would have a negative sign. In such cases the logarithm of the reciprocal of the transmission factor is written with a positive sign and designated as a transmission gain. (4)

TRANSMISSION LEVEL. The transmission level of the energy at any point in an energy transmission system is the rate of flow of that energy as expressed in terms of (1) a specified reference rate of flow and of (2) the transmission loss by which the actual rate of flow must be reduced to equal the reference rate. (4)

TRANSMISSION LOSS. Transmission loss is the reduction in the magnitude of some characteristic of a signal between two stated points in a transmission system. (9)

TRANSMISSOMETER. A light-path device for measuring in situ turbidity by relative light scattering and absorption of light transmitted. (35)

TRANSMITTING BAND RESPONSE. The transmitting band response of a sonar projector, for a given bearing and for a given frequency band, may be defined as the response measured by the quotient obtained by dividing (1) the index intensity of the acoustic energy radiated on the given bearing and in the given frequency band by the projector when receiving electric energy occupying the same frequency band by (2) the power of this received electric energy. (4)

TRANSMITTING DIRECTIVITY FACTOR. 1. The transmitting directivity factor of a sonar transducer, for a specified frequency, may be defined as the ratio of (1) the power per unit band of the acoustic energy radiated over all bearings and at the specified frequency by the transducer when receiving electric energy having a given power per unit band at the specified frequency to (2) the power per unit band of the acoustic energy which would be radiated over the same bearings and at the same frequency when receiving the same electric energy, if the transmitting response of the transducer for that frequency were the same for any bearing as for the maximum response reference bearing.

2. The transmitting directivity factor may also be defined as the ratio of (1) the power of the acoustic energy radiated over all bearings by the transducer when receiving sinusoidal electric waves of the specified frequency and having a given power to (2) the power of the acoustic energy which would be radiated over the same bearings and when receiving the same electric waves, if the transmitting response of the transducer for the specified frequency were the same for any bearing as for the maximum response reference bearing. (4)

THUNDERSQUALL. See SQUALL.

TRANSMITTING SPECTRUM FACTOR. The transmitting spectrum factor of a sonar transducer, for a specified bearing, for a specified frequency band, for a specified distribution of energy in that band, and for a specified reference frequency, is defined as the ratio of (1) the index intensity of the acoustic energy radiated over the specified bearing and in the specified frequency band by the transducer when receiving electric energy having a power per unit band which varies with frequency in the specified manner to (2) the index intensity of the acoustic energy which would be radiated over the same bearing and in the same frequency band when receiving the same electric energy if the transmitting response of the transducer for that bearing were the same for any frequency as for the specified reference frequency. (4)

TRANSPARENCY. The ability of water to transmit light of different wave lengths, usually measured in per cent of radiation which penetrates a distance of 1 meter. Transparency is the average of the depths at which a SECCHI DISK (about 30 centimeters in diameter) disappears and reappears. (15)

TRANSPONDER. An electronic device that receives a challenging signal and automatically transmits a response. The transponder consists of a receiver, which receives the signal impulses, and a responder (or transmitter) that returns signal impulses to the interrogator-responser. (42)

TRANS-TIDAL WAVES. Those waves having periods of 24 hours and greater.

TRANSVERSE BAR. A BAR which extends at approximately right angles to the shoreline. (27)

TRANSVERSE WAVE (DISTORTIONAL WAVE). A wave in which the direction of propagation of the wave is normal to the displacements of the medium, e.g., a vibrating string. The GRAVITY WAVE in which fluid parcels move in circular orbits is an example of a mixed transverse-longitudinal wave. The Rossby wave is also mixed, except in the case of zero current speed, when it is a transverse wave. (12)

TRAWL WINCH, DEEP SEA. A shipboard winch capable of paying out 3000 fathoms of cable in 30 minutes, it measures the cable tension and can be operated so as to recover 3000 fathoms of cable in 90 minutes with a ton on each end of the line. (35)

TRENCH. A long and narrow depression with relatively steep sides.

TRIAXON. See SPICULE.

TRI-FILTER HYDROPHOTOMETER. This device is basically identical to the DUAL-FILTER HYDROPHOTOMETER. It is, however, lighter and easier to maintain. The electrical circuit has been redesigned to sim-

plify operation and provide better linearity. In addition to the blue and red filters on the dual-filter hydrophotometer, a green filter is used on the tri-filter hydrophotometer. This instrument is designed for use in turbid estuarine and coastal regions and is not considered suitable for deep water transparency measurements. (35)

TROCHOIDAL WAVE. A progressive oscillatory wave whose form is that of a prolate cycloid or trochoid. It is approximated by waves of small amplitude. (11)

TROCHOPHORE. An invertebrate larva, commonly pear-shaped and with an equatorial band of CELIA. (19)

TROCHOID. As used in connection with wave motion, a curve described by a point within a circle that rolls along a straight line. The curve is also known as a prolate cycloid. The cross section of an ocean wave approximates in form a trochoid described with the rolling circle below the straight line. The resulting form has a comparatively sharp crest and flattened trough. (14)

TROPICAL MONTH. See DECLINATION.

TROPICAL SUBMERGENCE. See BIPOLARITY.

TROPIC CURRENTS. Tidal currents occurring semimonthly when the effect of the moon's maximum declination is greatest. At these times the tendency of the moon to produce a diurnal inequality in the current is at a maximum. (14)

TROPIC HIGH WATER INEQUALITY. See DIURNAL INEQUALITY.

TROPIC INEQUALITIES. Tropic high water inequality is the average difference between the two high waters of the day at the times of TROPIC TIDES. Tropic low water inequality is the average difference between the two low waters of the day at the times of tropic tides. Those terms are applicable only when the type of tide is semidiurnal or mixed. See TROPIC TIDES. (14)

TROPIC LOW WATER INEQUALITY. See DIURNAL INEQUALITY.

TROPIC RANGE. See GREAT TROPIC RANGE.

TROPIC TIDES. Tides occurring semimonthly when the effect of the moon's maximum declination is greatest. At these times there is a tendency for an increase in the diurnal range. The tidal planes pertaining to the tropic tides are designated as tropic higher high water, tropic lower high water, tropic higher low water, and tropic lower low water. (14)

TROPIC VELOCITY. The greater flood or greater ebb velocity at the time of TROPIC CURRENTS. (14)

TROPOPAUSE. The boundary or transition zone between the troposphere and the stratosphere. (42)

TROPOSPHERE. The lower layer of the earth's atmosphere, extending from the surface of the earth to an altitude of ten miles. Although the composition of the air remains more or less constant, its density decreases rather rapidly with altitude; 75% of the atmosphere's weight is found in the troposphere. (42)

TROUGH. 1. In meteorology, an elongated area of relatively low atmospheric pressure; the opposite of a RIDGE. The axis of a trough is the trough line.

This term is commonly used to distinguish the above from the closed circulation of a low (or cyclone); but a large-scale trough may include one or more lows, an upper-air trough may be associated with a lower-level low, and a low may have one or more distinct troughs radiating from it. (24)

2. A long depression of the sea floor, having relatively gentle sides, normally wider and shallower than a TRENCH. (26)

TRUE NORTH. The direction from any point on the earth's surface toward the geographic North Pole; the northerly direction along any projection of the earth's axis upon the earth's surface, e.g., along a longitude line. Except for much of navigational practice (which uses MAGNETIC NORTH), true north is the universal 0° (or 360°) mapping reference. True north differs from magnetic north by the magnetic DECLINATION at that geographic point. (24)

TRUNK BUOY. A mooring buoy having a pendant extending through an opening in the buoy, the ship's anchor chain or mooring line being secured to this pendant. (17)

TRUNK ROUTE DECCA. See DECTRA.

T-S CURVE. See TEMPERATURE-SALINITY DIAGRAM.

TSUSHIMA CURRENT. That part of the KUROSHIO flowing northeastward through Korea Strait and the Sea of Japan, following the northwest coast of Japan, and then curving southeastward to rejoin the main part of the Kuroshio. (17)

TRUMPET BUOY. A buoy provided with a trumpet having a distinctive tone and an adjustable characteristic. (17)

TRUNCATED LANDFORM. A landform cut off, especially by erosion, and forming a steep side or cliff. (27)

TSUNAMI (TIDAL WAVE). Tsunamis are ocean waves produced by sudden, large-scale motion of a portion of the ocean floor, as by volcanic eruption, earthquake, or landslide. If they are caused by a submarine earthquake, they are usually called seismic sea waves. Either a tsunami or a storm wave that overflows the land is popularly called a tidal wave, although it bears no relation to the tide.

Tsunamis usually occur in series, gradually increasing in height until a maximum is reached between about the third and eighth wave. Following the maximum, they again become smaller. Waves may continue to form for several hours, or even days. In deep water the wave height of a tsunami is probably never greater than two or three feet. Since the wave length is usually considerably more than 100 miles, the wave is not conspicuous at sea. In the Pacific, where most tsunamis occur, the wave period varies between about 15 and 60 minutes, and the speed in deep water is more than 400 knots. When a tsunami enters shoal water, it undergoes the same changes as other waves. Because of the great speed of a tsunami in relatively deep water, the slowing is relatively much greater than that of an ordinary wave created by wind. Therefore, the increase in height is also much greater. Tsunamis 50 feet in height or higher have reached the shore, inflicting widespread damage. (12)

TUBEWORMS. Segmented marine worms some of which secrete calcareous tubes. (15)

TUFA. A chemical sedimentary rock composed of calcium carbonate or silica. Tufa is included with rock on bottom sediment charts. On U. S.

Navy Hydrographic charts for the western coast of France the notation T may mean tangue, a calcareous deposit derived from a variety of marine organisms.

TUNICATES. A subphylum of marine invertebrate animals which includes ascidians or sea squirts, and salps. Ascidians are either compound or simple, and many species attach to submerged objects. Several species of salps are bioluminescent. (15)

TURBIDITES. Derived by TURBIDITY CURRENTS from the lands or from higher submarine terrain. (27)

TURBIDITY. The state or condition of having the transparence or translucence disturbed, as when sediment in water is stirred up, or when dust, haze, clouds, etc., appear in the atmosphere because of wind or vertical currents. (17)

TURBIDITY CURRENT. A gravity current resulting from a density increase by suspended material. Also called SUSPENSION CURRENT, and DENSITY CURRENT. (27)

TURBULENCE. The state or condition of being violently agitated or disturbed, as a stream which meets an obstacle, or air flowing over an uneven surface. (17)

TURBULENT FLOW. Fluid motion in which random motions of parts of the fluid are superimposed upon a simple pattern of flow. All or nearly all fluid flow displays some degree of turbulence. The opposite is STREAMLINE FLOW. (17)

TWO RANGE DECCA. Two-range Decca is a variant of the DECCA NAVIGATOR system. It was developed specifically for surveying and unlike conventional Decca, which utilizes permanently based transmitters ashore, the master is carried in a ship and the shore based equipment is designed for portability, as well as for the essential accuracy.

Since only two stations are used, the dial meter display consists of only 2 movements instead of the usual 4 in the standard Decca Navigator. (29)

TWZO. Trade Wind Zone Oceanography.

TYPE OF TIDE. The characteristic form of the tide with special reference to the relation of the diurnal and semidiurnal waves. Tides are sometimes classified as diurnal, semidiurnal, and mixed, but there are no sharply defined limits separating the groups. The tide is said to be diurnal when the diurnal wave predominates and only a single high and single low water occur each day during the greater part of the month. The tide is semidiurnal when the semidiurnal wave predominates and two high and two low waters occur each tidal day with a relatively small inequality in the high and low water heights. In the mixed type of tide the diurnal and semidiurnal waves are both important factors and the tide is characterized by a large inequality in the high or low water heights or in both. There will usually be two high and two low waters each day, but occasionally the tide will become diurnal. Also applicable to tidal currents. (14)

TYPHOON. A tropical cyclone originating in the western Pacific Ocean, particularly in the vicinity of the South China Sea or to the eastward of the Phillippine Islands. Such a disturbance is called a BAGUIO in the Philippine Islands. (17)

U

UDT. Underwater Demolition Team (USN).

UHF. Ultra High Frequencies (300 - 3000 megacycles).

ULTRA-GRAVITY WAVES. Those waves having periods ranging from 0.1 second to 1.0 second.

ULTRA LOW FREQUENCY OCEAN WAVE RECORDER. The instrument consists of a five-inch stand-pipe mounted vertically along a pier pile with its open end fifteen feet beneath mean sea level. Most of the pipe is filled with a highly refined petroleum oil. The movement of the oil column is impeded by a capillary. An air chamber above the air column is connected to an air reservoir, the volume of which can be readily adjusted. A fine capillary permits leakage of air between the reservoir and the atmosphere. The remaining part of the instrument consists of glass cylinders mounted above the deck level of the pier. The differential between the air pressure in the last glass cylinder and the atmospheric pressure actuates a strain gauge pressure transmitter, the output of which is recorded on shore. The capillary in the stand-pipe tends to suppress any short period vertical oscillation of the oil column due to wind waves or swell. The oil column does respond to the rise and fall of the tides, but due to the leakage of air through the air capillary in the reservoir, this very slow movement does not lead to appreciable pressure changes in the air pocket above the oil column. The pressure changes in the air pocket result mostly from periods intermediate between those of the swell and tides. The oil capillary connecting the first two glass cylinders suppresses the transmission of short period waves to the second air reservoir, whereas, the air capillary in the third cylinder reduces pressure changes of long periods. Each additional "stage" of the two cylinders thus has the characteristics of a band pass filter. (30)

ULTRAPLANKTON. See MARINE LIFE.

ULTRASONIC FREQUENCY. An ultrasonic frequency is a frequency lying above the audio frequency range. Thus it extends from roughly 20,000 cycles per second upward. (9)

ULTRASONICS. Ultrasonics is the technology of sound at frequencies above the audio range; i.e., above 20,000 cycles per second. (9)

ULTRASONIC SHIPBOARD WAVE HEIGHT SENSOR. A self-contained electronic system to measure and record the relative displacement of sea surface from mean sea level.

UN. United Nations.

UNCC. United Nations Cartographic Conference.

UNCONFORMITY ICEBERG. An ICEBERG consisting of more than one kind of ice, such as blue water-formed ice and NÉVÉ. Such an iceberg often contains many crevasses and silt bands. (17)

UNCONSOLIDATED SEDIMENTS. Deposits consisting of uncemented clastic or organic material. (27)

UNDERTOW. A CURRENT, below water surface, flowing seaward; also the receding water below the surface from waves breaking on a shelving beach. Actually "undertow" is largely mythical. As the backwash of each wave flows down the beach, a current is formed which flows seaward, however it is a periodic phenomenon. The most common phenomena expressed as "undertow" are actually the rip currents in the surf. Often uniform return flows seaward or lakeward are termed "undertow" though these flows will not be as strong as rip currents. (11)

UNDERWATER CAMERAS. Underwater cameras may be classified under two general categories; those operated by divers and swimmers, and those that are lowered with a winch and remotely operated by bottom contact, messenger, or mechanical means. The first category includes both still- and motion-picture cameras using either color or black and white film. The second category usually includes only still cameras. One type is the single shot, taking only one picture on each lowering. Another type is the multiple shot, taking a series of pictures during the lowering operation.

The single-shot, bottom-contact camera is designed to obtain photographs of the ocean bottom at great depths. It will take one picture on each lowering, and the camera shutter is tripped by contact with the bottom. The tripping mechanism obtains a small PHLEGER-TYPE core at the time of tripping. The camera is contained in a heavy pressure case capable of withstanding water pressures up to 12,000 pounds per square inch. (35)

UNDERWATER SOUND PROJECTOR. An Underwater Sound Projector is a transducer used to produce sound in water. The conversion from electrical energy to sound is achieved through the use of either the piezoelectric or magnetostrictive effect. When a piezoelectric material is used to generate underwater sound, the electric potential across the sample material is varied periodically at the frequency of the desired sound signal. Under this condition the piezoelectric material vibrates mechanically at this frequency; this vibration when properly coupled to the water, produces the sound of the desired frequency in the water.

If a rod of ferromagnetic material is brought into a magnetic field parallel to its ion axis the length is changed. This effect is called magnetostriction. Magnetostriction is applied to the production of sound waves as follows: a nickel rod is subjected to an alternating magnetic field by winding a coil of wire around it and sending an a.c. current through the coil. The rod is shortened periodically in response to the changing field. The natural frequency N of a rod of length L is

$$N = \frac{1}{22} \left(\frac{E}{P}\right)^{1/2} \qquad \begin{array}{l} E = \text{Modulus of elasticity} \\ P = \text{density of material} \end{array}$$

(30)

UNDERWAY BOTTOM SAMPLER. See SCOOPFISH.

UNDISTURBED WATER LEVEL. See STILL WATER LEVEL.

UNESCO. United Nations Educational, Scientific and Cultural Organization.

UNIDIRECTIONAL HYDROPHONE. A unidirectional hydrophone is a hydrophone that is responsive predominantly to sound incident from a single solid angle of one hemisphere or less. (1)

UNIDIRECTIONAL TRANSDUCER. In many practical transducer designs the active surface is mounted in a structure in such fashion that radiation or reception takes place on one side only. In such cases the unit will show maximum response along a single bearing only and is said to be unidirectional. (4)

UNILATERAL TRANSDUCER. A unilateral transducer is

a transducer that cannot be actuated at its outputs by waves in such a manner as to supply related waves at its inputs. (1)

UNIT AREA ACOUSTIC IMPEDANCE. The quotient obtained by dividing (1) the phasor corresponding, at a given frequency, to the acoustic pressure by (2) the phasor corresponding, at the same frequency, to the volume velocity per unit area. (4)

UNIVERSAL TIME. See GREENWICH MEAN TIME.

UNSA. United Nations Specialized Agencies.

UPCOAST. In United States usage; the coastal direction generally trending towards the north. (11)

UP DOPPLER. When a target is moving toward a transducer the echo will be of higher frequency than the reverberation regardless of whether the range is opening or closing. When the echo is of higher frequency than the reverberation it is said to have an Up Doppler. Similarly, when the echo is of lower frequency than the reverberation it is said to have a Down Doppler, which indicates a component of target motion away from the transducer. (4)

UPDRIFT. The direction opposite that of the predominant movement of littoral material. (11)

UPLIFT. The upward water pressure on the base of a structure or pavement. (11)

UPRUSH. See RUN-UP.

UPWELLING. The rising of water toward the surface from subsurface layers of a body of water. Upwelling is most prominent where persistent wind blows parallel to a coastline so that the resultant wind-driven current sets away from the coast (see EKMAN SPIRAL). It constitutes a distinct

climatogenetic influence by bringing colder water to the surface. Over the open ocean, upwelling occurs wherever the wind circulation is cyclonic, but is appreciable only in areas where that circulation is relatively permanent. It is also observable when the southern trade winds cross the equator.

The upwelled water, besides being cooler, is richer in plant nutrients, so that regions of upwelling are generally also areas of rich fisheries. (12)

URSTROMTHAL. A large channel cut by a substantial melt-water stream, flowing along the edge of an ICE-SHEET. (27)

URV. Underseas research vehicle.

USAID. United States Aid for International Development.

USC&GS. United States Coast & Geodetic Survey. The USC&GS is the nation's oldest (formed in 1807) scientific body and the chief civilian oceanographic agency in the U. S.

USCG. United States Coast Guard.

(US)GS. Geological Survey (Department of Interior).

USN. United States Navy.

(USN)HO. Hydrographic Office (although now officially designated U.S. Naval Oceanographic Office (NAVOCEANO) H. O. is still used in referring to charts and publications).

UST. Undersea Technology.

(US)WB. Weather Bureau.

UTS. Underwater Telephone System. A sonar system -- consisting of a transducer, a receiver-transmitter unit and a control box.

VACUOLE. A cavity within the PROTOPLASM containing a solution of sugars, salts, pigments, etc., together with colloidal materials. (18)

VACUUM. From a practical viewpoint, a condition where sufficient air has been removed from a container so that any remaining air will not affect the characteristics of the device beyond an allowable amount. Theoretically, a perfect vacuum is space from which all the air and gases have been removed; this is never attained in actual practice. (36)

VALLEY ICEBERG (DRYDOCK ICEBERG). An ICEBERG eroded in such a manner that a large U-shaped slot extends through the iceberg with large pinnacles or slabs on either side. Sometimes the slot is awash. These icebergs do not turn over, but sail on as majestically as a well-ballasted ship. Valley icebergs deteriorate chiefly by CALVING and melting at the water line. When the lightened iceberg rises a series of water lines circling the base is exposed. (25)

VAN DORN SAMPLER. This sediment sampler consists of a plexiglas cylinder closed at each end by an ordinary rubber force cup. The two cups are con-

nected by a length of surgical rubber tubing inside the cylinder, pre-stressed enough to permit the force cups to retain the sample in the cylinder. In the armed position the two cups are pulled outside the cylinder where they are restrained by a releasing mechanism attached to the outside wall. Two short loops of wire connect the cups to the releasing mechanism. The cups are released underwater by sending a messenger down the hydrographic wire. This sampler does not invert, which prevents use of reversing thermometers in conjunction with sampling. (30)

VDS. Variable-Depth Sonar.

VEGETATIVE EURYHALINE. See STENOHALINE.

VEGETATIVE STENOHALINE. See STENOHALINE.

VELOCIMETER. The Velocimeter is an instrument used for the in situ measurement of the speed of sound in the sea and other natural waters. The operation of the velocimeter is based upon the sing-around principle developed by C. E. Tschiegg and M. Greenspan of the National Bureau of Standards. Two electroacoustic transducers and a reflector are mounted to form a sound path of fixed length in water. This sound path along with the necessary amplifiers and blocking oscillator form the essential operating components of a sing-around circuit. In operation, a pulse of acoustic energy is transmitted through the water, received, amplified and used to generate another pulse of acoustic energy. The repetition or sing-around frequency of this regenerative action is dependent upon the transit time of the signal pulse and is therefore a measure of the propagation velocity. (30)

VELOCITY GRADIENT. Gradual changes in the velocity of propagation with distance within a single medium are known as velocity gradients. (4)

VELOCITY HYDROPHONE. A velocity hydrophone is a hydrophone in which the electric output substantially corresponds to the instantaneous particle velocity in the impressed sound wave. (1)

VELOCITY LEVEL. The velocity level, in decibels, of a sound is 20 times the logarithm to the base 10 of the ratio of the particle velocity of the sound to the reference particle velocity. The reference particle velocity shall be stated explicitly. (2)

VELOCITY OF SOUND. Sound velocity in the ocean varies roughly between 4800 feet per second (fps) and 5100 fps. At 70°F and with a normal salinity of 34 parts per thousand by weight, the sound velocity is 4935 fps at the ocean surface. (Speed of sound in air = 1090 ft./sec).

VENTRAL. Toward the lower side or belly; away from the back. Opposite to DORSAL. (19)

VERTEBRATE. An animal having a segmental "back-bone" or vertebral column. (19)

VIBRATING CORING TUBE. A sediment coring tube designed to vibrate in such a way as to overcome the resistance of compacted ocean floor sediments, sands and gravel.

VIBRATING WIRE TRANSDUCER. A device that can be used to measure ocean depth. The vibrating element is simply a very fine tungsten wire which is stretched in a magnetic field. The wire vibrates at some precise frequency which is determined by the length and tension of the wire. Pressure changes by varying the tension in the wire change the vibration frequency of the wire. (35)

VIBRATION. Vibration is an oscillation wherein the quantity is a parameter that defines the motion of a mechanical system. (2)

VIBROTRON. A pressure sensing transducer which converts hydrostatic pressure directly into an FM signal which can then be TELEMETERED.

VIGIA. A rock or shoal the existence or position of which is doubtful, or a warning note to this effect on a chart. (17)

VISCOSITY. The resistance of liquids, semi solids, and gases to movement or flow.

VISCOUS DAMPING. Viscous damping is the dissipation of energy that occurs when a particle in a vibrating system is resisted by a force whose magnitude is a constant independent of displacement and velocity, and whose direction is opposite to the direction of the velocity of the particle. (2)

VITAL CAPACITY. The term for the greatest volume of air that a man can expel from his lungs after a full inspiration. In other words, it is the greatest volume of air that can be moved in and out of the lungs in a single breath. The average man's vital capacity is between 4 and 5 liters. (37)

VIVIPAROUS. See OVIPAROUS.

VLF. Very Low Frequencies (10-30 kilocycles).

VNIRO. All-Union Research Institute of Marine Fisheries and Oceanography (USSR).

VOLCANIC ASH. Usually fine-grained material ejected by a volcano. Volcanic ash is classed as sand on bottom sediment charts.

VOLTAIC CELL. A cell consisting of two electrodes and one or more eletrolytes which, when connected in a closed circuit, will give out electrical energy.

VOLUME VELOCITY. Volume velocity is the rate of alternating flow of the medium through a specified surface due to a sound wave. (2)

VOLUNTARY APNEA. See BREATH HOLDING.

WAFC. West African Fisheries Commission.

WARP. To move, as a vessel, from one place to another by means of lines fastened to an object, such as a buoy, wharf, etc., secured to the ground. (17)

WARPING BUOY. A buoy so located that lines to it can be used for the movement of ships.

WASH AND STRAIN ICE FOOT. An ice foot formed from ice casts and slush and attached to a shelving beach, between the high and low water lines. High waves and spray may cause it to build up above the high water line. (17)

WATCH BUOY. See STATION BUOY.

WATER CLARITY METER (MOVABLE DISC TYPE). A visual photometer consisting of two discs of different

colors and sizes connected by a vertical shaft. The upper (gray, smaller) disc slides on the shaft so that it can be lifted above the fixed, lower (white, larger) disc by an auxiliary line. The upper disc is separated from the lower disc until the two appear to be equally luminous. Once the two are properly separated they will continue to match in homogeneous water regardless of the depth to which the apparatus is submerged.

The separation of the discs is a direct measure of the clarity of the water and can be converted to hydrological range by a multiplying factor. The hydrological range is that range at which the apparent contrast is two per cent; the apparent contrast is a function of the reflectivities of the two discs, their average depth, and the angle of sight to the discs. (35)

WATER CLARITY METER (PHOTOCELL TYPE). This meter was developed to permit underwater visibility readings by swimmers. It will measure and record surface illumination, the decrease of ambient light with depth, the attenuation of illumination of a beam of light beneath the surface, and the depth of the instrument. The underwater unit contains an Alpha-meter, which is a light source at a fixed distance from a photocell, to provide a measure of the attenuation of the beam of light; an h-meter, which is a photocell to measure ambient light; and a pressure transducer. Filters are used to make the photocell response similar to that of the human eye. The deck unit consists of a photocell for measuring surface illumination, an electronic unit, and a recorder. Any of the four parameters may be recorded individually or all in succession by switching. (35)

WATER COLOR. The apparent color of the surface layers of the sea caused by the reflection of certain components of the visible light spectrum coupled with the effects of dissolved material, concentration of PLANKTON, DETRITUS, or other matter Color of oceanic water varies from deep blue to yellow and is expressed by number values which are a variation of the FOREL SCALE. Plankton concentrations may cause a temporary appearance of red, white, green, or other colors. (15)

WATER-COMPRESSIBILITY. Water can be compressed only to a slight degree, the compressibility is so slight that even at the depth of a mile, a cubic foot of water weighs only about 1/2 pound more than that at the surface.

WATER CONTENT. Of a bottom sediment is a ratio obtained by multiplying the weight of the water in the sample by 100 and dividing the results by the weight of the dried sample; expressed as a percentage. (17)

WATERLINE ATTACK. CORROSION that takes place at the interface of the atmosphere and water on metallic structures partly immersed in the water.

WATER NOISE. The minimum ambient noise of practical significance is that due to movement of the water itself. The term water noise is used to designate acoustic energy resulting primarily from this cause. (4)

WATER SKY. Dark streaks, patches, or grayness on the underside of extensive cloud areas due to the absence of reflected light from open water areas. Water sky is darker than LAND SKY. (25)

WATERSPOUT. A small whirling storm over water, the chief characteristic of which is a funnel-shaped cloud extending, in a fully developed waterspout, from the surface of the water to the base of a cumulus type cloud. Only the lower part ordinarily has water, which may be drawn up by the action of the vortex or may be produced by condensation. Waterspouts usually rotate in the same direction as CYCLONES and are most frequent in the tropics. (17)

WAVE. A wave is a disturbance which is propagated in a medium in such a manner that at any point in the medium the quantity serving as measure of disturbance is a function of the time, while at any instant the displacement at a point is a function of the position of the point. Any physical quantity that has the same relationship to some independent variable (usually time) that a propagated disturbance has, at a particular instant, with respect to space, may be called a wave. (1)

WAVE, CAPILLARY. A wave whose velocity of propagation is controlled primarily by the surface tension of the liquid in which the wave is travelling. Water waves of a length less than one inch are considered to be capillary waves. (11)

WAVE CELERITY. See PHASE SPEED.

WAVE, CYCLOIDAL. A very steep, symmetrical wave whose crest forms an angle of 120°. The wave form is that of a cycloid. A TROCHOIDAL WAVE of maximum steepness. (11)

WAVE DIRECTION. The direction, in degrees true, from which the waves come. (35)

WAVE FILTER (FILTER). A wave filter is a transducer for separating waves on the basis of their frequency. It introduces relatively small insertion loss to waves in one or more frequency bands and relatively large insertion loss to waves of other frequencies. (9)

WAVE FORECASTING. The theoretical determination of future wave characteristics, usually from observed or predicted meteorological phenomena. (11)

WAVE FRONT. Wave front is an expression which is applied to a progressive wave in space at any given instant, and is the line or surface over which the phase is everywhere the same at the given instant. A wave front is particularly obvious in the case of surface waves on water, for all the points lying at the crest of the wave at any given instant are in the same phase. These points form a line and are an example of a case where the wave front is a line rather than a surface. (9)

WAVE GAGES. Ocean wave measurements may be made in several various ways. Capillary waves or those having a 10^{-2} WAVE PERIOD (in seconds) may be measured optically while GRAVITY (type) WAVES with a wave period characterized by 7 seconds are measured by electromechanical methods. For long (10^2 seconds) wave periods, pneumatic methods are employed; numerical methods on TRANSTIDAL (10^6 seconds) waves and Astronomical methods for waves having a wave period in the order of 10^8 seconds.
In general, the most common class of devices used are - Bottom Pressure Instruments, Floating Wave Gages, Fixed Wave Gages and Airborne Systems.
In obtaining wave height records from pressure transducers placed on the ocean floor, the measured pressure fluctuations due to the overlying wave are translated by appropriate theoretical equations into corresponding wave heights. The method is restricted however to so-called shallow water waves where the depth is less than half a wave length, and suffers in addition from the fact that high frequency components of the wave system become greatly attenuated with depth and may not even be sensed by the transducer.
A promising method for measuring waves at sea lies in the use of the SHIP-BORNE WAVE RECORDER. The device makes use of pressure sensors located on the ship's hull below the water surface. The heave of the vessel, determined from an accelerometer pickup, is effectively factored out of the total response, leaving only a record of wave height. A minor disadvantage of this method is that the presence and motion of the ship alters the wave pattern to some degree.
Another scheme of wave measurement is the wave pole, a spar-like floating buoy which uses a vertical wire whose resistance changes as a wave passes by it. The resulting voltage change, proportional to the wave height, is telemetered to shore or a nearby vessel and recorded. Although attempts are made to restrict the pole's motion in the seaway by means of damping devices, its excursions from a fixed position in space do lead to errors of measurement in varying degrees. (35)

WAVE GROUP. A series of waves in which the wave direction, WAVE LENGTH, and wave height vary only slightly. (11)

WAVE HEIGHT COEFFICIENT. The ratio of the wave height at a selected point to the deep water wave height. The REFRACTION COEFFICIENT multiplied by the SHOALING COEFFICIENT. (11)

WAVE INTERFERENCE. Wave interference is the phenomenon which results when waves of the same or nearly the same frequency are superposed and is

127

characterized by a spatial or temporal distribution of amplitude of some specified characteristic differing from that of the individual superposed waves. (2)

WAVE LENGTH. 1. The wave length of a periodic wave in an isotropic medium is the perpendicular distance between two wave fronts in which the displacements have a difference in phase of one complete period. (2)

2. The horizontal distance between successive ocean wave crests or the distance in meters traveled by a wave during the time interval of one complete cycle. It is equal to the velocity divided by the frequency. (36)

WAVE NUMBER. The reciprocal of wave length; the number of waves per unit distance in the direction of propagation; or, frequently, 2π times this quantity. Thus, in the simple harmonic component sin k(x - ct), the wave number is ambiguously k or $k/2\pi$. (12)

WAVE OF TRANSLATION. A wave in which the individual particles of the medium are shifted in the direction of wave travel, as ocean waves in shoal waters; in contrast with an OSCILLATORY WAVE, in which only the form advances, the individual particles moving in closed orbits, as ocean waves in deep water. (17)

WAVE PERIOD. In a train of identical waves the period is the time elapsed between the passage of a given phase on one wave and the arrival of the same phase on the next succeeding wave, as observed from a fixed station.

WAVE PROPAGATION. The radiation, as from an antenna of r-f energy into space, or of sound energy into a conducting medium. (10)

WAVE SPECTRUM. In ocean wave studies, a graph showing the distribution of wave heights with respect to frequency in a wave record. (12)

WAVE SPEED. See PHASE SPEED.

WAVE STEEPNESS. Of a water-surface wave, the ratio of wave height to wave length. (12)

WAVE SYSTEM. In ocean wave studies, a group of waves having the same height, direction, and length. Ocean surface waves are generally composed of a number of superimposed wave systems. (12)

WAVE VELOCITY. Wave velocity is a vector quantity that specifies the speed and direction with which a sound wave travels through a medium. (2)

WB. U. S. Weather Bureau.

W/D. Weight-displacement ratio.

WDC. World Data Center.

WEATHER PATROL SHIP. See OCEAN STATION VESSEL.

WEATHER SHIP. See OCEAN STATION VESSEL.

WEDGE. See RIDGE.

WEST AUSTRALIA CURRENT. A seasonal Indian Ocean current flowing along the west coast of Australia. In the northern hemisphere winter it flows northward from off Cape Leeuwin to Northwest Cape, where it curves northwestward to continue as part of the SOUTH EQUATORIAL CURRENT. The west Australia current is formed from the northern part of the west wind drift current and a current setting westerly along the south coast of Australia, and is the eastern part of the general counterclockwise

oceanic circulation of the southern part of the Indian Ocean. In the northern hemisphere summer, this northward flowing current is replaced by a southwesterly and southerly flow from the Arafura Sea to the vicinity of Cape Leeuwin, where it merges with the WEST WIND DRIFT CURRENT. (17)

WESTERLIES. 1. Specifically: the dominant west-to-east motion of the atmosphere, centered over the middle latitudes of both hemispheres. At the earth's surface, the westerly belt extends, on the average, from about 35° to 65° latitude. At upper levels, the westerlies extend farther equatorward and poleward. The equatorward boundary is fairly well defined by the SUBTROPICAL HIGH-PRESSURE BELT; the poleward boundary is quite diffuse and variable.

2. Generally, any winds with components from the west. (14)

WEST GREENLAND CURRENT. An Atlantic Ocean current flowing northwestward and northward along the southwest and west coast of Greenland from off Cape Farewell, the southern tip of Greenland, through Davis Strait and into Baffin Bay. The west Greenland current is the continuation, along the west coast of Greenland, of the EAST GREENLAND CURRENT. (17)

WESTON PHOTRONIC CELL. See BARRIER LAYER CELL.

WEST WIND DRIFT CURRENT. A circumpolar ocean current flowing eastward around Antarctica, and having its northern limits determined by the southern limits of Australia, New Zealand, South America, and Africa, and by the general oceanic circulation of the South Pacific, South Atlantic, and Indian Oceans. The west wind drift current is fed by several southward flowing currents, and in turn, it augments certain northward flowing currents, notably the PERU CURRENT of the South Pacific Ocean and the BENGUELA CURRENT of the South Atlantic Ocean. That part of the west wind drift current flowing eastward in the immediate vicinity of Cape Horn is called CAPE HORN CURRENT. (17)

WEST WIND DRIFT. (see ANTARCTIC CIRCUMPOLAR CURRENT)

WET-BULB TEMPERATURE. 1. Isobaric wet-bulb temperature: The temperature an air parcel would have if cooled adiabatically to saturation at constant pressure by evaporation of water into it, all latent heat being supplied by the parcel.

2. Adiabatic wet-bulb temperature (or pseudo wet-bulb temperature): The temperature an air parcel would have if cooled adiabatically to saturation and then compressed adiabatically to the original pressure in a saturation-adiabatic process. This is the wet-bulb temperature as read off the thermodynamic diagram and is always less than the isobaric wet-bulb temperature, usually by a fraction of a degree centigrade.

3. The temperature read from the wet-bulb thermometer (See PSYCHROMETER). The thermodynamics of this thermometer is still under discussion, but for practical purposes the temperature so obtained is identified with the isobaric wet-bulb temperature. (14)

WET DENSITY. Of a bottom sediment sample is the ratio of the weight of the sample to its volume. (15)

WET DOCK. See DOCK.

WET SUIT. See RUBBER SUIT.

WHARF. A structure serving as a berthing place for vessels. A wharf approximately parallel to the shore line, accommodating ships on one side only, and usually of solid construction, as distinguished from open pile construction, is called a quay. A wharf extending into the water, with accommodations for ships on both sides, is called a PIER. See DOCK, JETTY, LANDING, MOLE. (17)

WHISTLE BUOY. A buoy equipped with a whistle. In the United States a whistle buoy is usually a conical buoy with a whistle on top. (17)

WHITE NOISE. White noise is a noise whose spectrum density (or spectrum level) is substantially independent of frequency over a specified range. (2)

WHO. World Health Organization.

WHOI. Woods Hole Oceanographic Institution.

WHOLE GALE. See GALE.

WIANCKO PRESSURE-MEASURING SYSTEM. This pressure measuring system is used to measure and record water pressure changes of 0.1 inch to 80.0 inches to a depth of 200 feet. The system includes three basic units. The underwater unit consists of a differential pressure gauge in a housing which also contains a hydraulic filter to compensate for static pressures and a calibration relay circuit. The differential pressure gauge produces an electrical signal which is proportional to the pressure variation by changing the ratio of two inductances. The electronic unit contains two resistances which complete a bridge circuit with the two inductances and produce a d.c. voltage proportional to the pressure variations. The recording unit is a recording milliammeter which serves as the indicating device for the pressure variation. (35)

WILLIWAW. A sudden blast of wind descending from a mountainous coast to the sea, especially in the vicinity of either the Strait of Magellan or the Aleutian Islands. (17)

WILLY-WILLY. A tropical cyclone which originates over the Timor Sea and moves southwest and then southeast across the interior of northwestern Australia. (17)

WINCH. Essentially the winch is a piece of the deck machinery of an oceanographic research ship which is used to lower and raise various pieces and types of equipment and devices such as current meters, hydrophones, corers, plankton nets and numerous other types of equipment.

The largest type of winch used by oceanographic research ships is the deep-sea anchoring winch. This winch uses steel wire rope in lengths of 20,000 to 35,000 feet. Some winches use specially tapered wire, while others use wire of about 1/2-inch diameter. The tapered wire can be used to greater depths than the untapered wire because it has been calculated that a vertical steel wire of any diameter will not support its own weight with a safety factor of two if it is more than 30,000 feet long (Von Arx, 1954, after Stommel). Such a winch is used for deep-sea anchoring at great depths for periods ranging from a few hours to a month. Other uses to which this winch is put include bottom dredging, towing large midwater trawls, taking large bottom cores, and obtaining samples of sea water for carbon-14 (C^{14}) analysis.

The winch the oceanographer probably uses the most is a medium size winch which holds 20,000- to 30,000-foot lengths of wire rope. This wire is about 5/32 inch in diameter and is usually stainless steel. The winch is a high-speed type and is the one from which the majority of oceanographic instruments are lowered. It is used for water sampling bottles, current meters, underwater cameras, small coring devices, small dredges, plankton nets, various temperature measuring instruments, and numerous other types of equipment.

One of the smallest winches used on an oceanographic ship is the bathythermograph, or BT, winch.

This winch is used to lower the BT, both while underway and when lying-to on station. The BT is a recording thermometer capable of registering temperature against depth down to 900 feet. The winch uses about 2,500 feet of 3/32-inch diameter stainless steel wire. It is sometimes used in shallow water for taking small bottom samples when underway with a specially designed bottom sampler called a "SCOOPFISH". Mechanical current meters and vertical hand plankton nets are sometimes lowered from the BT winch. (35)

WIND CHOP. See CHOP.

WIND CURRENT. A current created by the action of the wind. From theoretical considerations, currents produced by winds in the open sea will set to the right of the direction towards which the wind is blowing if in the northern hemisphere and to the left of this direction if in the southern hemisphere. (14)

WIND SET-UP. See SET-UP WIND.

WIND TIDE. See SET-UP WIND.

WIND WAVE. A wave created by the action of the wind. The ordinary waves which are continually breaking on the beaches are usually of this type. It is not necessary that the wind be blowing in the immediate vicinity as such waves may result from winds far out to sea. (14)

WINTER ICE. Ice created in a single season, and therefore less than a year old. It is usually less than 12 feet thick. (17)

WIRE ANGLE REMOTE INDICATOR. The instrument is clamped on the hydrographic wire, after the wire has been paid out to the working position. The remote indicators are mounted in the pilot house, permitting the ship's engines to be used in maneuvering to obtain zero wire angle. The sensing element of the wire angle remote indicator is a 180° POTENTIOMETER. The sliding arm of the potentiometer is attached to a heavy pendulum. Two potentiometers are mounted at right angles to each other to furnish the desired directional indication. The entire case of the sensing unit is filled with damping fluid to minimize undesirable pendulum motion. The angle indications are given in terms of degrees fore and aft and port and starboard. (30)

WIRE DRAG. A buoyed wire towed at a given depth to determine whether any isolated rocks, small shoals, etc., extend above that depth, or for determining the least depth of an area. (27)

WIRE ROPE. Various constructions of wire rope are designated by the number of strands in the rope and the number of wires in each strand.

The following are brief definitions of some common terms encountered:

Airplane Strand: A small 7- or 19-wire galvanized strand made from plow steel or crucible steel wire.

Cable Laid Rope: A compound laid rope consisting of several ropes or several layers of strands laid together into one rope, as, for instance, 6 by 6 by 7.

Crane Rope: Wire rope consisting of 6 strands of 37 wires around a hemp center.

Elevator Rope: Wire rope usually made of iron and composed of 6 strands of 19 wires each, and a hemp core.

Extra-flexible Hoisting Rope: A rope consisting of 8 strands of 19 wires each with a large hemp center.

Flat Rope: A rope consisting of alternate right and left lay rope strands, each rope strand consisting of 4 strands of 7 wires, all sewed together with a number of soft iron sewing wires.

(continued on next page)

Flattened Strand Rope: A wire rope having non-cylindrical strands, usually of the oval or triangular type; the center wire of each strand is an oval or a triangular wire.

Guy Rope: Glavanized rope consisting of 6 strands, 7 wires each, and a hemp core.

Guy Strand: Glavanized 7-wire strand.

Hand Rope: Flexible rope consisting of 6 ropes, each composed of 6 strands, 7 wires each, and 7 hemp cores.

Haulage Rope: Rope usually composed of 6 strands, 37 wires, and a hemp core, or 6 strands, 24 wires, and 7 hemp cores.

Hawser: Wire rope usually consisting of 6 strands, 37 wires, and a hemp core, or 6 strands, 24 wires, and 7 hemp cores.

Hoisting Rope: Rope consisting of 6 strands of 19 wires each, with a hemp center.

Lang Lay Rope: Wire rope in which both the wires in the strand and the strands in the rope are twisted in the same direction.

Lay: The pitch or angle of the helix of the wires or strands of a rope, usually expressed by the ratio of the diameter of the strand or rope to the length required for one complete twist.

Left-lay Rope: Wire rope, the strands of which form a left-hand helix like a left-hand screw thread.

Left Twist: Same as right lay, and corresponds to a right-hand screw thread.

Non-spinning Rope: A rope wire consisting of 18 strands of 7 wires each, in two layers; the inner layer consists of 6 strands Lang lay and left lay around a small hemp core, and the outer of 12

strands regular lay, right-hand lay. Will carry a load on a single end without untwisting.

Regular Lay: Strands twisted to the right and rope twisted to the left. Helix of strands takes the direction of a right-hand screw thread.

Reverse Laid Rope: A wire rope with alternate strands right and left lay.

Rheostat Rope: A small rope consisting of 8 strands of 7 wires each.

Right Lay: Known also as regular lay; strands twisted to the right and rope twisted to the left; corresponds to a right-hand screw thread.

Right Twist: Corresponds to left lay, or to a left-hand screw thread.

Running Rope: A flexible rope of 6 strands, 12 wires each, and 7 hemp cores.

Special Flexible Hoisting Rope: A wire rope consisting of 6 strands of 37 wires each, and a hemp core.

Standing Rope: Another term applied to galvanized guy rope which consists of 6 strands, 7 wires, and a hemp core.

Towing Hawser: A large flexible wire rope made of galvanized wires. Usual construction, 6 strands of 37 wires each, or 6 strands of 24 wires each.

Transmission Rope: Rope composed of 6 strands, 7 wires each, and a hemp core.

__WMO.__ World Meteorological Organization.

__WOO.__ World Oceanographic Organization.

__WRECK BUOY.__ A buoy marking the location of a wreck. (17)

XYZ

__XANTHOPHYLLS.__ Yellow or orange pigments, one of the two chief groups of the CAROTENOIDS; occur in the plastids. (18)

__X-1 HYDROPHOTOMETER.__ A transistorized self-calibrating device used to measure light transmission through a fixed distance in sea water.

__X-RAY.__ Artificial radiations similar to gamma rays but less penetrating in nature, they are produced by electronic means which excite electrons near the nucleus of the atom. They have been used in photographing opaque bodies, treating cancer, research, etc. (39)

__YAW.__ Oscillation of a ship about the vertical axis. (12)

__YELLOW SUBSTANCE.__ Kalle (1938) has shown that in sea water water soluble pigments of yellow color are present. These pigments appear to be related to the humic acid, but their chemical composition has not been thoroughly examined, for which reason Kalle calls them "yellow substance". This yellow substance seems to occur in greatest abundance in coastal aread, but Kalle has demonstrated its presence in the open ocean as well and believes that it represents a fairly stable metabolic product related to the phytoplankton of the sea. The selective absorption of this yellow substance may then be responsible, in part, for the character of the absorption in coastal water and for shift of the land of minimum absorption would lower wave length. (13)

__YIELD POINT.__ It is only for those materials that with increasing stress show a gradual departure

from elastic behavior and thus exhibit a stress-strain curve that it is necessary to define the onset of plastic yielding in terms of yield strength. Many steels exhibit a rather abrupt yielding and may show an initial increase of strain without any appreciable increase of stress when yielding occurs. Such materials are said to exhibit a yield point, the yield point being defined as "the stress in a material at which there occurs a marked increase in strain without an increase in stress." This definition of yield point is that presented in the ASTM Standards and forms the basis for yield-point specifications.

__YIELD STRENGTH.__ A measure of resistance to plastic deformation of a material subjected to a specified type of loading. The stress at which a material exhibits a specified limiting permanent deformation. A practical approximation of Elastic Limit. Yield Strength is usually determined by one of two common methods: "offset" or "strain under load". Offset Yield Strength is determined from a Stress-Strain Diagram; it is the stress corresponding to the

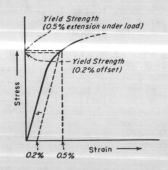

intersection with the curve of a line that is parallel to the straight-line portion of the curve and intersects the 0-stress axis at a strain equal to a specified offset. Offset is usually specified as 0.2%. Where stress-strain behavior of a material is known, Yield Strength may be given as the stress corresponding to a specified strain, a quantity that can be determined by direct measurement and without a Stress-Strain Diagram. This method is used primarily in determining Tensile Yield Strength of copper and copper alloys. Specified deformation is 0.5% extension under load which corresponds to an offset of about 0.35%. Without a Stress-Strain Diagram, however, Yield Strength at a specified offset cannot be compared with Yield Strength at a specified strain under load with any degree of certainty. Yield Strength may also be determined as the stress required to produce a specified Permanent Set, but this method involves trial-and-error procedure and is seldom used. Depending on type of loading involved, Yield Strength may be known as Compressive Yield Strength, Flexural Yield Strength, Shear Yield Strength, Tensile Yield Strength or Torsional Yield Strength. Yield Strength, alone, is generally assumed to refer to Tensile Yield Strength.

YIELD STRENGTH ELONGATION. A measure of Ductility of a material. The strain or Elongation corresponding to the Yield Strength.

YOUNG'S MODULUS. The modulus of elasticity of a material or the quotient obtained by dividing the stress per square inch by the elongation in one inch caused by this stress.

"Z" NUMBER. The atomic number of an element.

ZOOSPORE. A motile, usually naked and flagellated asexual spore (as of an alga). (20)

ZYGOTE. A fertilized egg resulting from the union of two gametes of opposite king, ovum and sperm.(19)

APPENDIX

Miscellaneous Astronomical Constants...........134

Miscellaneous Terrestrial Constants...........134

Gross Properties Of Sea Water.................134

Heat Properties Of Sea Water..................135

Pressure In Sea Water, PSIG...................135

Water Masses Of The World Ocean...............136

Characteristics Of Individual Seas............137

Gross Structure Of The Deep-Sea Floor.........138

Hypsographic Curve Showing The Area Of The
  Earth's Solid Surface Above Any Given
  Level Of Elevation Or Depth.................139

Wave And Sea Scale For Fully Arisen Sea.......140

Relative Frequency Of Waves Of Different Height
  In Different Regions........................141

Length Of Storm Waves Observed In Different
  Oceans......................................141

Deep-Ocean Surface Waves......................142

Alteration Of The Characteristics Of Waves As
  They Cross A Shoal..........................142

Units Of Depth Measurement On Charts Of
  Various Nations.............................143

Elements Present In Solution In Sea Water,
  Excluding Dissolved Gases...................144

Approximate Amount of Minerals In One Cubic
  Mile Of Sea Water...........................144

Electromotive Force Series....................145

Classification Of Marine Environments.........146

Animal Forms In The Oceans....................147

Marine Life -- Sharks.........................148

Marine Life -- Other Forms....................149

Soil Classification Systems...................150

Nomograph For The Determination Of Density
  From Salinity And Temperature Of Sea Water...151

Velocity Of Sound In Selected Materials At
  Ambient Conditions..........................152

Comparison Of Units For Underwater Sound.......153

Acoustic Absorption Coefficient Nomogram.......154

Survey Of Oceanographic Instrumentation.......155

Physical Properties Of Aluminum Alloys
  Considered For Deept Submergence............158

Comparison Of Properties Of Low Density Solids.158

Bulk Moduli Of Buoyancy Materials At 10,000
  PSIG Hydrostatic Pressure...................159

Estimated Strength Ranges For Susceptibility
  To Cracking In Sea Water, Fresh Water, Or
  Humid Atmospheres...........................159

Capabilities Of Concrete Hydrostatic
  Compressive Load Of 3000 PSI................160

Comparison Of Low Density Liquids.............160

A Summary Of Characteristics Of Surface
  Navigation Systems..........................161

U.S. Navy Standard Air Decompression Table.....163

U.S. Navy Standard Air Decompression Table
  For Exceptional Exposures...................164

"No Decompression" Limits And Repetitive Group
  Designation Table For "No Decompression"
  Dives.......................................165

Surface Interval Credit Table.................166

Repetitive Dive Timetable.....................167

Oxygen Consumption And Respiratory Minute
  Volume At Different Work-Rates..............168

Per cent Change in Buoyancy Of Unicellular Foam
  Rubber Swim Suit............................168

Scientific Information Activities Of The
  Department Of The Navy......................169

MISCELLANEOUS ASTRONOMICAL CONSTANTS*

Angular velocity of earth rotation . . . . -0.729211×10^{-4} sec^{-1}
Mean solar day . . . . 86,400 sec = 1.0027379 sidereal day
Sidereal day . . . . 86,164.09054 mean solar sec
           (23 hr 56 min 4.09054 sec)
Solar parallax . . . . 8.80 sec of arc
Mean distance of sun . . . . 1.4945×10^{8} km
Mean density of sun . . . . 1.41 gm/cm^{3}
Solar diameter . . . . 1.393×10^{6} km
Obliquity of the ecliptic . . . . 23°26'59''
†Tidal constituents, mean increase in hour angle
     of sun . . . . 15°/hr
     celestial longitude of sun . . . . 0.0411°/hr
     celestial longitude of moon . . . . 0.5490°/hr
     celestial longitude of lunar perigee . . . . . . 0.0046°/hr
Mean distance of moon from earth . . . . 384,393 km
Moon's sidereal period . . . . 27.322 days
Moon's synodic period . . . . 29.5 ± 0.5 days
Earth's mass . . . . 5.975×10^{27} gm
Sun's mass . . . . 1.987×10^{33} gm
           (330,000 earth masses)
Moon's mass . . . . 7.343×10^{25} gm
           (1/81.56 earth mass)
Gravitation constant G . . . . $(6.670 \pm 0.005) \times 10^{-8}$
           dyne · cm^{2}/gm^{2}
§Acceleration due to gravity g
     sea level, 0° latitude . . . . 978.039 cm/sec^{2}
     sea level, 90° latitude . . . . 983.217 cm/sec^{2}

* Adapted from *Smithsonian Physical Tables*, 1954 (Smithsonian Miscellaneous Collections, Vol. 120), 9th revised ed., prepared by W. E. Forsythe, Washington, D.C.: The Smithsonian Institution.
† P. Schureman, 1940, *Manual of Harmonic Analysis and Prediction of Tides*, 2nd ed., U.S. Coast and Geodetic Survey Special Publication No. 98, Washington, D.C.: U.S. Government Printing Office; A. T. Doodson and H. D. Warburg, 1941, *Admiralty Manual of Tides*, London: H.M. Stationery Office.
§ Based on a U.S. Coast and Geodetic Survey formula.

MISCELLANEOUS TERRESTRIAL CONSTANTS*

Area of the earth . . . . 510.100×10^{6} km^{2}
Area of the land . . . . 148.847×10^{6} km^{2}
Area of the oceans . . . . 361.254×10^{6} km^{2}
Mean depth of oceans . . . . 3.790 km
Volume of the oceans . . . . 1.369×10^{9} km^{3}
Percent ocean volume colder than 10°C 93%
Percent ocean volume colder than 4°C 76%
Mean depth of thermocline . . . . 0.2 km
Volume of lower atmosphere . . . . 4×10^{9} km^{3}
Standard sea level pressure of
     atmosphere . . . . 1.01325×10^{6} dynes/cm^{2}
Approximate pressure gradient of
     oceans . . . . 0.1 atm/m or 0.5 lb/in^{2}/ft
Maximum insolation at top of
     atmosphere . . . . 2 ly/min
24-hr mean insolation at top of
     atmosphere . . . . 0.5 ly/min
24-hr mean insolation at surface . . . . 0.25 ly/min
Mean temperature of earth surface . . . . 287°K
Mean albedo of earth 0.34
†Heat flux through sea floor . . . . 1.2×10^{-6} ly/sec
§Evaporation rate from oceans . . . . 93 — 106 cm/year
Ellipticity of earth 1/297
Equatorial radius . . . . 6378 km

* *Smithsonian Meteorological Tables*, 1951 (Smithsonian Miscellaneous Collections, Vol. 114), 6th revised ed., prepared by Robert J. List, Washington, D.C.: The Smithsonian Institution.
† R. Revelle and A. E. Maxwell, 1952, *Nature, Lond.*, 170: 199–200.
§ G. Wüst, 1936, *Länderkundliche Forschung*, Festschrift Norbert Krebs: 347–359; H. Mosby, 1936, *Ann. Hydrogr., Berl.*, 64: 281–286.

GROSS PROPERTIES OF SEA WATER

(For physical units and chemical definitions see B. Helland-Hansen, J. P. Jacobsen, and T. G. Thompson, 1948, *Un. géod. géophys. int., Ass. Océanogr. phys. Publ. Sci.,* 9: 28 pp.)

Characteristic density, $f(s, t, p)$ . . . . 1.025 gm/cm^{3}
Velocity of sound, $f(s, t, p)$ . . . . at surface = 1448.6 m/sec
Specific heat, $Cp\,f\,(s)$ . . . . 0.932 cal/gm/°C at 35 °/$_{00}$
Adiabatic lapse rate, $f(s, p)$ . . . . approx. 0.1°C/km
Maximum surface temperature . . . . 32°C
Minimum surface temperature . . . . −2°C
Median surface temperature . . . . 20°C
Average temperature . . . . 3.8°C
Latent heat of fusion and vaporization . . . . . same as pure water

SPECIFIC HEAT AT CONSTANT PRESSURE FOR VARIOUS SALINITIES*

S (°/$_{00}$)	0	5	10	15	20	25	30	35	40
C_p (cal/gm/°C)	1.000	0.982	0.968	0.958	0.951	0.945	0.939	0.932	0.926

EFFECTS OF PRESSURE ON THE PROPERTIES OF SEA WATER AT 0°C AND SALINITY OF 35 °/$_{00}$*

Pressure, decibars	Density, gm/cm^{3}	Speed of sound, m/sec	Adiabatic temperature change, °C/1000 decibars
0	1.02813	1448.6	0.035
2,000	1.03748	1484.4	0.072
4,000	1.04640	1519.7	0.104
6,000	1.05495	1554.2	0.133
8,000	1.06315	1587.7	0.159
10,000	1.07104	1620.0	0.181

* Adapted from R. B. Montgomery, 1957, "Oceanographic Data," pp. 2–115 to 2–124, *American Institute of Physics Handbook*, New York: McGraw-Hill.

Property	Symbol	Formula	Fundamental Dimensions	Metric System Units	Range of Values	References	Remarks
a) Coefficient of thermal expansion	e	$e = \frac{1}{a_{s,P,t}} \left(\frac{d\sigma_{s,p,t}}{dt} \right)$ a = specific volume	$1/\theta$ θ = temp.	$1/°C$	$e = -105 \times 10^{-6}$ at Patmos t = 2°C s = 0‰ $e = 334 \times 10^{-6}$ at Patmos t = 30°C s = 35‰	Knudsen's Hydrographical Tables, 1901. Bekman 1908; reported by Sverdrup, Johnson and Fleming, 1942, and Defant, 1961	
b) Coefficient of thermal conductivity	γ	$\gamma = \frac{-dQ/dt}{dt/dn}$ $\frac{dQ}{dt}$ = amount of heat in gram calories per second conducted through a surface of 1 cm². $\frac{dt}{dn}$ = change in temperature per cm parallel to heat flow.	$\frac{ML}{T^3\theta}$ M = mass L = length T = time θ = temp.	$\frac{gram/centimeter}{(second)^3 °C}$	$\gamma < 1.39 \times 10^{-3}$ at Patmos t = 15°C s = 0‰ But increases with increasing pressure and temperature.	Sverdrup, Johnson, and Fleming, 1942	Note 1: Since turbulent motion prevails in the sea, and "eddy" coefficient must be introduced which is many times larger.
					$\gamma = 1.4000 \times 10^{-3}$ at Patmos s = 0‰ $\gamma = 1.337 \times 10^{-3}$ at Patmos s = 40‰	Defant, 1961	Values based on ratios of thermal capacities of equal volumes.
c) Heat Capacity 1) Specific heat at constant pressure	Cp	Defined as the number of calories required to increase the temperature of 1 g of a substance 1°C.	ML^2/T^2 M = mass L = length T = time	$\frac{gram/centimeter)^2}{(second)^2}$	Cp = 1.000 at Patmos t = 17.5°C S = 0‰ Cp = 0.926 at Patmos t = 17.5°C S = 40‰	Kuwahara, 1939, at Patmos and 0°C: Cp = 1.005-0.004136S + 0.000010985² - 0.000001324S³ Krummel, 1907 at Patmos and 17.5°C: Cp = f(s) in tabular form. Ekmann, 1914 at Patmos and 34.85‰: a) Cp = f(T) in tabular form. b) $\frac{dCp}{dp} = -10^5 \frac{T}{PJ} \left(\frac{de}{dt} te^2 \right)$, where, P is pressure in meters, T is absolute temperature, E is the density, J = mechanical equipment of heat, and e = coefficient of thermal	Relationship between cp and cu is $Cu = Cp - \frac{Te^2}{PKJ}$, where, e = coefficient of thermal expansion, T = closure temperature, P = density, k = true compressibility, and J = mechanical equivalent of heat.
2) Specific heat at constant volume	Cv	Defined as the ratio of its thermal capacity to that of distilled water. Defined at 15° C.	Unity				
d) Latent heat of fusion	—	Defined as the quantity of heat necessary to change one gram of solid to a liquid with no temperature change.	$\frac{L^2}{T^2}$	$\frac{(centimeters)^2}{(second)^2}$	For distilled water at 0°C: 79.71 gram-calories/gram	Handbook of chemistry and physics 40th edition, Hodgman, C.D. et el.	Not well investigated for sea water.
e) Latent heat of evaporation	—	Defined as the quantity of heat necessary to change one gram of liquid to a gas with no temperature change. L = 596 - 0.52 t	L^2/T^2	$\frac{(centimeters)^2}{(second)^2}$	For distilled water at 0°C: 595.9 gram-calories/gram at 30°C: 579.5 gram-calories/gram	Handbook of chemistry and physics 40th edition, Hodgman, C.D. et al.	Not well investigated for sea water.

TABLE OF PRESSURE IN THE SEA, IN PSIG

(at Salinity 35°/oo and Temperature 0°C)

Depth (Meters*)	0	100	200	300	400	500	600	700	800	900
0	——	146	293	438	585	731	877	1024	1172	1318
1000	1465	1611	1758	1906	2052	2200	2347	2495	2641	2788
2000	2934	3082	3231	3379	3527	3674	3822	3970	4118	4266
3000	4415	4563	4712	4859	5008	5156	5304	5455	5603	5752
4000	5900	6050	6198	6347	6496	6646	6794	6943	7094	7243
5000	7393	7542	7691	7841	7992	8141	8289	8440	8591	8740
6000	8890	9040	9190	9341	9493	9642	9793	9944	10093	10244
7000	10395	10547	10698	10899	11000	11151	11302	11454	11605	11755
8000	11908	12059	12209	12363	12514	12666	12817	12969	13122	13276
9000	13426	13577	13729	13882	14033	14186	14337	14489	14643	14796

*To convert to feet multiply by 3.281

Water Masses of the Atlantic Ocean

North Atlantic	Temp. (°C)	Salinity (°/oo)	South Atlantic	Temp. (°C)	Salinity (°/oo)
1. North Polar water	-1 to +2	34.9	1. South Atlantic central water	+5 to +16	34.3 to 35.6
2. Subarctic water	+3 to +5	34.7 to 34.9	2. Antarctic inter-mediate water	+3 to +5	34.1 to 34.6
3. North Atlantic central water	+4 to +17	35.1 to 36.2	3. Subantarctic water	+3 to +9	33.8 to 34.5
4. North Atlantic deep water	+3 to +4	34.9 to 35.0	4. Antarctic circum-polar water	+0.5 to +2.5	34.7 to 34.8
5. North Atlantic bottom water	+1 to +3	34.8 to 34.9	5. South Atlantic deep and bottom water	0 to +2	34.5 to 34.9
6. Mediterranean water	+6 to +10	35.3 to 36.4	6. Antarctic bottom water	-0.4	34 to 36

Water Masses of the Indian Ocean

	Temp. (°C)	Salinity (°/oo)
1. Equatorial water	4 to 16	34.8 to 35.2
2. Indian central water	6 to 15	34.5 to 35.4
3. Antarctic intermediate water	2 to 6	34.4 to 34.7
4. Subantarctic water	2 to 8	34.1 to 34.6
5. Indian Ocean deep and antarctic circumpolar water	0.5 to 2	34.7 to 34.75
6. Red Sea water	9	35.5

Water Masses of the Pacific Ocean

North Pacific	Temp. (°C)	Salinity (°/oo)	South Pacific	Temp. (°C)	Salinity (°/oo)
1. Subarctic water	2 to 10	33.5 to 34.4	1. Eastern South Pacific water	9 to 16	34.3 to 35.1
2. Pacific equatorial water	6 to 16	34.5 to 35.2	2. Western South Pacific water	7 to 16	34.5 to 35.5
3. Eastern North Pacific water	10 to 16	34.0 to 34.6	3. Antarctic Inter-mediate water	4 to 7	34.3 to 34.5
4. Western North Pacific water	7 to 16	34.1 to 34.6	4. Subantarctic water	3 to 7	34.1 to 34.6
5. Arctic Intermediate water	6 to 10	34.0 to 34.1	5. Pacific deep water and Antarctic cir-cumpolar water	(-1) to 3	34.6 to 34.7
6. Pacific deep water and Arctic cir-cumpolar water	(-1) to 3	34.6 to 34.7			

WAVE AND SEA SCALE FOR FULLY ARISEN SEA

SEA-GENERAL DESCRIPTION	(BEAUFORT) WIND FORCE	WIND DESCRIPTION	RANGE (KNOTS)	WIND VELOCITY (KNOTS)	WAVE HEIGHT FEET AVERAGE	SIGNIFICANT	AVERAGE 1/10 HIGHEST	SIGNIFICANT RANGE OF PERIODS (SECONDS)	T_{max} (PERIOD OF MAXIMUM ENERGY OF SPECTRUM)	$\bar{T}$ (AVERAGE PERIOD)	$\bar{\lambda}$ (AVERAGE WAVE LENGTH)	MINIMUM FETCH (NAUTICAL MILES)	MINIMUM DURATION (HOURS)
Sea like a mirror.	U	Calm	< 1	0	0	0	0	–	–	–	–	–	–
Ripples with the appearance of scales are formed, but without foam crests.	1	Light Airs	1-3	2	0.05	0.08	0.10	≤1.2 sec	0.7	0.5	10 in.	5	18 min.
Small wavelets, short but pronounced; crests have a glassy appearance, but do not break.	2	Light Breeze	4-6	5	0.18	0.29	0.37	0.4-2.8	2.0	1.4	6.7 ft.	8	39 min.
Large wavelets, crests beging to break. Foam of glassy appearance. Perhaps scattered white horses.	3	Gentle Breeze	7-10	8.5	0.6	1.0	1.2	0.8-5.0	3.4	2.4	20	9.8	1.7 hrs.
				10	0.88	1.4	1.8	1.0-6.0	4	2.9	27	10	2.4
Small waves, becoming larger; fairly frequent white horses.	4	Moderate Breeze	11-16	12	1.4	2.2	2.8	1.0-7.0	4.8	3.4	40	18	3.8
				13.5	1.8	2.9	3.7	1.4-7.6	5.4	3.9	52	24	4.8
				14	2.0	3.3	4.2	1.5-7.8	5.6	4.0	59	28	5.2
				16	2.9	4.6	5.8	2.0-8.8	6.5	4.6	71	40	6.6
Moderate waves, taking a more pronounced long form; many white horses are formed. (Chance of some spray).	5	Fresh Breeze	17-21	18	3.8	6.1	7.8	2.5-10.0	7.2	5.1	90	55	8.3
				19	4.3	6.9	8.7	2.8-10.6	7.7	5.4	99	65	9.2
				20	5.0	8.0	10	3.0-11.1	8.1	5.7	111	75	10
Large waves begin to form; the white foam crests are more extensive everywhere. (Probably some spray).	6	Strong Breeze	22-27	22	6.4	10	13	3.4-12.2	8.9	6.3	134	100	12
				24	7.9	12	16	3.7-13.5	9.7	6.8	160	130	14
				24.5	8.2	13	17	3.8-13.6	9.9	7.0	164	140	15
				26	9.6	15	20	4.0-14.5	10.5	7.4	188	180	17
Sea heaps up and white foam from breaking waves begins to be blown in streaks along the direction of the wind. (Spindrift begins to be seen).	7	Moderate Gale	28-33	28	11	18	23	4.5-15.5	11.3	7.9	212	230	20
				30	14	22	28	4.7-16.7	12.1	8.6	250	280	23
				30.5	14	23	29	4.8-17.0	12.4	8.7	258	290	24
				32	16	26	33	5.0-17.5	12.9	9.1	285	340	27
Moderately high waves of greater length; edges of crests break into spindrift. The foam is blown in well marked streaks along the direction of the wind. Spray affects visibility.	8	Fresh Gale	34-40	34	19	30	38	5.5-18.5	13.6	9.7	322	420	30
				36	21	35	44	5.8-19.7	14.5	10.3	363	500	34
				37	23	37	46.7	6-20.5	14.9	10.5	376	530	37
				38	25	40	50	6.2-20.8	15.4	10.7	392	600	38
				40	28	45	58	6.5-21.7	16.1	11.4	444	710	42
High waves. Dense streaks of foam along the direction of the wind. Sea begins to roll. Visibility affected.	9	Strong Gale	41-47	42	31	50	64	7-23	17.0	12.0	492	830	47
				44	36	58	73	7-24-2	17.7	12.5	534	960	52
				46	40	64	81	7-25	18.6	13.1	590	1110	57
Very high waves with long overhanging crests. The resulting foam is in great patches and is blown in dense white streaks along the direction of the wind. On the whole the surface of the sea takes a white appearance. The rolling of the sea becomes heavy and shock-like. Visibility is affected.	10	Whole Gale	48-55	48	44	71	90	7.5-26	19.4	13.8	650	1250	63
				50	49	78	99	7.5-27	20.2	14.3	700	1420	69
				51.5	52	83	106	8-28.2	20.8	14.7	736	1560	73
				52	54	87	110	8-28.5	21.0	14.8	750	1610	75
				54	59	95	121	8-29.5	21.8	15.4	810	1800	81
Exceptionally high waves. Sea completely covered with long white patches of foam lying in direction of wind. Everywhere edges of wave crests are blown into froth. Visibility affected.	11	Storm	56-63	56	64	103	130	8.5-31	22.6	16.3	910	2100	88
				59.5	73	116	148	10-32	24	17.0	985	2500	101
Air filled with foam and spray. Sea white with driving spray; visibility very seriously affected.	12	Hurricane	64-71	> 64	> 80	> 128	> 164	10-(35)	(26)	(18)			

CHARACTERISTICS OF INDIVIDUAL SEAS (Lyman, 1960)

Sea	Area (10^9 m^2)	Mean Depth (meters)	Volume (10^{12} m^3)
Tributary to Arctic Ocean			
Norwegian Sea	1383	1742	2408
Greenland Sea	1205	1444	1740
Barents Sea	1405	229	322
White Sea	90	89	8
Kara Sea	883	118	104
Laptev Sea	650	519	338
East Siberian Sea	901	58	53
Chukchi Sea	582	88	51
Beaufort Sea	476	1004	478
Baffin Bay	689	861	593
Tributary to North Atlantic			
North Sea	600	91	55
Baltic Sea	386	86	33
Mediterranean Sea	2516	1494	3758
Black Sea	461	1166	537
Caribbean Sea	2754	2491	6860
Gulf of Mexico	1543	1512	2332
Gulf of St. Lawrence	238	127	30
Hudson Bay	1232	128	158
Tributary to South Atlantic			
Gulf of Guinea	1533	2996	4,592
Tributary to Indian Ocean			
Red Sea	450	558	251
Persian Gulf	241	40	10
Arabian Sea	3863	2734	10,561
Bay of Bengal	2172	2586	5,616
Andaman Sea	602	1096	660
Great Australian Bight	484	950	459
Tributary to North Pacific			
Gulf of California	177	818	145
Gulf of Alaska	1327	2431	3,226
Bering Sea	2304	1598	3,683
Okhotsk Sea	1590	859	1,365
Japan Sea	978	1752	1,713
Yellow Sea	417	40	17
East China Sea	752	349	263
Sulu Sea	420	1139	478
Celebes Sea	472	3291	1,553
In both North and South Pacific			
South China Sea	3685	1060	3,907
Makassar Strait	194	967	188
Molukka Sea	307	1880	578
Ceram Sea	187	1209	227
Tributary to South Pacific			
Java Sea	433	46	20
Bali Sea	119	411	49
Flores Sea	121	1829	222
Savu Sea	105	1701	178
Banda Sea	695	3064	2,129
Ceram Sea	187	1209	227
Timor Sea	615	406	250
Arafura Sea	1037	197	204
Coral Sea	4791	2394	11,470

(From McGraw-Hill Yearbook of Science and Technology, Copyright 1960. McGraw-Hill Book Company, Inc. Used by permission)

PACIFIC OCEAN

Western Pacific Basins	Central Pacific Basins	Eastern Pacific Basins
I. Philippines Basin	IX. North Pacific Basin	XIII. Guatemala Basin
A. Riu-Kiu Trench (7,507 m.)	E. Aleutian Trench (7,679 m.)	XIV. Peru Basin
B. Philippines Trench	F. Kurile Trench (9,587 m.)	L. Atacama Trench (7,634 m.)
(10,497 m.)	G. Japan Trench (10,554 m.)	XV. Pacific Antarctic Basin
II. Western Caroline Basin	H. Bonin Trench (9,156 m.)	
C. Western Caroline Trench	X. Mariana Basin	**East Asiatic Basins of Marginal Seas**
(8,138 m.)	J. Mariana Trench (10,899 m.)	XVI. Bering Basin
III. Eastern Caroline Basin	XI. Central Pacific Basin	XVII. Okhotsk Basin
IV. Solomon Basin	XII. South Pacific Basin	XVIII. Japan Basin
D. Bougainville-New Britain	K. Tonga-Kermadec Trench	XIX. South China Basin
Trench (9,140 m.)	(10,633 m.)	
V. Coral Basin		**Basins of the Austral-Asian Mediterranean**
VI. New Hebrides Basin		XX. Sulu Basin
VII. Fiji Basin		XXI. Celebes Basin
VIII. East Australia Basin		XXII. Banda Basin

ATLANTIC OCEAN

Western Atlantic Basins	Eastern Atlantic Basins
XXIII. Labrador Basin	XXX. West Europe Basin
XXIV. Newfoundland Basin	XXXI. Iberia Basin
XXV. North America Basin	XXXII. Canaries Basin
N. Puerto Rico Trough	XXXIII. Cape Verde Basin
(9,219 m.)	XXXIV. Sierra Leone Basin
XXVI. Guiana Basin	XXXV. Guinea Basin
XXVII. Brazil Basin	XXXVI. Angola Basin
XXVIII. Argentina Basin	XXXVII. Cape Basin
XXIX. South Antilles Basin	XXXVIII. Agulhas Basin
Basins of the Arctic Mediterranean	XXXIX. Atlantic-Indian Antarctic
XL. North Polar Basin	Basin
XLI. Greenland Basin	M. South Sandwich Trench
XLII. Norway Basin	(8,264 m.)
Basins of the American Mediterranean	**Basins of the European Mediterranean**
XLIII. Mexico Basin	XLVI. Balearic Basin
XLIV. Yucatan Basin	XLVII. Tyrrhenian Basin
O. Cayman Trough (7,200 m.)	XLVIII. Ionian Basin
XLV. Caribbean Basin	XLIX. Levant Basin

INDIAN OCEAN

Western Indian Basins	Eastern Indian Basins
L. Arabian Basin	LV. India-Australia Basin
LI. Somali Basin	P. Sunda Trench (7,455 m.)
LII. Mascarenes Basin	LVI. South Australia Basin
LIII. Madagascar Basin	LVII. Eastern Indian Antarctic
LIV. Natal Basin	Basin
XXXIX. Atlantic-Indian Antarctic	
Basin	

Data on the maximum depths of the deep sea trenches is based on observations up to 1954.

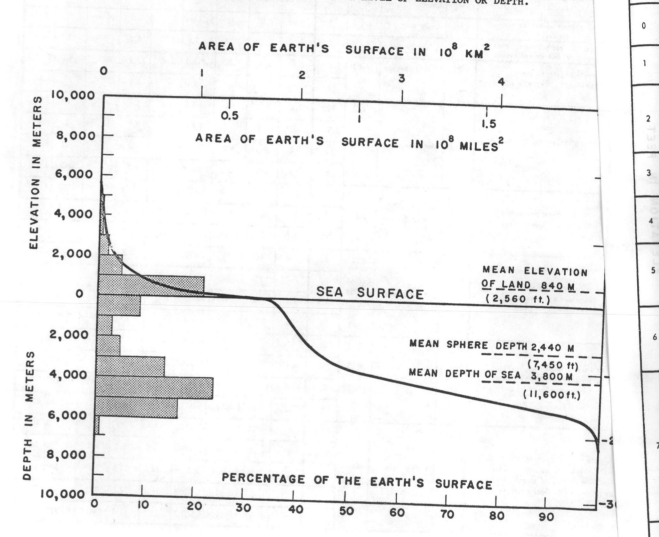

HYPSOGRAPHIC CURVE SHOWING THE AREA OF THE EARTH'S SOLID SURFACE ABOVE ANY GIVEN LEVEL OF ELEVATION OR DEPTH.

(The smooth curve represents the cumulative summation of areas denoted by shaded bars.)

CHARACTERISTICS OF INDIVIDUAL SEAS (Lyman, 1960)

Sea	Area $(10^9 \ m^2)$	Mean Depth (meters)	Volume $(10^{12} \ m^3)$
Tributary to Arctic Ocean			
Norwegian Sea	1383	1742	2408
Greenland Sea	1205	1444	1740
Barents Sea	1405	229	322
White Sea	90	89	8
Kara Sea	883	118	104
Laptev Sea	650	519	338
East Siberian Sea	901	58	53
Chukchi Sea	582	88	51
Beaufort Sea	476	1004	478
Baffin Bay	689	861	593
Tributary to North Atlantic			
North Sea	600	91	55
Baltic Sea	386	86	33
Mediterranean Sea	2516	1494	3758
Black Sea	461	1166	537
Caribbean Sea	2754	2491	6860
Gulf of Mexico	1543	1512	2332
Gulf of St. Lawrence	238	127	30
Hudson Bay	1232	128	158
Tributary to South Atlantic			
Gulf of Guinea	1533	2996	4,592
Tributary to Indian Ocean			
Red Sea	450	558	251
Persian Gulf	241	40	10
Arabian Sea	3863	2734	10,561
Bay of Bengal	2172	2586	5,616
Andaman Sea	602	1096	660
Great Australian Bight	484	950	459
Tributary to North Pacific			
Gulf of California	177	818	145
Gulf of Alaska	1327	2431	3,226
Bering Sea	2304	1598	3,683
Okhotsk Sea	1590	859	1,365
Japan Sea	978	1752	1,713
Yellow Sea	417	40	17
East China Sea	752	349	263
Sulu Sea	420	1139	478
Celebes Sea	472	3291	1,553
In both North and South Pacific			
South China Sea	3685	1060	3,907
Makassar Strait	194	967	188
Molukka Sea	307	1880	578
Ceram Sea	187	1209	227
Tributary to South Pacific			
Java Sea	433	46	20
Bali Sea	119	411	49
Flores Sea	121	1829	222
Savu Sea	105	1701	178
Banda Sea	695	3064	2,129
Ceram Sea	187	1209	227
Timor Sea	615	406	250
Arafura Sea	1037	197	204
Coral Sea	4791	2394	11,470

(From McGraw-Hill Yearbook of Science and Technology,
Copyright 1960. McGraw-Hill Book Company, Inc.
Used by permission)

PACIFIC OCEAN

Western Pacific Basins	Central Pacific Basins	Eastern Pacific Basins
I. Philippines Basin A. Riu-Kiu Trench (7,507 m.) B. Philippines Trench (10,497 m.) II. Western Caroline Basin C. Western Caroline Trench (8,138 m.) III. Eastern Caroline Basin IV. Solomon Basin D. Bougainville-New Britain Trench (9,140 m.) V. Coral Basin VI. New Hebrides Basin VII. Fiji Basin VIII. East Australia Basin	IX. North Pacific Basin E. Aleutian Trench (7,679 m.) F. Kurile Trench (9,587 m.) G. Japan Trench (10,554 m.) H. Bonin Trench (9,156 m.) X. Mariana Basin J. Mariana Trench (10,899 m.) XI. Central Pacific Basin XII. South Pacific Basin K. Tonga-Kermadec Trench (10,633 m.)	XIII. Guatemala Basin XIV. Peru Basin L. Atacama Trench (7,634 m.) XV. Pacific Antarctic Basin

Eastern Pacific Basins (continued)
East Asiatic Basins of Marginal Seas XVI. Bering Basin XVII. Okhotsk Basin XVIII. Japan Basin XIX. South China Basin
Basins of the Austral-Asian Mediterranean XX. Sulu Basin XXI. Celebes Basin XXII. Banda Basin

ATLANTIC OCEAN

Western Atlantic Basins	Eastern Atlantic Basins
XXIII. Labrador Basin XXIV. Newfoundland Basin XXV. North America Basin N. Puerto Rico Trough (9,219 m.) XXVI. Guiana Basin XXVII. Brazil Basin XXVIII. Argentina Basin XXIX. South Antilles Basin	XXX. West Europe Basin XXXI. Iberia Basin XXXII. Canaries Basin XXXIII. Cape Verde Basin XXXIV. Sierra Leone Basin XXXV. Guinea Basin XXXVI. Angola Basin XXXVII. Cape Basin XXXVIII. Agulhas Basin XXXIX. Atlantic-Indian Antarctic Basin M. South Sandwich Trench (8,264 m.)
Basins of the Arctic Mediterranean XL. North Polar Basin XLI. Greenland Basin XLII. Norway Basin	
Basins of the American Mediterranean XLIII. Mexico Basin XLIV. Yucatan Basin O. Cayman Trough (7,200 m.) XLV. Caribbean Basin	**Basins of the European Mediterranean** XLVI. Balearic Basin XLVII. Tyrrhenian Basin XLVIII. Ionian Basin XLIX. Levant Basin

INDIAN OCEAN

Western Indian Basins	Eastern Indian Basins
L. Arabian Basin LI. Somali Basin LII. Mascarenes Basin LIII. Madagascar Basin LIV. Natal Basin XXXIX. Atlantic-Indian Antarctic Basin	LV. India-Australia Basin P. Sunda Trench (7,455 m.) LVI. South Australia Basin LVII. Eastern Indian Antarctic Basin

Data on the maximum depths of the deep sea trenches is based on observations up to 1954.

HYPSOGRAPHIC CURVE SHOWING THE AREA OF THE EARTH'S SOLID
SURFACE ABOVE ANY GIVEN LEVEL OF ELEVATION OR DEPTH.

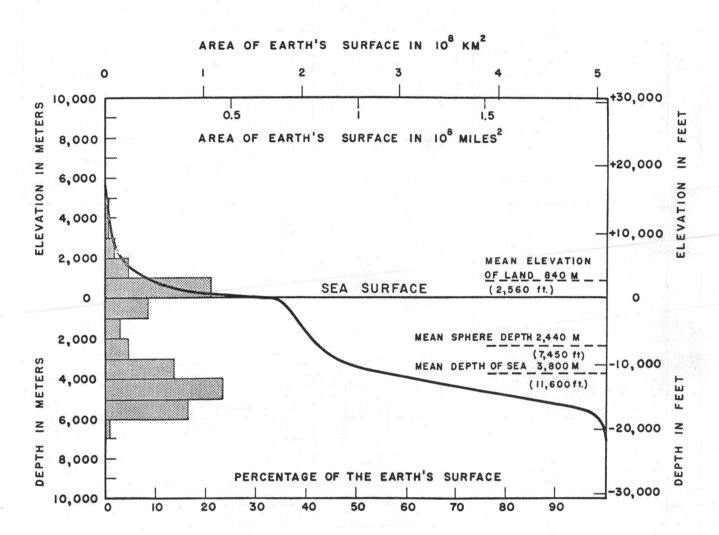

(The smooth curve represents the cumulative summation of areas denoted by shaded bars.)

WAVE AND SEA SCALE FOR FULLY ARISEN SEA

SEA STATE	SEA-GENERAL DESCRIPTION	(BEAUFORT) WIND FORCE	WIND DESCRIPTION	RANGE (KNOTS)	WIND VELOCITY (KNOTS)	WAVE HEIGHT FEET AVERAGE	SIGNIFICANT	AVERAGE 1/10 HIGHEST	SIGNIFICANT RANGE OF PERIODS (SECONDS)	T_{max} (PERIOD OF MAXIMUM ENERGY OF SPECTRUM)	$\bar{T}$ (AVERAGE PERIOD)	$\bar{\lambda}$ (AVERAGE WAVE LENGTH)	MINIMUM FETCH (NAUTICAL MILES)	MINIMUM DURATION (HOURS)
0	Sea like a mirror.	U	Calm	< 1	0	0	0	0	–	–	–	–	–	–
0	Ripples with the appearance of scales are formed, but without foam crests.	1	Light Airs	1-3	2	0.05	0.08	0.10	≤1.2 sec	0.7	0.5	10 in.	5	18 min.
1	Small wavelets, short but pronounced; crests have a glassy appearance, but do not break.	2	Light Breeze	4-6	5	0.18	0.29	0.37	0.4-2.8	2.0	1.4	6.7 ft.	8	39 min.
1	Large wavelets, crests begin to break. Foam of glassy appearance. Perhaps scattered white horses.	3	Gentle Breeze	7-10	8.5	0.6	1.0	1.2	0.8-5.0	3.4	2.4	20	9.8	1.7 hrs.
					10	0.88	1.4	1.8	1.0-6.0	4	2.9	27	10	2.4
2	Small waves, becoming larger; fairly frequent white horses.	4	Moderate Breeze	11-16	12	1.4	2.2	2.8	1.0-7.0	4.8	3.4	40	18	3.8
					13.5	1.8	2.9	3.7	1.4-7.6	5.4	3.9	52	24	4.8
3					14	2.0	3.3	4.2	1.5-7.8	5.6	4.0	59	28	5.2
					16	2.9	4.6	5.8	2.0-8.8	6.5	4.6	71	40	6.6
4	Moderate waves, taking a more pronounced long form; many white horses are formed. (Chance of some spray).	5	Fresh Breeze	17-21	18	3.8	6.1	7.8	2.5-10.0	7.2	5.1	90	55	8.3
					19	4.3	6.9	8.7	2.8-10.6	7.7	5.4	99	65	9.2
					20	5.0	8.0	10	3.0-11.1	8.1	5.7	111	75	10
5	Large waves begin to form; the white foam crests are more extensive everywhere. (Probably some spray).	6	Strong Breeze	22-27	22	6.4	10	13	3.4-12.2	8.9	6.3	134	100	12
					24	7.9	12	16	3.7-13.5	9.7	6.8	160	130	14
					24.5	8.2	13	17	3.8-13.6	9.9	7.0	164	140	15
6					26	9.6	15	20	4.0-14.5	10.5	7.4	188	180	17
	Sea heaps up and white foam from breaking waves begins to be blown in streaks along the direction of the wind. (Spindrift begins to be seen).	7	Moderate Gale	28-33	28	11	18	23	4.5-15.5	11.3	7.9	212	230	20
					30	14	22	28	4.7-16.7	12.1	8.6	250	280	23
					30.5	14	23	29	4.8-17.0	12.4	8.7	258	290	24
					32	16	26	33	5.0-17.5	12.9	9.1	285	340	27
7	Moderately high waves of greater length; edges of crests break into spindrift. The foam is blown in well marked streaks along the direction of the wind. Spray affects visibility.	8	Fresh Gale	34-40	34	19	30	38	5.5-18.5	13.6	9.7	322	420	30
					36	21	35	44	5.8-19.7	14.5	10.3	363	500	34
					37	23	37	46.7	6-20.5	14.9	10.5	376	530	37
					38	25	40	50	6.2-20.8	15.4	10.7	392	600	38
					40	28	45	58	6.5-21.7	16.1	11.4	444	710	42
8	High waves. Dense streaks of foam along the direction of the wind. Sea begins to roll. Visibility affected.	9	Strong Gale	41-47	42	31	50	64	7-23	17.0	12.0	492	830	47
					44	36	58	73	7-24.2	17.7	12.5	534	960	52
					46	40	64	81	7-25	18.6	13.1	590	1110	57
9	Very high waves with long overhanging crests. The resulting foam is in great patches and is blown in dense white streaks along the direction of the wind. On the whole the surface of the sea takes a white appearance. The rolling of the sea becomes heavy and shock-like. Visibility is affected.	10	Whole Gale	48-55	48	44	71	90	7.5-26	19.4	13.8	650	1250	63
					50	49	78	99	7.5-27	20.2	14.3	700	1420	69
					51.5	52	83	106	8-28.2	20.8	14.7	736	1560	73
					52	54	87	110	8-28.5	21.0	14.8	750	1610	75
					54	59	95	121	8-29.5	21.8	15.4	810	1800	81
	Exceptionally high waves. Sea completely covered with long white patches of foam lying in direction of wind. Everywhere edges of wave crests are blown into froth. Visibility affected.	11	Storm	56-63	56	64	103	130	8.5-31	22.6	16.3	910	2100	88
					59.5	73	116	148	10-32	24	17.0	985	2500	101
	Air filled with foam and spray. Sea white with driving spray; visibility very seriously affected.	12	Hurricane	64-71	> 64	>80	>128	>164	10-(35)	(26)	(18)			

RELATIVE FREQUENCY OF WAVES OF DIFFERENT HEIGHTS IN DIFFERENT REGIONS

Ocean Region	Height of Waves in feet					
	0-3	3-4	4-7	7-12	12-20	20
	%	%	%	%	%	%
North Atlantic (between Newfoundland and England)	20	20	20	15	10	15
Mid-equatorial Atlantic	20	30	25	15	5	5
South Atlantic, (latitude of Argentina)	10	20	20	20	15	10
North Pacific (latitude of Oregon and south of Alaskan Peninsula)	25	20	20	15	10	10
East equatorial Pacific	25	35	25	10	5	5
West wind belt of South Pacific (latitude of Southern Chile)	5	20	20	20	15	15
North Indian Ocean (Northeast monsoon season)	55	25	10	5	0	0
North Indian Ocean (Southwest monsoon season)	15	15	25	20	15	10
Southern Indian Ocean (between Madagascar and northern Australia)	35	25	20	15	5	5
West wind belt of southern Indian Ocean (on route between Cape of Good Hope and southern Australia)	10	20	20	20	15	15

(Bigelow and Edmondson, 1962, adapted from a chart, based on 40,164
extracts from sailing ships' log books, in Schumacher, 1939.)

LENGTHS OF STORM WAVES OBSERVED IN DIFFERENT OCEANS

Ocean Area	Wave Length (Feet)			Number of Cases
	Maximum	Minimum	Average	
North Atlantic	559	115	303	15
South Atlantic	701	82	226	32
Pacific	765	80	242	14
Southern Indian	1121	108	360	23
China Sea	261	160	197	3

(Bigelow and Edmondson, 1952)

DEEP-OCEAN SURFACE WAVES (Munk, 1951)

Classification	Period	Usual Generating Force	Comments
Capillary waves	less than 0.1 sec	Wind (or non-linear actions of steep gravity waves)	Surface tension is restoring force
Ultra-gravity waves	from 0.1 sec to 1 sec	Wind (or non-linear actions of steep gravity waves)	Combination of surface tension and gravity restoring force
Ordinary gravity waves	from 1 sec to 30 sec	Wind (most often generates 5 to 15 sec period waves)	Usual type experienced on ocean surface
Infra-gravity waves	from 30 sec to 5 min	Meteorological factors	Can cause dangerous oscillation in offshore installations
Long-period waves	from 5 min to 12 hrs	Storms and earthquakes	
Ordinary tide waves	from 12 hrs to 24 hrs	Sun and moon	
Trans-tidal waves	24 hrs and up	Meteorologic factors Sun and moon	May contain solar and lunar tidal components or even seasonal water level variations

(Copyright, Council on Wave Research)

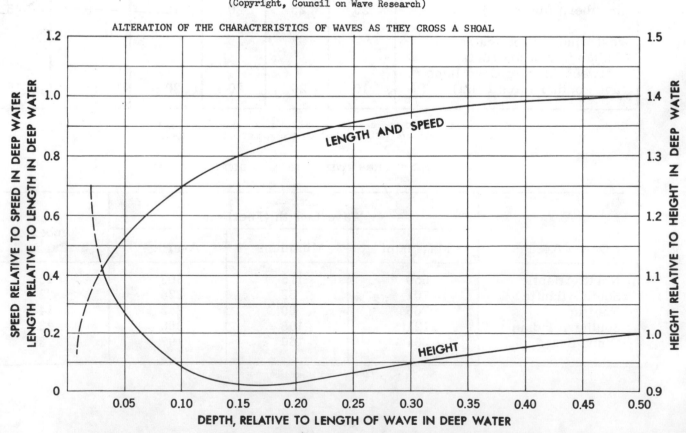

ALTERATION OF THE CHARACTERISTICS OF WAVES AS THEY CROSS A SHOAL

UNITS OF DEPTH MEASUREMENT ON CHARTS OF VARIOUS NATIONS

Nation	Unit of depth measurement	Equivalent in United States Units	
		Feet	Fathoms
Argentina	Braza	6.000	1.000
Australia	Fathom	6.000	1.000
Belgium	Metre	3.281	0.547
Brazil	Metro	3.281	0.547
Canada	Fathom	6.000	1.000
Chile	Metro	3.281	0.547
Denmark	Favn	6.176	1.029
	Meter	3.281	0.547
Finland	Metre	3.281	0.547
France	Metre	3.281	0.547
Germany	Meter	3.281	0.547
Great Britain	Fathom	6.000	1.000
Greece	Metre (Metpa)	3.281	0.547
Italy	Metre	3.281	0.547
Japan	Metre	3.281	0.547
Netherlands	Vadem	5.905	0.984
	Meter	3.281	0.547
Norway	Favn	6.176	1.029
	Meter	3.281	0.547
Portugal	Metro	3.281	0.547
Russia (USSR)	Sazhen'	6.000	1.000
	Metre	3.281	0.547
Thailand	Metre	3.281	0.547
Spain	Metro	3.281	0.547
Sweden	Famn	5.844	0.974
	Meter	3.281	0.547
Turkey	Fathom (Kulac)	6.000	1.000
Uruguay	Metro	3.281	0.547
Yugoslavia	Metar	3.281	0.547

ELEMENTS PRESENT IN SOLUTION IN SEA WATER, EXCLUDING DISSOLVED GASES

Element	Concentration (g/ton)	Element	Concentration (g/ton)
Cl	18,980	Pb	0.004-0.005
Na	10,556	Se	0.004
Mg	1,272	Sn	0.003
S	884	Cs	approximately 0.002
Ca	400	U	0.00015-0.0016
K	380	Mo	0.003-0.002
Br	65	Ga	0.0005
C (inorganic)	28	Ni	0.0001-0.0005
Sr	13	Th	0.0005
(SiO$_2$)	0.01-7.0	Ce	0.0004
B	4.6	V	0.0003
Si	0.02-4.0	La	0.0003
C (organic)	1.2-3.0	Y	0.0003
Al	0.16-1.9	Hg	0.0003
F	1.4	Ag	0.00015-0.0003
N (as nitrate)	0.001-0.7	Bi	0.0002
N (as organic nitrogen)	0.03-0.2	Co	0.0001
Rb	0.2	Sc	0.00004
Li	0.1	Au	0.000004-0.000008
P (as phosphate)	0.001-0.10	Fe (in true solution)	10^{-9}
Ba	0.05	Ra	2.10^{-11}-3.10^{-10}
I	0.05	Ge	Present
N (as nitrite)	0.0001-0.05	Ti	Present
N (as ammonia)	0.005-0.05	W	Present
As (as arsenite)	0.003-0.024	Cd	Present in marine organisms
Fe	0.002-0.02	Cr	Present in marine organisms
P (as organic phosphorus)	0-0.016	Tl	Present in marine organisms
Zn	0.005-0.05	Sb	Present in marine organisms
Cu	0.001-0.09	Zr	Present in marine organisms
Mn	0.001-0.01	Pt	Present in marine organisms

APPROXIMATE AMOUNT OF MINERALS IN ONE CUBIC MILE OF SEA WATER

Mineral	Amount (tons)
Sodium chloride (common salt)	128,284,000
Magnesium chloride	17,947,000
Magnesium sulphate	7,816,000
Calcium sulphate	5,940,000
Potassium sulphate	4,068,000
Calcium carbonate (lime)	580,000
Magnesium bromide	358,000
Bromine	300,000
Strontium	60,000
Boron	21,000
Fluorine	6,400
Barium	900
Iodine	100 to 12,000
Arsenic	45 to 367
Rubidium	198
Silver	up to 45
Copper, Manganese, Zinc, Lead	10 to 30
Gold (dissolved)	4
Radium	5 g

ELECTROMOTIVE FORCE SERIES

METAL	ION.	STANDARD ELECTRODE POTENTIAL AT 25°C. (Volts)
Potassium	K^+	-2.922
Sodium	Na^+	-2.712
Magnesium	Mg^{++}	-2.34
Aluminum	Al^{+++}	-1.67
Zinc	Zn^{++}	-0.76
Chromium	Cr^{+++}	-0.71
Iron	Fe^{++}	-0.44
Cadmium	Cd^{++}	-0.44
Nickel	Ni^{++}	-0.25
Tin	Sn^{++}	-0.14
Lead	Pb^{++}	-0.13
Hydrogen	H^+	0.00 (Reference)
Copper	Cu^{++}	0.34
Silver	Ag^+	0.80
Palladium	Pd^{++}	0.83
Mercury	Hg^{++}	0.85
Platinum	Pt^{++}	1.20
Gold	Au^{+++}	1.68

CLASSIFICATION OF MARINE ENVIRONMENTS

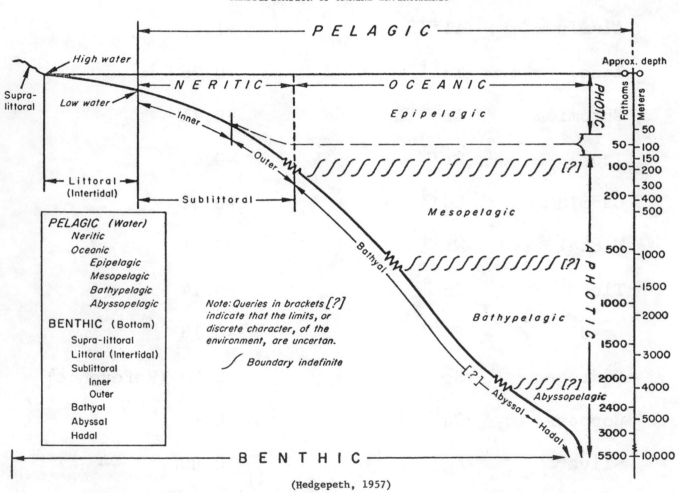

(Hedgepeth, 1957)

ANIMAL FORMS IN THE OCEAN.

Division	System or Province	Zone	Ecological Groups	Plant and Animal Forms		
Benthic	Littoral	Littoral Sublittoral	Benthos (sea floor animals)	1. Sessile - (immobile)	(Sponges, mussels, oysters, crinoids, corals, hydroids, bryozoans, barnacles)	
				Tube worms Seaweeds and sea grasses Diatoms		
	Deep-Sea	Bathyal Abyssal Hadal		2. Creeping forms - (crabs, lobsters, copepods, amphipods) Crustaceans Protozoans Snails Bivalves		
				3. Burrowing forms - (clams, worms) Crustaceans Echinoderms		
Pelagic	Neritic Oceanic	Epipelagic Mesopelagic	Nekton (swimming animals)	Squids Fishes Whales		
			Plankton (floating animals or floating plants)	Floating and Drifting Life 1. Zooplankton - feebly swimming or floating animals 2. Phytoplankton - microscopic floating plants		

Name	Danger [1]	Maximum size	Appearance [2]	Behavior	Where found
White shark	4+	30 feet	Slaty brown to black on back.	Savage, aggressive	Oceanic; tropical, subtropical, warm temperate belts, especially in Australian waters.
Mako shark	4+	30 feet	Slender form, deep blue gray on back.	Savage	Oceanic, tropical, and warm temperate belts.
Porbeagle shark	2+	12 feet	Dark bluish gray on back.	Sluggish except when pursuing prey.	Continental waters of Northern Atlantic. Allied forms in North Pacific, Australia and New Zealand.
Tiger shark	2+	30 feet	Short snout, sharply pointed tail.	Can be vigorous and powerful.	Tropical and subtropical belts of all oceans, inshore and offshore.
Lemon shark	2+	11 feet	Yellowish brown on back, broadly rounded snout.	Found in salt water creeks, bays, and sounds.	Inshore western Atlantic, northern Brazil to North Carolina, tropical West Africa.
Lake Nicaragua shark.	2+	10 feet	Dark gray on back.	Found in shallow water.	Fresh water species of Lake Nicaragua.
Dusky shark	1+	14 feet	Bluish or leaden gray on back.	Found in shallow water.	Tropical and warm temperate waters on both sides of Atlantic.
White-tipped shark.	3+	13 feet	Light gray to slaty blue on back.	Indifferent, fearless.	Tropical and subtropical Atlantic and Mediterranean. Deep offshore waters.
Sand shark	2+	10 feet	Bright gray-brown on back.	Stays close to bottom.	Indo-Pacific, Mediterranean, tropical West Africa, South Africa, Gulf of Maine to Florida, Brazil, Argentina.
Gray nurse shark.	3+	10 feet	Pale gray on back	Swift and savage	Australia.
Ganges River shark.	4+	7 feet	Gray on back	Ferocious, attacks bathers.	Indian Ocean to Japan, ascends fresh water rivers.
Hammerhead shark.	4+	15 feet	Ashy-gray on back, flat, wide head.	Powerful swimmers.	Warm temperate zone of all oceans including Mediterranean Sea, out at sea or close inshore.

[1] 1+ means minimum danger, 4+ means maximum danger.
[2] All sharks listed are some shade of white on lower half.

Name	Danger	Maximum size	Appearance	Behavior	Where found
Great barracuda	4+	6–8 feet	Long, slender, large mouths.	Swift, fierce, attracted easily.	Tropical and subtropical waters, West Indies, Brazil, northern Florida, In the Indo-Pacific from Red Sea to Hawaiian Islands.
Groupers	2+	12 feet, 700 lbs.	Bulky type of body.	Curious, bold, voracious feeders.	Around rocks, caverns, old wrecks.
Moray eels	1+	10 feet	Long, narrow, snakelike.	Attack when provoked.	Tropical and subtropical, bottom dwellers.
Killer whales	4+		Jet black head and back, white under parts.	Ruthless, ferocious.	All oceans and seas, tropical to polar. *Caution*—leave water immediately if sighted.
Sea lions	1+		Resemble seals but larger.	Curious, fast swimmers.	Northern waters.
Sea urchins	2+		Small spiny animals.	Spines, needle sharp, small venomous pincers.	Tropical and temperate zones, ocean floor on rocks and coral reefs.
Corals	1+			Extremely sharp	Tropical and subtropical waters.
Barnacles, mussels.	1+			Deep cuts	Rocks, pilings, wrecks.
Giant clams	2+	Several hundred pounds.		Traps legs and arms between shells.	Abound in tropical waters.
Portuguese man-o-war.	3+	6 in. in diameter.	Tentacles up to 50 feet long.	Stings with cells on tentacles.	Tropical waters.
Sea wasp	4+		Tentacles up to 50 feet long.	Stings with cells on tentacles.	Northern Australia, Philippines, Indian Ocean.
Octopuses	2+	25 feet	Arms radiating from head.	Hold with tentacles, bite also.	Underwater caves.
Cone shells	2+		Colorful shells	Penetrates skin with venom filled teeth on proboscis (trunk).	Widespread.
Horned sharks	1+		Spines anterior to back fins.		
Stingrays	1+	Several feet	Spine on top of tail, flat body.	Drives spine into leg when stepped on.	Tropical to temperate waters.
Catfish	1+		Venomous dorsal and pectoral spines.		Tropical and temperate, mostly fresh water, some marine.
Weeverfish	1+		Venomous dorsal and pectoral spines.	Toxic to the nervous system and blood, extremely painful.	Eastern Atlantic and Mediterranean.
Scorpionfish	1+		Venomous back anal, and pelvic spines.	Toxic to the nervous system and blood.	Tropical and temperate.
Sea snakes	3+	9 feet	Resembles snakes, venomous fangs.	Boldness varies	Tropical Pacific and Indian Ocean. River mouths to far at sea.

SOIL CLASSIFICATION SYSTEMS

1. Wentworth's Size Classification:

Grade Limits (Diameters)	Name
Above 256 mm.	Boulder
256 - 64 mm.	Cobble
64 - 4 mm.	Pebble
4 - 2 mm.	Granule
2 - 1 mm.	Very coarse sand
1 - 1/2mm.	Coarse sand
1/2 - 1/4mm.	Medium sand
1/4 - 1/8mm.	Fine sand
1/8 -1/16mm.	Very fine sand
1/16 -1/256mm.	Silt
Below 1/256mm.	Clay

2. U. S. Army Corps of Engineers' Classification

Grade Limits (Diameters)		Name
Greater than 76.2 mm.		Cobbles
76.2 -	25.4	Coarse gravel
25.4 -	4.76	Medium gravel
4.76 -	2.00	Fine gravel
2.00 -	0.42	Coarse sand
0.42 -	0.074	Fine sand
If liquid limit is 27 or less and plasticity index (based upon -40 fraction) is less than 6		Silt
If liquid limit is 27 or less and plasticity index (based on -40 fraction) is 6 or greater		Clay

3. U. S. Bureau of Soils' Classification

Grade Limits (Diameters)		Name
2	- 1 mm.	Fine gravel
1	- 1/2 mm.	Coarse sand
1/2	- 1/4 mm.	Medium sand
1/4	- 1/10 mm.	Fine sand
1/10	- 1/20 mm.	Very fine sand
1/20	- 1/200 mm.	Silt
Below 1/200 mm.		Clay

4. Atterberg's Size Classification

Grade Limits (Diameters)		Name
2,000 -	200 mm.	Blocks
200 -	20 mm.	Cobbles
20 -	2 mm.	Pebbles
2 -	0.2 mm.	Coarse sand
0.2 -	0.02 mm.	Fine sand
0.02 -	0.002 mm.	Silt
Below 0.002 mm.		Clay

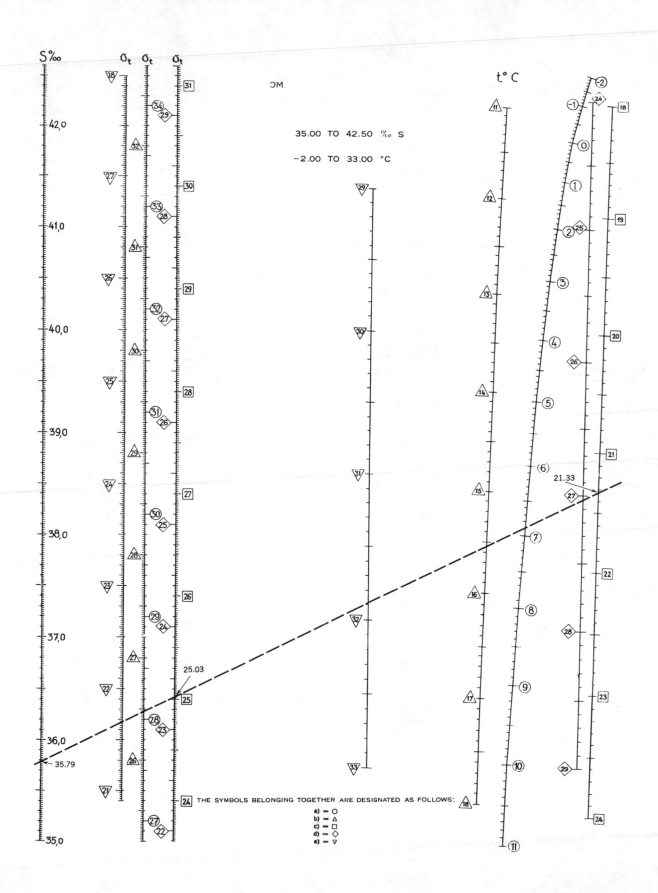

35.00 TO 42.50 ‰ S

−2.00 TO 33.00 °C

THE SYMBOLS BELONGING TOGETHER ARE DESIGNATED AS FOLLOWS:

a) = ○
b) = △
c) = □
d) = ◇
e) = ▽

(U.S. Navy Hydrographic Office, H.O. 607)

VELOCITY OF SOUND IN SELECTED MATERIALS

AT AMBIENT CONDITIONS

Material	Specific Gravity	Sound Velocity km/sec	Sound Velocity ft/sec	Ratio velocity/sp gr
Rubber (soft)	0.95	0.054	177	0.057
Air	0.0012	0.332	1,088	276.0
Lead	11.3	1.227	4,026	0.11
Water (air free)	0.998	1.461	4,794	1.46
Water (sea)	1.026	1.500	4,927	1.46
Copper	8.9	3.560	11,670	0.40
Iron and Soft Steel	7.7	5.000	16,410	0.65
Glass	2.3	5.000	16,410	2.18
Aluminum	2.7	5.104	16,740	1.89

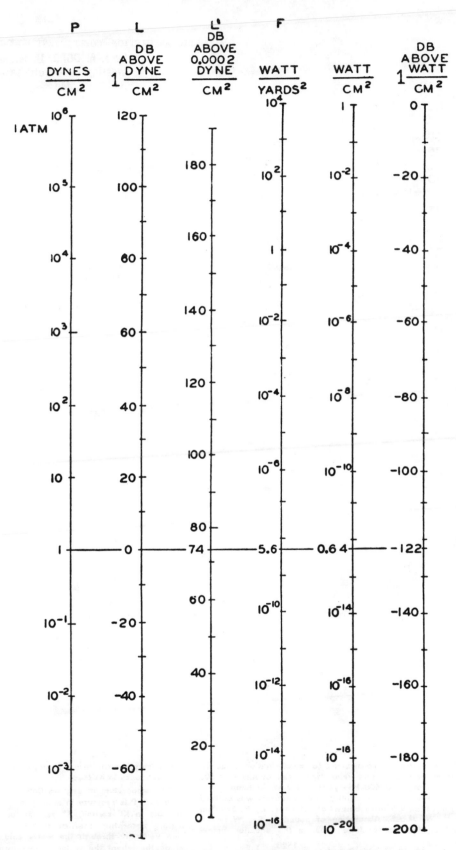

COMPARISON OF UNITS FOR UNDERWATER SOUND.

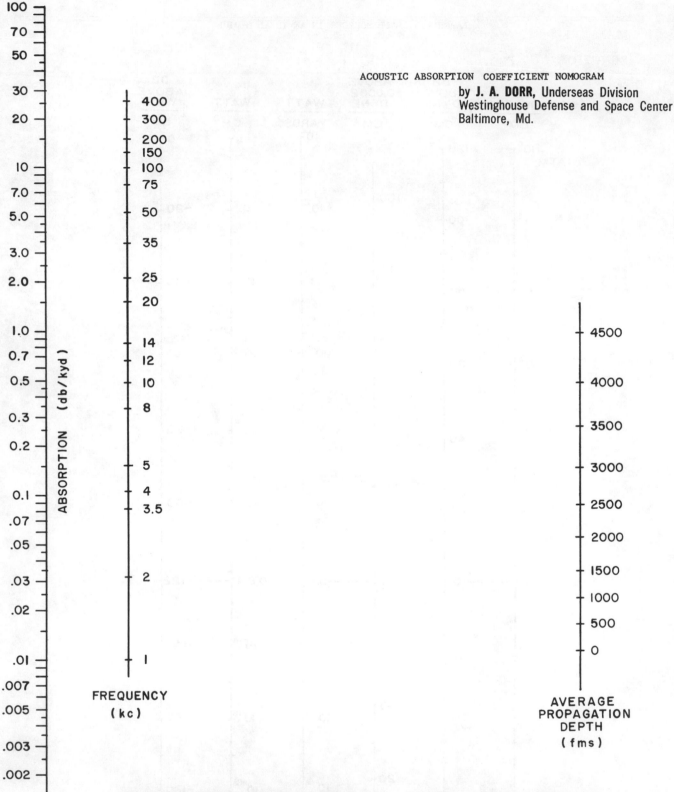

ACOUSTIC ABSORPTION COEFFICIENT NOMOGRAM

by **J. A. DORR,** Underseas Division
Westinghouse Defense and Space Center
Baltimore, Md.

ABSORPTION (db / kyd)

FREQUENCY
(kc)

AVERAGE
PROPAGATION
DEPTH
(fms)

This nomogram is constructed for determination of acoustic absorption coefficient values for ocean depths to 4,500 fathoms, from 1 to 400 kilocycles at sea water temperature of 3° Celsius and 35% salinity. The nomogram was derived from equation 9 (shown below) of the paper by M. Schulkin and H. W. Marsh, Absorption of Sound in Sea Water, J. Brit, IRE, Vol. No. 6, June 1963. In the equation below

$$F_t = 21.9 \times 10 \left(6 - \frac{1520}{T + 273} \right)$$

α is absorption coefficient in nepers per meter; F_t is relaxation frequency in KC/sec.

T is temperature in degrees Celsius; S is salinity in parts/thousand; P is pressure in atmosphere; F is the independent variable in KC/second; 3° temperature value permits estimating absorption coefficients for both acoustic transmission vertically through the water column and horizontally at depths where the water temperature is less than about 10°.

$$\alpha = \left[\frac{2.34 \times 10^{-6} SF_t F^2}{F_t^2 + F^2} + \frac{3.38 \times 10^{-6} F^2}{F_t} \right] \times (1 - 6.54 \times 10^{-4} P)$$

154

MEASURE-MENT FUNCTION	DEVICES	CHARACTERISTICS AND LIMITATIONS	COMMENTS
Ocean Temperature	Mechanical (BT) Bathythermograph	Depth: 0 to 900 feet/Accuracy: ± 10 feet Temperature: −2.2 to 32°C/ Accuracy: ± 0.1°C Poor accuracy	In temperature measurement work the Mechanical Bathythermograph has long been the oceanographer's workhorse. The "BT," together with those previously noted herein, and an airborne radiation thermometer (for surface depths, temperature range—2 to 35°C, accuracy ± 0.2°C), comprise for the most part present-day temperature instrumentation. Various telemetering and self-containing recording systems, infra red devices, temperature probes, and electronic Bathythermographs (Hytech) are also being used, developed, and evaluated. Specifications for improved systems have been documented as those requiring repeatability and accuracy ± 0.1°C (for buoyancy problems the accuracy may be approximately ± .05°C), quick reaction time sensors, durability, watertightness, linear output and standardization of output signals compatible to computer and machine tabulation.
	Deep-Sea Reversing Thermometer	Depth: 0 to 20,000 feet/Accuracy: ± 100 feet Temperature: −2 to 30°C/Accuracy: ± 0.01°C Not continuous; too delicate	
	Wire-Wound Resistance Thermometer	Depth: Surface Temperature: −5 to 30°C and −25 to 5°C/Accuracy: ± 0.1°C Poor accuracy except near surface	
	Thermocouple	Depth: 0 to 200 feet Temperature: −50 to 10°C/Accuracy: ± 0.5°C Requires laborious calibration: thermocouple reference junctions must be kept at a constant known temperature	
Depth	**Edo 255** (Depth of bottom)	Accuracy: 0.1% of depth Experiences numerous breakdowns	Depth is most difficult to measure accurately. New depth measuring devices, for example, require pressure transducers which are expendable, adaptable for use with various kinds of arrays, and reproducable. In this context, more accurate transducers are coveted by the researcher. New developments in this field primarily include the strain gauge transducers for unlimited depth measurements with an accuracy of ± 1 foot in 1,000 feet. The strain gauge principle has merit because it is more feasible to use a pressure sensitive device (in an environment where the *pressure* varies from 0.44 to 0.46 psi per foot of *depth*) and then convert pressure to depth.
	Unprotected Mercury Thermometer	Probable error of depths: ± 15 feet for depths less than 3,000 feet; at greater depths to about 0.5% Too delicate; has limited application; is not continuous	
	Mechanical Pressure Transducer (Bourdon tube, bellows, helical coil, aneroid, etc.)	Depth: 0 to 1,500 feet/Accuracy: ± 15 feet Erratic	
	Electronic Pressure Transducer ("Vibration," strain gauge, variable reluctance gauge, etc.)	Depth: 0 to 1,500 feet/Accuracy: ± 4 feet (Accuracy of the transducer is generally limited by the recording apparatus) Erratic; transducer accuracy is limitation	
Conductivity/ Salinity	**Sea Water Sampler** Nansen Bottle Volumetric Method (Titration) Conductivity Bridge Salinometer (University of Washington)	Salinity Accuracy: ± 0.02 part per thousand Salinity Accuracy: ± 0.005 part per thousand Repeatability: ± 0.001 part per thousand Is not continuous; requires laborious analysis of samples	Although measuring techniques being used for salinity *in situ* and probes for conductivity are deemed by some as "acceptable," many suggestions for improvement in this field have been put forth to provide accuracy for use in coastal waters—portability of the equipment, automated collection equipment, sensor capability of 20–40 parts per thousand ocean salinity range, accuracy ± .001 part per thousand (classical hydrography demands salinity measurements approximately ± .01 per cent relative), equipment capable of easy calibration and alignment, non-polarized electrodes, etc. Miniaturized transistor salinometers, conductivity-temperature indicators, temperature-chlorinity titrators, neutron absorption, salinity-temperature-depth recorders, etc., are also being used to some extent by various activities.
	Electrical Method Conductivity Cell Foxboro Company Serfass Bridge	Accuracy: ± 0.1 part per thousand Accuracy: ± 1.0 part per thousand (0.1 part per thousand if calibrated before and after use) Becomes unstable because of change in cell characteristics; actual measurements are largely empirical in nature and a basically incorrect assumption is technically made that the ocean water composition is constant	

Ocean Currents	Mechanical Current Meter (Ekman)	Speed: 0.15 to 2.5 knots/Accuracy: ±0.1 knot Direction: 0 to 360 degrees/Accuracy: ±10 degrees Not continuous or deck-reading	Various methods are being considered for current measurement such as a suspended-drop current meter (Lamont Geological Observatory), the Savonius Rotor, etc., to improve these instruments and their operating limits. Broad design criteria for further new developments have been documented as: A need for a good solid-state type of current meter design with a speed range of 0.1 to 10.0 knots, accuracy: ±0.1 knot (lower thresholds and accuracies desired for special research projects), direction: ±10 degrees, depth range: unlimited in some designs (but not necessarily for those with the speed ranges, accuracies, and directions mentioned above), simplicity in over-all design and operation, rugged, minimum maintenance, standardization of output signal range, and stability in three dimensional space. Standardization of output signals should be compatible to present machine tabulation and/or computers.
	Electro-Mechanical Current Meter Types Price Meter	Speed: 0.1 to 6.5 knots/ Accuracy: ±0.1 knot Direction: None Marginal accuracy; maintenance problems	
	Roberts Meter Mod. 3	Speed: 0.2 to 7.0 knots/Accuracy: ±0.1 knot Direction: 0 to 360 degrees/Accuracy: ±10 degrees High threshold level; maintenance problems	
	Low Velocity Types Hytech Crouse-Hinds	Speed: 0.1 to 7.0 knots/Accuracy: ±0.1 knot Direction: 0 to 360 degrees/Accuracy: ±10 degrees	
	Pruitt	Speed: 0.04 to 7.0 knots/Accuracy: ±0.01 knot Direction: 0 to 360 degrees/Accuracy: ±10 degrees	
	CM-3 (Japanese)	Speed: 0.2 to 5.0 knots/Accuracy: ±0.1 knot Direction: 0 to 360 degrees/Accuracy: ±10 degrees	
	Geomagnetic Electro Kinetograph (GEX)	Uncertain	
	Photographic Type (German paddle wheel)	Speed: 0.3 to 3.0 knots/Accuracy: ±0.1 knot Direction: 0 to 360 degrees/Accuracy: ±10 degrees	
	Parachute Drogues	(Speeds and accuracies determined from two tests by the Hydrographic Office)	
	Drift Bottle	Crude, slow, and uncertain	
Transparency and Visibility Determinations	Submarine Photometer	Depth: Approximately 500 feet	An example of a new design is the tele-recording bathyphotometer (Boden, Kampa, & Snodgrass). Sophistications of all these instruments and new designs which also assist in the determination of currents and biological conditions should employ automatic calibration, an ease of alignment, an ability to determine suspended particles in the ocean (by size, number, and type), an ability to measure attenuation of ambient light with depth, capable of transparency measurement in relatively clear open ocean water, have a design simplicity, be capable of measurement of number of wavelengths, and be dependable.
	Hydrophotometer Mark 2	Depth: 200 feet	
	Secchi Disc	Depth: 20 feet (maximum)	
Density	No direct measuring instrument	No *direct* measuring device available for continuous measurements with the accuracy ±10⁻⁶ desired	New instruments should not be sensitive to gravity dissolved gases, acceleration and organic matter in sample. Direct, accurate, density measuring systems are being sought.
Tide	Portable tide gauge	Not bottom mounted, self-contained, or unattended	Nearly all the tide gauges in the U. S. are operated by the U. S. Coast and Geodetic Survey. Systems under consideration and in development include tide-buoy telemetering with output signals appropriate for computer work. Some advanced design criteria and the problems involved for improved gauges are: accurate determination of a vertical datum, crustal movements, classification of tides affecting different coast lines, attain accuracy of ±0.01 foot, determine parallax and declination cycles, tidal pulsations in deep ocean water, and tidal buildup.

Bottom Topography and Sediment Structure	Deep-Sea Multi-Shot Camera (Type III, Navy Electronics Laboratory)	Depth: Greater than 20,000 feet Number of photographs per operation: approximately 55	Future designs ideally would provide: high power transducers, broad-band energy sources, high repetition rates, short pulse length for thin-bed resolution, a cored sediment more representative of *in situ* conditions, improved release mechanisms, deeper sediment penetration, non-distortion of sediment sample, adequate sediment samples for comprehensive laboratory analysis, optimum physical dimensions of piston corers, and portable shipboard analysis kits.
	Mechanical Bottom Signalling Device "The Ball Breaker"	Depth: Unlimited	
	Substrata Acoustic Probe (Marine Sonoprobe)	Depth: 700 feet Sediment penetration: 200 feet	
	Precision Depth Recorder (Times Facsimile Corp.) and AN/UQN (Edo)	Depth: Up to 18,000 feet Sediment penetration: 120 feet (extreme maximum)	
	Fathometer—Echo Sounder (Model 255B-EDO Corp.)	Depth: 2.5 to 1,500 feet/Accuracy: ±1 to 6 feet depending on depth scale in use Sediment penetration: undetermined	
	Corers: **Gravity Type** Phleger	Depth: Unlimited—determined by length of lowering cable Sediment penetration: 4 feet	
	Piston Type Kullenburg Ewing	Depth: Unlimited Sediment penetration: 6 to 12 feet Depth: Unlimited Sediment penetration: 20 to 60 feet	
	Grab Samplers Clamshell Snapper	Depth: Unlimited Sediment penetration: Surface	
	Mud Sampler	Same as above Most now restricted in performance. More precision required. Longer cores are required.	
Marine Biology	Meter or Half-Meter Plankton Samplers	Towing speeds: Not greater than 2 knots	Biological instrumentation is primarily mechanical. Basic problem is the collection of specimens from all depths. Specimens here, however, mean living material varying in size from the ultramicroscopic to whales. Most devices then must be highly specialized and capable of collecting specimens horizontally and vertically, capturing the more active swimmers, securing undamaged specimens, recording exactly the amount of water sampled and depth, sampling over long distances, and sampling several depths simultaneously.
	Clarke-Bumpus Plankton Sampler (Woods Hole Oceanographic Institution)	Same as above	
	Midwater Trawl	Same as above	
	Hi-Speed Sampler (Scripps Institution of Oceanography)	Towing speeds: 8 to 12 knots	
	Hardy Continuous Plankton Recorder (British, used by Woods Hole Oceanographic Institution)	Towing speeds: 15 knots	
	Convex-Concave Fouling Plates	Plates in the environment from 1 month to 2 years	

COMPARISON OF PROPERTIES OF LOW DENSITY SOLIDS

Material	Density	Bulk Modulus $\times 10^5$ psi	Comments and Limitation
Lithium metal	0.53	22	Reacts vigorously with water releasing hydrogen. It must be contained in suitable non-corrosive metal containers which reduce buoyancy.
Wood	0.4-1.3	--	Has low compressive strength, absorbs water rapidly at pressures greater than 500 psi.
Solid Polyethylene, Polypropylene	0.9-0.95	2.6	Marginal compressive strength. Low buoyancy.
Expanded plastics	wide range	--	Have low strength. Are permeable to water and must be packaged in a barrier material.
Inorganic foams	wide range	--	Have low strength or open celled structure.
Syntactic foam	0.65-0.75	5.5	Offer exceptional promise for use at 10,000 psi.

PHYSICAL PROPERTIES OF ALUMINUM ALLOYS CONSIDERED FOR DEEP SUBMERGENCE

Alloy Desig- nation	Density 16/in.^{3}	Modulus			Poisson's Ratio	Coef. of Exp. 10^{-6} in./in. F (68-212)	Melting Range
		Tension in 10^6 psi	Compres- sion in 10^6 psi	Rigidity in 10^6 psi			
5083	0.096	10.2	10.4	3.85	0.33	13.2	1075-1185
5086	0.096	10.2	10.4	3.85	0.33	13.2	1084-1184
5454	0.097	10.2	10.4	3.85	0.33	13.2	1115-1195
5456	0.096	10.2	10.4	3.85	0.33	13.2	1060-1180
7002	0.099	10.3	--	3.90	0.33	--	1065-
7005	0.101	10.3	10.5	3.90	0.33	13.2	1125-1195
7106	0.099	10.3	10.5	3.90	0.33	13.3	1090-1195
7039	0.0988						

BULK MODULI OF BUOYANCY MATERIALS
AT 10,000 PSIG HYDROSTATIC PRESSURE.

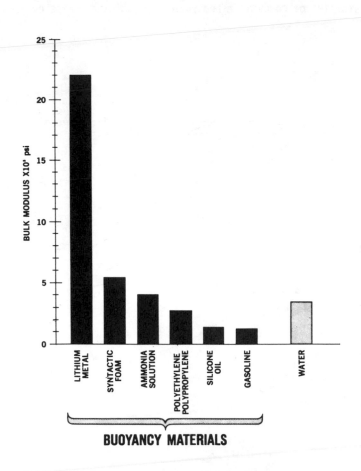

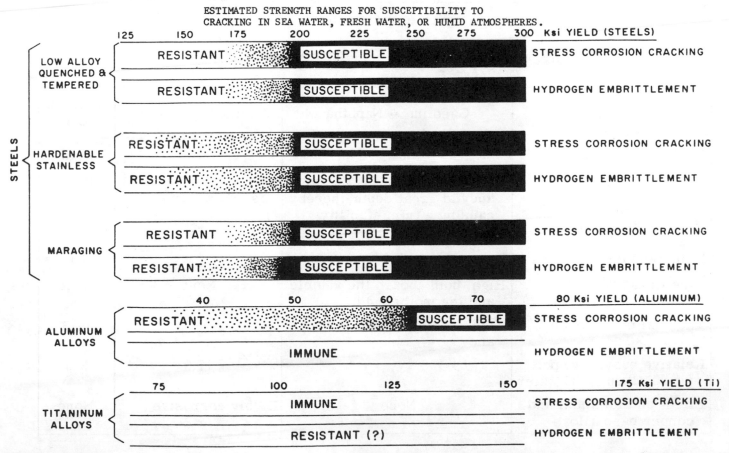

ESTIMATED STRENGTH RANGES FOR SUSCEPTIBILITY TO
CRACKING IN SEA WATER, FRESH WATER, OR HUMID ATMOSPHERES.

CAPABILITIES OF CONCRETE HYDROSTATIC COMPRESSIVE STRESS OF 3000 PSI.

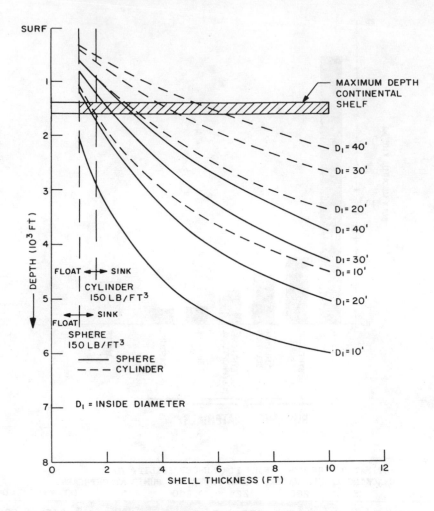

COMPARISON OF LOW DENSITY LIQUIDS.

Property	Gasoline & Naphtha	Ammonia Solutions	Silicone Oil
Cost	Low	Low	High
Compressibility	High, causing a loss of buoyancy at great depth, thereby causing a trim stability problem	Low, nearly the same as sea water	High
Bulk Modulus $\times 10^5$ psi	1.4	4	1.5
Fire Hazard	High, both aboard the vehicle and the mother ship	None	None
Thermal contraction	High, causing a loss in buoyancy	----	----
Relative buoyancy, pcf. (at 20°C) in 20°C water	17	17.5	3-7
Effect on aluminum and copper base alloys	None	Highly corrosive	None

A SUMMARY OF THE CHARACTERISTICS OF SURFACE NAVIGATION SYSTEMS

SYSTEM and associated names	FREQUENCY BAND	TYPE	MAXIMUM RANGE (Miles)	PRESENT STATUS	PLOTTING METHOD	ACCURACY (Average)	EQUIPMENT NEEDED ON SHIP
CONSOL Consolan Sonne	200 to 500 kc	Navigation	1500 miles	Used in Europe and U.S.	Bearings	0.5% Bearing	Low frequency receiver.
DECCA NAVIGATOR	100 kc	Navigation	300 miles	Used in Europe, Canada & So. Asia	Hyperbolic	300 ft.	Special receivers and phase meters.
SURVEY DECCA	100 kc	Surveying	100 miles	Various countries	Hyperbolic	100 ft.	Special receivers and phase meters.
DECCA HI-FIX	2000 kc	Surveying		Experimental	Circular or Hyperbolic	25 to 50 ft.	Special transmitter and receiver and phase meters for circular use.
TWO-RANGE DECCA	100 kc	Surveying	100 miles	Various Countries	Circular	50 ft	Special receivers, transmitters and phase meters.
DECTRA	100 kc	Trackline Navigation	2000 miles	North Atlantic	Hyperbolic	10 miles	Special receivers and phase meters.
DELRAC	10 kc	Navigation	5000 miles	Experimental	Hyperbolic	5 miles	Special receivers and phase meters.
EPI	2 Mcs	Surveying	400 miles	U.S.	Circular	300 ft.	Special transmitter and receiver.
GEE	60 Mcs	Navigation	100 miles	Obsolete	Hyperbolic	300 ft.	GEE receiver.
GEODIMETER Mark I, II, III and IV	Light waves	Distance Measuring	25 miles	Various countries		1/500,000	
LAMBDA DECCA	100 kc	Surveying	200 miles	Experimental	Circular	100 ft.	Special transmitter, receivers and phase meters.
LORAC	2 Mcs	Surveying	100 miles	Various countries	Hyperbolic		
LORAN A	2 Mcs	Navigation	750 miles	Atlantic and Pacific	Hyperbolic	1% of the distance	Special Loran Receiver.
LORAN B	2 Mcs	Navigation	750 miles	Experimental	Hyperbolic	0.01% of distance	Special Receiver.
LORAN C	100 kc	Navigation	1500 miles	Experimental	Hyperbolic	0.1% of distance	Special Receiver.
MAP	RADAR	Surveying	50 miles	New	Circular	50 ft.	Radar and special MAP attachments.
MICRODIST	9 Kmc	Distance Measuring	25 miles	Experimental		1/100,000	
MPFS	Radar	Surveying	50 miles	New	Bearings	0.04° Bearing	Special Radar and control equipment.
NAVARHO	100 kc	Navigation	1500 miles	Experimental	Hyperbolic		Special Receiver and display unit.
OMEGA	10 kc	Navigation	5000 miles	Experimental	Hyperbolic	2 miles	Special Receiver and display unit.
PULSED LIGHT	Light waves	Distance measuring	5 miles	Experimental		3 ft.	

161

SYSTEM and associated names	FREQUENCY BAND	TYPE	MAXIMUM RANGE (Miles)	PRESENT STATUS	PLOTTING METHOD	ACCURACY (Average)	EQUIPMENT NEEDED ON SHIP
RAYDIST (E, R,N, and ER)	2 Mcs	Surveying	150 miles	Obsolete except for special purposes.	Hyperbolic	200 ft.	Special Receiver and Phase meters.
RAYDIST (DM)	2 Mcs	Surveying	150 miles	Various countries	Circular	30 ft.	Special Receiver and Phase meters.
SHORAN Hiran	250 Mcs	Surveying	4 miles	Various countries	Circular	50 ft.	Special Transmitter and Receiver.
RANA	2 Mcs	Surveying	100 miles	France and Possesions	Hyperbolic	100 ft.	Special Receivers and Phase meters.
TELLUROMETER (Hydrodist)	3 Kmc	Distance Measuring	25 miles	Various countries		1/100,000	
SOFAR	Sound Waves	Rescue	4000 miles	Obsolete	Hyperbolic		Special bomb.
RAFOS	Sound waves	Navigation	Classified	Experimental	Triangulation	Classified	Sound wave receiver.

(Instrument Division--U.S. Coast & Geodetic Survey--October 1963)

DEPTH (ft)	BOTTOM TIME (mins)	TIME TO FIRST STOP	50	40	30	20	10	TOTAL ASCENT TIME	REPET. GROUP
40	200						0	0.7	•
	210	0.5					2	2.5	N
	230	0.5					7	7.5	N
	250	0.5					11	11.5	O
	270	0.5					15	15.5	O
	300	0.5					19	19.5	Z
50	100						0	0.8	•
	110	0.7					3	3.7	L
	120	0.7					5	5.7	M
	140	0.7					10	10.7	M
	160	0.7					21	21.7	N
	180	0.7					29	29.7	O
	200	0.7					35	35.7	O
	220	0.7					40	40.7	Z
	240	0.7					47	47.7	Z
60	60						0	1.0	•
	70	0.8					2	2.8	K
	80	0.8					7	7.8	L
	100	0.8					14	14.8	M
	120	0.8					26	26.8	N
	140	0.8					39	39.8	O
	160	0.8					48	48.8	Z
	180	0.8					56	56.8	Z
	200	0.6				1	69	70.6	Z
70	50						0	1.2	•
	60	1.0					8	9.0	K
	70	1.0					14	15.0	L
	80	1.0					18	19.0	M
	90	1.0					23	24.0	N
	100	1.0					33	34.0	N
	110	0.8				2	41	43.8	O
	120	0.8				4	47	51.8	O
	130	0.8				6	52	58.8	O
	140	0.8				8	56	64.8	Z
	150	0.8				9	61	70.8	Z
	160	0.8				13	72	85.8	Z
	170	0.8				19	79	98.8	Z
80	40						0	1.3	•
	50	1.2					10	11.2	K
	60	1.2					17	18.2	L
	70	1.2					23	24.2	M
	80	1.0				2	31	34.0	N
	90	1.0				7	39	47.0	N
	100	1.0				11	46	58.0	O
	110	1.0				13	53	67.0	O
	120	1.0				17	56	74.0	Z
	130	1.0				19	63	83.0	Z
	140	1.0				26	69	96.0	Z
	150	1.0				32	77	110.0	Z
90	30						0	1.5	•
	40	1.3					7	8.3	J
	50	1.3					18	19.3	L
	60	1.3					25	26.3	M
	70	1.2				7	30	38.2	N
	80	1.2				13	40	54.2	N
	90	1.2				18	48	67.2	O
	100	1.2				21	54	76.2	Z
	110	1.2				24	61	86.2	Z
	120	1.2				32	68	101.2	Z
	130	1.0			5	36	74	116.0	Z
100	25						0	1.7	•
	30	1.5					3	4.5	I
	40	1.5					15	16.5	K
	50	1.3				2	24	27.3	L
	60	1.3				9	28	38.3	N
	70	1.3				17	39	57.3	O
	80	1.3				23	48	72.3	O
	90	1.2			3	23	57	84.2	Z
	100	1.2			7	23	66	97.2	Z
	110	1.2			10	34	72	117.2	Z
	120	1.2			12	41	78	132.2	Z
110	20						0	1.8	•
	25	1.7					3	4.7	H
	30	1.7					7	8.7	J
	40	1.5				2	21	24.5	L
	50	1.5				8	26	35.5	M
	60	1.5				18	36	55.5	N
	70	1.3			1	23	48	73.3	O
	80	1.3			7	23	57	88.3	Z
	90	1.3			12	30	64	107.3	Z
	100	1.3			15	37	72	125.3	Z

DEPTH (ft)	BOTTOM TIME (mins)	TIME TO FIRST STOP	50	40	30	20	10	TOTAL ASCENT TIME	REPET. GROUP
120	15						0	2.0	•
	20	1.8					2	3.8	H
	25	1.8					6	7.8	I
	30	1.8					14	15.8	J
	40	1.7				5	25	31.7	L
	50	1.7				15	31	47.7	N
	60	1.5			2	22	45	70.5	O
	70	1.5			9	23	55	88.5	O
	80	1.5			15	27	63	106.5	Z
	90	1.5			19	37	74	131.5	Z
	100	1.5			23	45	80	149.5	Z
130	10						0	2.2	•
	15	2.0					1	3.0	F
	20	2.0					4	6.0	H
	25	2.0					10	12.0	J
	30	1.8				3	18	22.8	M
	40	1.8				10	25	36.8	N
	50	1.7			3	21	37	62.7	O
	60	1.7			9	23	52	85.7	Z
	70	1.7			16	24	61	102.7	Z
	80	1.5		3	19	35	72	130.5	Z
	90	1.5		8	19	45	80	153.5	Z
140	10						0	2.3	•
	15	2.2					2	4.2	G
	20	2.2					6	8.2	I
	25	2.0				2	14	18.0	J
	30	2.0				5	21	28.0	K
	40	1.8			2	16	26	45.8	N
	50	1.8			6	24	44	75.8	O
	60	1.8			16	23	56	96.8	Z
	70	1.7		4	19	32	68	124.7	Z
	80	1.7		10	23	41	79	154.7	Z
150	5						0	2.5	C
	10	2.3					1	3.3	E
	15	2.3					3	5.3	G
	20	2.2				2	7	11.2	H
	25	2.2				4	17	23.2	K
	30	2.2				8	24	34.2	L
	40	2.0			5	19	33	59.0	N
	50	2.0			12	23	51	88.0	O
	60	1.8		3	19	26	62	111.8	Z
	70	1.8		11	19	39	75	145.8	Z
	80	1.7	1	17	19	50	84	172.7	Z
160	5						0	2.7	D
	10	2.5					1	3.5	F
	15	2.3				1	4	7.3	H
	20	2.3				3	11	16.3	J
	25	2.3				7	20	29.3	K
	30	2.2			2	11	25	40.2	M
	40	2.2			7	23	39	71.2	N
	50	2.0		2	16	23	55	98.0	Z
	60	2.0		9	19	33	69	132.0	Z
	70	1.8	1	17	22	44	80	165.8	Z
170	5						0	2.8	D
	10	2.7					2	4.7	F
	15	2.5				2	5	9.5	H
	20	2.5				4	15	21.5	J
	25	2.3			2	7	23	34.3	L
	30	2.3			4	13	26	45.3	M
	40	2.2		1	10	23	45	81.2	O
	50	2.2		5	18	23	61	109.2	Z
	60	2.0	2	15	22	37	74	152.0	Z
	70	2.0	8	17	19	51	86	183.0	Z
180	5						0	3.0	D
	10	2.8					3	5.8	F
	15	2.7				3	6	11.7	I
	20	2.5			1	5	17	25.5	K
	25	2.5			3	10	24	39.5	L
	30	2.5			6	17	27	52.5	N
	40	2.3		3	14	23	50	92.3	O
	50	2.2	2	9	19	30	65	127.2	Z
	60	2.2	5	16	19	44	81	167.2	Z
190	5						0	3.2	D
	10	2.8				1	3	6.8	G
	15	2.8				4	7	13.8	I
	20	2.7			2	6	20	30.7	K
	25	2.7			5	11	25	43.7	M
	30	2.5		1	8	19	32	62.5	N
	40	2.5		8	14	23	55	102.5	O
	50	2.3	4	13	22	33	72	146.3	Z
	60	2.3	10	17	19	50	84	182.3	Z

(U.S. Navy Diving Manual)

U.S. NAVY STANDARD AIR DECOMPRESSION TABLE FOR EXCEPTIONAL EXPOSURES.

DEPTH (ft.)	BOTTOM TIME (Min.)	TIME TO FIRST STOP	130	120	110	100	90	80	70	60	50	40	30	20	10	TOTAL ASCENT TIME
40	360	0.5													23	24
	480	0.5													41	42
	720	0.5													69	70
60	240	0.7												2	79	82
	360	0.7												20	119	140
	480	0.7												44	148	193
	720	0.7												78	187	266
80	180	1.0												35	85	121
	240	0.8											6	52	120	179
	360	0.8											29	90	160	280
	480	0.8											59	107	187	354
	720	0.7										17	108	142	187	455
100	180	1.0										1	29	53	118	202
	240	1.0										14	42	84	142	283
	360	0.8									2	42	73	111	187	416
	480	0.8									21	61	91	142	187	502
	720	0.8									55	106	122	142	187	613
120	120	1.3										10	19	47	98	176
	180	1.2									5	27	37	76	137	283
	240	1.2									23	35	60	97	179	395
	360	1.0								18	45	64	93	142	187	550
	480	0.8							3	41	64	93	122	142	187	653
	720	0.8							32	74	100	114	122	142	187	772
140	90	1.5									2	14	18	42	88	166
	120	1.5									12	14	36	56	120	240
	180	1.3								10	26	32	54	94	168	386
	240	1.2							8	28	34	50	78	124	187	511
	360	1.0						9	32	42	64	84	122	142	187	683
	480	1.0						31	44	59	100	114	122	142	187	800
	720	0.8					16	56	88	97	100	114	122	142	187	923
170	90	1.8							12	12	14	34	52	120		232
	120	1.5						2	10	12	18	32	42	82	156	356
	180	1.3					4	10	22	28	34	50	78	120	187	535
	240	1.3					18	24	30	42	50	70	116	142	187	681
	360	1.2				22	34	40	52	60	98	114	122	142	187	873
	480	1.0			14	40	42	56	91	97	100	114	122	142	187	1006
200	5	3.2													1	5
	10	3.0												1	4	8
	15	2.8											1	4	10	18
	20	2.8											3	7	27	40
	25	2.8											7	14	25	49
	30	2.7										2	9	22	37	73
	40	2.5									2	8	17	23	59	112
	50	2.5									6	16	22	39	75	161
	60	2.3								2	13	17	24	51	89	199
	90	1.8					1	10	10	12	12	30	38	74	134	323
	120	1.7				6	10	10	10	24	28	40	64	98	180	472
	180	1.3		1	10	10	18	24	24	42	48	70	106	142	187	684
	240	1.3		6	20	24	24	36	42	54	68	114	122	142	187	841
	360	1.2	12	22	36	40	44	56	82	98	100	114	122	142	187	1057
210	5	3.3													1	5
	10	3.2												2	4	10
	15	3.0											1	5	13	22
	20	3.0											4	10	23	40
	25	2.8										2	7	17	27	56
	30	2.8										4	9	24	41	81
	40	2.7									4	9	19	26	63	124
	50	2.5								1	9	17	19	45	80	174
220	5	3.5													2	6
	10	3.3												2	5	11
	15	3.2											2	5	16	27
	20	3.0										1	3	11	24	43
	25	3.0										3	8	19	33	66
	30	2.8									1	7	10	23	47	91
	40	2.8									6	12	22	29	68	140
	50	2.7								3	12	17	18	51	86	190

DEPTH (ft.)	BOTTOM TIME (Min.)	TIME TO FIRST STOP	130	120	110	100	90	80	70	60	50	40	30	20	10	TOTAL ASCENT TIME
230	5	3.7													2	6
	10	3.3											1	2	6	13
	15	3.3											3	6	18	31
	20	3.2										2	5	12	26	49
	25	3.2										4	8	22	37	75
	30	3.0									2	8	12	23	51	99
	40	2.8								1	7	15	22	34	74	156
	50	2.8								5	14	16	24	51	89	202
240	5	3.8													2	6
	10	3.5											1	3	6	14
	15	3.5											4	6	21	35
	20	3.3										3	6	15	25	53
	25	3.2									1	4	9	24	40	82
	30	3.2									4	8	15	22	56	109
	40	3.0								3	7	17	22	39	75	166
	50	2.8							1	8	15	16	29	51	94	217
250	5	3.8												1	2	7
	10	3.7											1	4	7	16
	15	3.5										1	4	7	22	38
	20	3.5										4	7	17	27	59
	25	3.3									2	7	10	24	45	92
	30	3.3									6	7	17	23	59	116
	40	3.2								5	9	17	19	45	79	178
	60	2.7						4	10	10	12	22	36	64	126	297
	90	2.2		8	10	10	10	10	10	28	28	44	68	98	186	513
	120															
	180		(SEE EXTREME EXPOSURES BELOW)													
	240															
260	5	4.0												1	2	7
	10	3.8											2	4	9	19
	15	3.7										2	4	10	22	42
	20	3.5									1	4	7	20	31	67
	25	3.5									3	8	11	23	50	99
	30	3.3								2	6	8	19	26	61	125
	40	3.2							1	6	11	16	19	49	84	190
270	5	4.2												1	3	9
	10	4.0											2	5	11	22
	15	3.8										3	4	11	24	46
	20	3.7									2	3	9	21	35	74
	25	3.5								2	3	8	13	23	53	106
	30	3.5								3	6	12	22	27	64	138
	40	3.3							5	6	11	17	22	51	88	204
280	5	4.3												2	2	9
	10	4.0										1	2	5	13	25
	15	3.8									1	3	4	11	26	49
	20	3.8									3	4	8	23	39	81
	25	3.7								2	5	7	16	23	56	113
	30	3.5							1	3	7	13	22	30	70	150
	40	3.3						1	6	6	13	17	27	51	93	218
290	5	4.5												2	3	10
	10	4.2										1	3	5	16	30
	15	4.0									1	3	6	12	26	52
	20	4.0									3	7	9	23	43	89
	25	3.8								3	5	8	17	23	60	120
	30	3.7							1	5	6	16	22	36	72	162
	40	3.5						3	5	7	15	16	32	51	95	264
300	5	4.7												3	3	11
	10	4.3										1	3	6	17	32
	15	4.2									2	3	6	15	26	56
	20	4.0								2	3	7	10	23	47	104
	25	3.8							1	3	6	8	19	26	61	128
	30	3.8							2	5	7	17	22	39	75	171
	40	3.7						4	6	9	15	17	34	51	90	234
	60	3.0		4	10	10	10	10	10	14	28	32	50	90	187	458
	90															
	120		(SEE EXTREME EXPOSURES BELOW)													
	180															

(Rev. 1958)

EXTREME EXPOSURES – 250 AND 300 FT.

DEPTH (ft.)	BOTTOM TIME (Min.)	TIME TO FIRST STOP	200	190	180	170	160	150	140	130	120	110	100	90	80	70	60	50	40	30	20	10	TOTAL ASCENT TIME
250	120	1.8							5	10	10	10	10	16	24	24	36	48	64	94	142	187	682
	180	1.5					4	8	8	10	22	22	24	32	42	44	60	84	114	122	142	187	929
	240	1.5					9	14	21	22	22	40	40	42	56	76	98	100	114	122	142	187	1107
300	90	2.3					3	8	8	10	10	10	10	16	24	24	34	48	64	90	142	187	691
	120	2.0				4	8	8	8	10	14	24	24	24	34	42	58	66	102	122	142	187	887
	180	1.7	6	8	8	8	14	20	21	21	28	40	40	48	56	82	98	100	114	122	142	187	1165

(U.S. Navy Diving Manual)

"NO DECOMPRESSION" LIMITS AND REPETITIVE GROUP DESIGNATION TABLE FOR "NO DECOMPRESSION" DIVES.

DEPTH (ft.)	NO DECOMPRESSION LIMITS (Min.)	REPETITIVE GROUPS														
		A	B	C	D	E	F	G	H	I	J	K	L	M	N	O
10	–	60	120	210	300											
15	–	35	70	110	160	225	350									
20	–	25	50	75	100	135	180	240	325							
25	–	20	35	55	75	100	125	160	195	245	315					
30	–	15	30	45	60	75	95	120	145	170	205	250	310			
35	310	5	15	25	40	50	60	80	100	120	140	160	190	220	270	310
40	200	5	15	25	30	40	50	70	80	100	110	130	150	170	200	
50	100	–	10	15	25	30	40	50	60	70	80	90	100			
60	60	–	10	15	20	25	30	40	50	55	60					
70	50	–	5	10	15	20	30	35	40	45	50					
80	40	–	5	10	15	20	25	30	35	40						
90	30	–	5	10	12	15	20	25	30							
100	25	–	5	7	10	15	20	22	25							
110	20	–	–	5	10	13	15	20								
120	15	–	–	5	10	12	15									
130	10	–	–	5	8	10										
140	10	–	–	5	7	10										
150	5	–	–	5												
160	5	–	–	–	5											
170	5	–	–	–	5											
180	5	–	–	–	5											
190	5	–	–	–	5											

(Rev. 1958)

INSTRUCTIONS FOR USE

I. "No decompression" limits

This column shows at various depths greater than 30 feet the allowable diving times (in minutes) which permit surfacing directly at 60 ft. a minute with no decompression stops. Longer exposure times require the use of the Standard Air Decompression Table (Table 1-5).

II. Repetitive group designation table

The tabulated exposure times (or bottom times) are in minutes. The times at the various depths in each vertical column are the maximum exposures during which a diver will remain within the group listed at the head of the column.

To find the repetitive group designation at surfacing for dives involving exposures up to and including the "no decompression limits": Enter the table on the exact or next greater depth than that to which exposed and select the listed exposure time exact or next greater than the actual exposure time. The repetitive group designation is indicated by the letter at the head of the vertical column where the selected exposure time is listed.

For example: A dive was to 32 feet for 45 minutes. Enter the table along the 35 ft. depth line since it is next greater than 32 ft. The table shows that since group "D" is left after 40 minutes exposure and group "E" after 50 minutes, group "E" (at the head of the column where the 50 min. exposure is listed) is the proper selection.

Exposure times for depths less than 40 ft. are listed only up to approximately five hours since this is considered to be beyond field requirements for this table.

(U.S. Navy Diving Manual)

	Z	O	N	M	L	K	J	I	H	G	F	E	D	C	B	A
REPETITIVE GROUP AT THE END OF THE SURFACE INTERVAL																
Z	0:10-0:22	0:34	0:48	1:02	1:18	1:36	1:55	2:17	2:42	3:10	3:45	4:29	5:27	6:56	10:05	12:00*
O		0:10-0:23	0:36	0:51	1:07	1:24	1:43	2:04	2:29	2:59	3:33	4:17	5:16	6:44	9:54	12:00*
N			0:10-0:24	0:39	0:54	1:11	1:30	1:53	2:18	2:47	3:22	4:04	5:03	6:32	9:43	12:00*
M				0:10-0:25	0:42	0:59	1:18	1:39	2:05	2:34	3:08	3:52	4:49	6:18	9:28	12:00*
L					0:10-0:26	0:45	1:04	1:25	1:49	2:19	2:53	3:36	4:35	6:02	9:12	12:00*
K						0:10-0:28	0:49	1:11	1:35	2:03	2:38	3:21	4:19	5:48	8:58	12:00*
J							0:10-0:31	0:54	1:19	1:47	2:20	3:04	4:02	5:40	8:40	12:00*
I								0:10-0:33	0:59	1:29	2:02	2:44	3:43	5:12	8:21	12:00*
H									0:10-0:36	1:06	1:41	2:23	3:20	4:49	7:59	12:00*
G										0:10-0:40	1:15	1:59	2:58	4:25	7:35	12:00*
F											0:10-0:45	1:29	2:28	3:57	7:05	12:00*
E												0:10-0:54	1:57	3:22	6:32	12:00*
D													0:10-1:09	2:38	5:48	12:00*
C														0:10-1:39	2:49	12:00*
B															0:10-2:10	12:00*
A																0:10-12:00*

REPETITIVE GROUP AT THE BEGINNING OF SURFACE INTERVAL (FROM PREVIOUS DIVE)

(Rev. 1958)

INSTRUCTIONS FOR USE

Surface interval time in the table is in <u>hours</u> and <u>minutes</u> ("7:59" means 7 hours and 59 minutes). The surface interval must be at least 10 minutes.

Find the repetitive <u>group designation letter</u> (from the <u>previous dive</u> schedule) on the diagonal slope. Enter the table horizontally to select the listed surface interval time that is exactly or <u>next greater</u> than the actual surface interval time. The repetitive group designation for the <u>end</u> of the surface interval is at the head of the vertical column where the selected surface interval time is listed. For example — a previous dive was to 110 ft. for 30 minutes. The diver remains on the surface 1 hour and 30 minutes and wishes to find the new repetitive group designation: The repetitive group from the last column of the 110/30 schedule in the Standard Air Decompression Tables is "J". Enter the surface interval credit table along the horizontal line labeled "J". The 1 hour and 47 min. listed surface interval time is <u>next greater</u> than the actual 1 hour and 30 minutes surface interval time. Therefore, the diver <u>has lost</u> sufficient inert gas to place him in group "G" (at the head of the vertical column selected).

*NOTE: Dives following surface intervals of <u>more</u> than 12 hours are not considered repetitive dives. <u>Actual</u> bottom times in the Standard Air Decompression Tables may be used in computing decompression for such dives.

REPET. GROUPS	REPETITIVE DIVE DEPTH (Ft.)															
	40	50	60	70	80	90	100	110	120	130	140	150	160	170	180	190
A	7	6	5	4	4	3	3	3	3	3	2	2	2	2	2	2
B	17	13	11	9	8	7	7	6	6	6	5	5	4	4	4	4
C	25	21	17	15	13	11	10	10	9	8	7	7	6	6	6	6
D	37	29	24	20	18	16	14	13	12	11	10	9	9	8	8	8
E	49	38	30	26	23	20	18	16	15	13	12	12	11	10	10	10
F	61	47	36	31	28	24	22	20	18	16	15	14	13	13	12	11
G	73	56	44	37	32	29	26	24	21	19	18	17	16	15	14	13
H	87	66	52	43	38	33	30	27	25	22	20	19	18	17	16	15
I	101	76	61	50	43	38	34	31	28	25	23	22	20	19	18	17
J	116	87	70	57	48	43	38	34	32	28	26	24	23	22	20	19
K	138	99	79	64	54	47	43	38	35	31	29	27	26	24	22	21
L	161	111	88	72	61	53	48	42	39	35	32	30	28	26	25	24
M	187	124	97	80	68	58	52	47	43	38	35	32	31	29	27	26
N	213	142	107	87	73	64	57	51	46	40	38	35	33	31	29	28
O	241	160	117	96	80	70	62	55	50	44	40	38	36	34	31	30
Z	257	169	122	100	84	73	64	57	52	46	42	40	37	35	32	31

(Rev. 1958)

INSTRUCTIONS FOR USE

The bottom times listed in this table are called "residual nitrogen times" and are the times a diver is to consider he has already spent on bottom when he starts a repetitive dive to a specific depth. They are in minutes.

Enter the table horizontally with the repetitive group designation from the Surface Interval Credit Table. The time in each vertical column is the number of minutes that would be required (at the depth listed at the head of the column) to saturate to the particular group.

For example — the final group designation from the Surface Interval Credit Table, on the basis of a previous dive and surface interval, is "H". To plan a dive to 110 feet, determine the "residual nitrogen time" for this depth required by the repetitive group designation: Enter this table along the horizontal line labeled "H". The table shows that one must start a dive to 110 feet as though he had already been on the bottom for 27 minutes. This information can then be applied to the Standard Air Decompression table or "No Decompression" Table in a number of ways:

(1) Assuming a diver is going to finish a job and take whatever decompression is required, he must add 27 minutes to his actual bottom time and be prepared to take decompression according to the 110 foot schedules for the sum or equivalent single dive time.

(2) Assuming one wishes to make a quick inspection dive for the minimum decompression, he will decompress according to the 110/30 schedule for a dive of 3 minutes or less (27 + 3 = 30). For a dive of over 3 minutes but less than 13, he will decompress according to the 110/40 schedule (27 + 13 = 40).

(3) Assuming that one does not want to exceed the 110/50 schedule and the amount of decompression it requires, he will have to start ascent before 23 minutes of actual bottom time (50 - 27 = 23).

(4) Assuming that a diver has air for approximately 45 minutes bottom time and decompression stops, the possible dives can be computed: A dive of 13 minutes will require 23 minutes of decompression (110/40 schedule), for a total submerged time of 36 minutes. A dive of 13 to 23 minutes will require 34 minutes of decompression (110/50 schedule), for a total submerged time of 47 to 57 minutes. Therefore, to be safe, the diver will have to start ascent before 13 minutes or a standby air source will have to be provided.

(U.S. Navy Diving Manual)

PER CENT CHANGE IN BUOYANCY OF
UNICELLULAR FOAM RUBBER SWIM SUIT
(INCLUDING BOOTS, HOOD AND GLOVES)
WITH DEPTH.

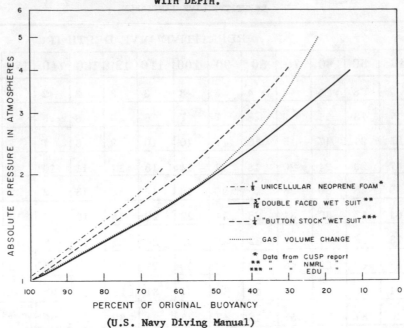

(U.S. Navy Diving Manual)

OXYGEN CONSUMPTION AND RESPIRATORY MINUTE
VOLUME AT DIFFERENT WORK-RATES.

Activity [1]		Oxygen consumption [2] in liters/min. [3] (STPD) [4]	Respiratory minute volume [5] liters [3] (BTPS) [6]
REST	Bed rest (basal)	0.25	6
	Sitting quietly	.30	7
	Standing still	.40	9
LIGHT WORK	**Slow walking on hard bottom**	0.6	13
	Walking, 2 mph	.7	16
	Swimming, 0.5 knot (slow)	.8	18
MODERATE WORK	**Slow walking on mud bottom**	1.1	23
	Walking, 4 mph	1.2	27
	Swimming, 0.85 knot (av. speed)	1.4	30
	Max. walking speed, hard bottom	1.5	34
HEAVY WORK	**Swimming, 1.0 knot**	1.8	40
	Max. walking speed, mud bottom	1.8	40
	Running, 8 mph	2.0	50
SEVERE WORK	**Swimming, 1.2 knots**	2.5	60
	Uphill running	4.0	95

NOTES

[1] Underwater activities are in heavy type.

[2] All figures are average values. There is considerable variation between individuals. (See fig. 1-26 for range found in underwater swimming.)

[3] One liter equals approximately one quart.

[4] STPD means standard conditions (see 1.3.4(10)).

[5] The RMV values are approximate for the corresponding oxygen consumption. Individual variations are large.

[6] BTPS means body temperature, existing barometric pressure, saturated with water vapor at body temperature.

(U.S. Navy Diving Manual)

BUREAU OF MEDICINE AND SURGERY. In addition to
providing for medical care for naval personnel,
the Bureau conducts medical and dental research
and is responsible for the prevention and control
of disease in naval combat forces. (40)

BUREAU OF NAVAL PERSONNEL. The Navy's recruiting,
replacement, education and training programs are
administered by this Bureau. It engages in personnel research to determine personnel and training requirements for new weapon and support systems.
(40)

BUREAU OF NAVAL WEAPONS. In 1959, the Bureau of
Ordnance and the Bureau of Aeronautics were combined to form the Bureau of Naval Weapons. The
new Bureau is responsible for the design, development, and testing of all naval weapons, missiles,
aircraft, space vehicles, and supporting equipment.
(40)

BUREAU OF SHIPS. This Bureau is responsible for
the design and development of naval vessels. It
conducts and sponsors materials research with em-
phasis on protection against chemical, biological,
and radiological warfare effects, and develops
special devices such as respiratory protective
apparatus, diving apparatus, and radio, radar, and
sonar equipment and accessories. (40)

BUREAU OF SUPPLIES AND ACCOUNTS. This Bureau conducts or sponsors research projects in advanced
logistics, supply and food engineering, special-
purpose clothing, cargo handling, and packaging
and preservation. (40)

CHIEF OF NAVAL OPERATIONS. The Office of the Chief
of Naval Operations, with headquarters in the Pen-
tagon Building, Washington, D.C., 20350, formulates
the Navy's research and development requirements
and program objectives. It has jurisdiction over
the following installations.

The Naval Oceanographic Office, which is the
principal source of oceanographic and hydrographic
data and charts in the United States;

The Naval Observatory, which conducts research
in astronomy and derives the most accurate possible
time from its observations for dissemination by the
appropriate authorities; and

The Navy Department Library in the Main Navy
Building, Washington, D.C., 20360. (40)

NATIONAL OCEANOGRAPHIC DATA CENTER. The Naval
Oceanographic Office administers the National
Oceanographic Data Center (NODC) established in
1960 at the Navy Yard Annex, Washington, D.C.,
20390, as a national clearinghouse for oceanographic data. Policies of the Center are determined jointly by a Policy Board comprised of representatives of the sponsoring agencies - the Office

of Naval Research and Oceanographic Office; the
Coast and Geodetic Survey and the Weather Bureau
(both of which are activities of the U.S. Depart-
ment of Commerce); the Bureau of Commercial
Fisheries of the Department of the Interior; the
National Science Foundation; the Atomic Energy
Commission; and the U.S. Coast Guard (Treasury
Department).

The nucleus of the Center's collection is
the bathythermograph and oceanographic station
data collected and processed by the Oceanographic
Office and consists of approximately 5 million
punched cards of physical and chemical data and
several million wave and sea surface temperature
observations in various forms. Oceanographic
station data are largely North Atlantic Ocean
observations, but increasing amounts of Pacific
and Indian Ocean data are being processed. The
Center also collects pertinent technical reports,
journals, and scientific literature in the major
European languages, including Russian and Japanese.
Information is exchanged with oceanographic organizations in the United States and abroad. (40)

NAVAL BIOLOGICAL LABORATORY. The Naval Biological
Laboratory (NBL), located in Oakland, Calif., and
maintaining additional facilities on the campus of
the University of California at Berkeley, is
operated under contract by the University of California. Its staff is augmented by a research unit
assigned by the Bureau of Medicine and Surgery.
The Laboratory is concerned chiefly with the study
of selected epidemiological characteristics and
aerobiologic behavior of disease agents. (40)

NAVAL OCEANOGRAPHIC OFFICE. This office (until
July 1962 known as the U.S. Navy Hydrographic
Office) traces its origin to 1830 when the Navy
established a Depot of Charts and Instruments to
collect and to assume responsibility for the care
and issue of charts and navigational instruments
to U.S. naval ships. The mission of the Oceanographic Office, located at Suitland, Md. (mailing
address: Washington, D.C., 20390), includes preparation of hydrographic and other navigational charts
and publications, and the conduct of applied
oceanographic programs for the Navy. The Office
collects, analyzes and evaluates worldwide data
for dissemination in the form of charts, tables,
publications, and technical reports.

The U. S. Naval Oceanographic Office collects
and generates information in the following subject
fields:

Oceanography and Hydrography: Ocean soundings
and depth profiles; bottom sediments and topography; ocean wave characteristics; wave forecasting and hindcasting; production of least-time
tracks for optimum ship routing; internal waves;
ocean currents; surface and subsurface thermal
structure; heat exchange between sea and atmosphere;

ice physics; ice reconnaissance and prediction; submarine oceanographic observations (temperature, salinity, bottom pressure, sound velocity, ambient light, relative waterflow, etc.); microbathymetry survey techniques; biological fouling; flushing and dispersion of contaminants in marine areas; correlating environmental phenomena associated with harbors; visibility; acoustic reflectivity; bioluminescence; ambient noise; and unusual marine phenomena. (40)

NAVAL OCEANOGRAPHIC OFFICE LIBRARY. The library houses a unique reference collection in oceanography and the allied sciences, consisting of approximately 100,000 bound volumes and the reports of several hundred oceanographic surveys prepared by institutions in the United States and abroad. About 500 periodicals are received regularly by the Library. There are also special collections of all Office publications, of all publications issued by the International Hydrographic Bureau at Monaco since 1921, and of foreign sailing directions since 1920. At least 30 percent of the Library's holdings are obtained from sources outside the United States. Library services are extended primarily to personnel of the Naval Oceanographic Office but are made available to others on a need-to-know basis. (40)

NAVAL RESEARCH ADVISORY COMMITTEE. This committee consists of 15 eminent civilian scientists. They advise the Chief of Naval Operations and Chief of Naval Research (of the Office of Naval Research) on research trends and potentialities as they relate to naval operations. (40)

OCEANOGRAPHIC INSTRUMENTATION CENTER. The Naval Oceanographic Office administers the Oceanographic Instrumentation Center organized in February 1962 as a prototype facility of a proposed National Oceanographic Instrumentation Test and Calibration Center. Located at the U.S. Naval Station, Washington Navy Yard Annex, Washington, D.C., 20390, the Center has a broad program for the development, testing, evaluation, and calibration of oceanographic instruments, and serves as a clearinghouse for information on oceanographic and geophysical survey instrumentation. (40)

OFFICE OF NAVAL MATERIAL. This office is concerned with the development of new production methods to meet the material requirements of the Operating Forces and with inspection techniques. It issues an annual publication, Navy Research and Development Problems, setting forth the current scientific and engineering needs of the Navy in 10 scientific areas (chemical sciences, data processing, electronic sciences, energy conversion, engineering mechanics, fabrication technology, life sciences, marine sciences, materials sciences, and physical sciences). (40)

OFFICE OF NAVAL PETROLEUM AND OIL SHALE RESERVES. This office explores, develops, and conserves naval petroleum reserves. It serves as the principal Navy Department advisory office on all matters relating to crude petroleum and oil shale, both domestic and foreign. (40)

OFFICE OF NAVAL RESEARCH. The Office of Naval Research plans and coordinates research and certain aspects of exploratory development throughout the Navy and conducts or sponsors its own projects in the physical, engineering, life, psychological, environmental, and social sciences. It has primary responsibility for the design, development, and modification of training devices and training aids. (40)

UNDERWATER SOUND REFERENCE LABORATORY. The Underwater Sound Reference Laboratory (USRL) was originally established in 1941 as two laboratories under the Office of Scientific Research and Development - one located at Orlando, Fla., the other at Mountain Lakes, N.J. In 1946 the Orlando facilities became a laboratory of the Office of Naval Research and assumed its present title.
    The Underwater Sound Reference Laboratory has the most complete facilities for making underwater sound studies in the United States. Special anechoic chambers and other structures are set in its lake, which is considered the quietest water site in the world. The Laboratory is responsible for research and development in underwater sound detection, analysis, and measurement. It develops new and improved methods and instruments for measuring acoustic characteristics. (40)

1. A Practical Dictionary of Underwater Acoustic Devices, Taylor, John M., Jr. (Editor), USN Underwater Sound Reference Laboratory, June 1953.

2. American Standard Acoustical Terminology, American Standards Association, Inc., 25 May 1960.

3. Principles of Underwater Sound Summary Technical Report of Division 6, NDRC, 1946.

4. Fundamentals of Sonar, Horton, J. Warren, U. S. Naval Institute, Annapolis, Md., 1957.

5. Frequency-Modulated Sonar Systems, Underwater Sound Equipment IV, Summary Technical Report of Division 6, NDRC, 1946.

6. Basic Methods for the Calibration of Sonar Equipment, Summary Technical Report of Division 6, NDRC, Vol. 10, 1946.

7. Scanning Sonar Systems, Underwater Sound Equipment III, Vol. 16, Summary Technical Report of Division 6, NDRC, 1946.

8. Search and Screening, Koopman, Bernard Osgood, Operations Evaluation Group Report No. 56, 1946.

9. Glossary of Terms Frequently Used in Acoustics, American Institute of Physics, October 1960.

10. Shipboard Electronic Equipments, NAVPERS 10794, 1955.

11. Shore Protection, Planning and Design, Beach Erosion Board, Tech. Rept. No. 4, Appendix A, Glossary of Terms, 1961.

12. American Practical Navigator (Bowditch), Part Six, Oceanography, Hydrographic Office Publication No. 9, 1958.

13. The Oceans, Sverdrup, H. U., Martin W., and Fleming, Richard H., Prentice-Hall Inc., Englewood Cliffs, N. J., 1942.

14. Tide and Current Glossary, Schureman, Paul, U. S. Department of Commerce, Coast and Geodetic Survey Special Publication No. 228, 1949.

15. Glossary of Oceanographic Terms, U. S. Navy Hydrographic Office, H. O. Special Publication SP-35, January 1960.

16. The Quality of the Bottom - A Glossary of Terms, Berninghausen, William H., U. S. Navy Hydrographic Office, H. O. Special Publication SP-56, November 1961.

17. Navigation Dictionary, U. S. Navy Hydrographic Office, H. O. Pub. No. 220, 1956.

18. Botany, Wilson, Carl E., The Dryden Press, New York, N. Y., 1952.

19. General Zoology, Storer, Tracy I., McGraw-Hill, New York and London, 1943, 1st Edition, 7th Impression.

20. Webster's Third New International Dictionary (Unabridged), G and C Merriam Company, Publishers, Springfield, Mass., 1964.

21. Invertebrate Fossils, Moore, R. C., Lalicker, C. G., and Fischer, A. G., McGraw-Hill Book Co. Inc., New York, N. Y., 1952.

22. Dictionary of Geological Terms, Rice, C. M. (Exclusive of stratigraphic formations and paleontologic genera and species), Edwards Brothers, Inc., Ann Arbor, Michigan, 1952.

23. Glossary of Geology and Related Sciences (with Supplement), American Geological Institute, Second Edition, November, 1960.

24. Glossary of Meteorology, Huschke, Ralph E. (Ed.), American Meteorological Society, 1959.

25. A Functional Glossary of Ice Terminology, U. S. Navy Hydrographic Office, H. O. Publication No. 609, 1952.

26. Bathymetric Nomenclature Adopted at the 62nd Meeting of the Board of Geographic Names, July 19, 1960.

27. Handbook of Underwater Engineering, Part I, The Environment, Robert Taggart Inc., April 1964. (Unpublished Manuscript).

28. Development of Environmental Sensing Buoys, Marine Sciences Dept., U. S. Naval Oceanographic Office, Washington, D. C., Report No. 0-19-63, (Unpublished Manuscript).

29. A Summary of The Characteristics of Surface Navigation Systems, U. S. Coast and Geodetic Survey (Instrument Division), Oct. 1963.

30. Private Communications from Dr. Fred Alt, USNAVOCEANO to Don Groves, 19 March 1965 and 30 March 1965.

31. Short Glossary of Space Terms, NASA SP-1, March 1962.

32. Oceanographic Instrumentation, Publication No. 309, NAS-NRC, 1952.

33. Basic Enlisted Submarine Text, Nav. Pers., No. 10490.

34. Proceedings of Inter Agency Committee on Oceanography of the Federal Council For Science and Technology USA - Proceedings Government Industry Oceanographic Instrumentation Symposium, 1961, Miller-Columbian Reporting Service, Washington, D. C.

35. Terms and descriptions bearing this reference number have been gathered and edited from several sources both oral and written. The major written sources from which some terms have been extracted verbatim are as follows:

    Barnes, H., Oceanography and Marine Biology, George Allen & Unwin, Ltd., London, 1959.

    Instruction Manual for Oceanographic Observations, Hydrographic Office Pub. No. 607, Reprint of 2nd edition, 1959.

    Terry, Richard D., Oceanography - Its Tools, Methods, Resources and Applications, Unpublished (Autonetics - a Division of North American Aviation, Inc.).

    References No. 27, 32 and 34.

    Special publication No. 41, Oceanographic Instrumentation USHO, Oct. 1960.

    Marine Sciences Instrumentation, Vol. 1 - A publication of Instrument Society of America, 1961, Plenum Press, N. Y.

36. Shipboard Electronic Equipments, NAVPERS, No. 10794.

37. Submarine Medicine Practice, NAVMEDP, No. 5054, 1956.
    U. S. Navy Diving Manual, NAVSHIPS, No. 250-538 1963.

38. American Institute of Physics Glossary, 1962.

39. Atomic Terms To Live With, prepared by Educational Section, American Museum, Atomic Energy, Oak Ridge, Tenn.

40. Scientific Information Activities of Federal Agencies, NSF (63-42), No. 20, Nov. 1963, Supt. Documents, Wash., D. C.

41. Mechanical Properties and Tests, from Materials & Methods, July 1954 issue, Reinhold Publishing Corporation, 430 Park Avenue, New York, N.Y.

42. Air Force Missile Test Center Missile Glossary, Air Force Missile Test Center, Patrick Air Force Base, Fla.

NOTES